Warp-Drawing Machine

Patented May 20, 1913

Spooler

Patented Nov. 11, 1913

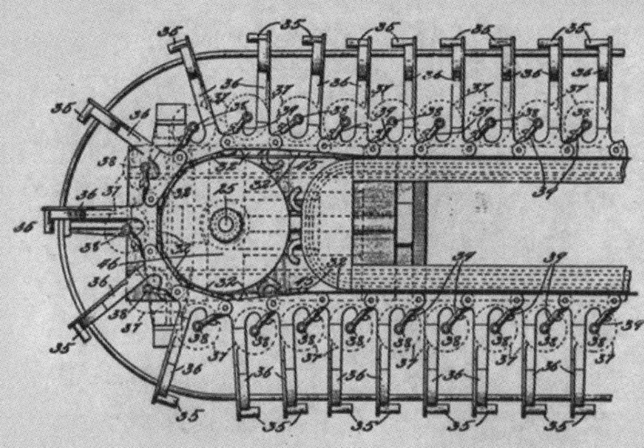

Warp-Tying Machine

Patented Nov. 25, 1913

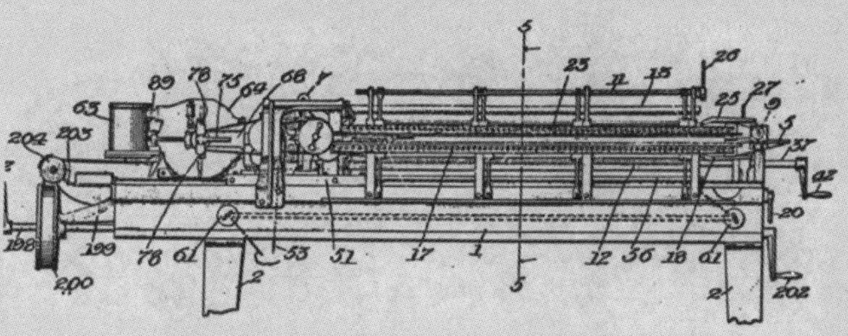

Winder

Patented July 18, 1914

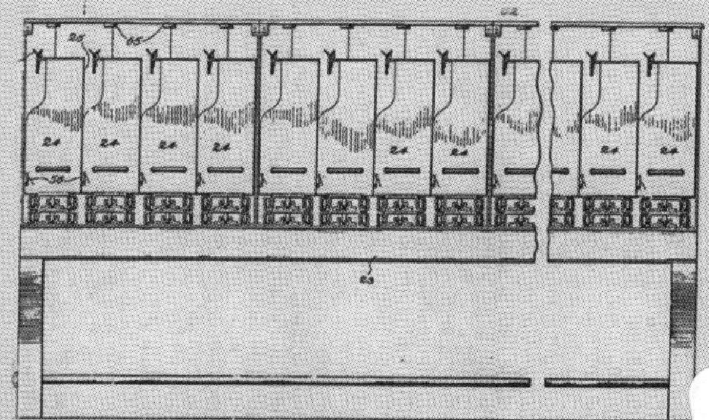

Warping Apparatus

Patented Dec. 12, 1916

MASTER INVENTOR

MASTER INVENTOR

How Howard Colman Created a Multi-National Corporation

JON LUNDIN

Amphitryon

Frontispiece: The last photograph of Howard Colman, taken in 1942; his daughter Dorothy would later describe it as a "grim pose but a very good picture."

 For information address Amphitryon Publishers, 1907 Kishwaukee Street, Rockford, Illinois 61104-5121.

Library of Congress Cataloging-in-Publication Data

Lundin, Jon.

Master Inventor: How Howard Colman Created a Multi-National Corporation/ Jon Lundin

Includes chronology and index.

ISBN 0-9791622-0-3

1. Colman, Howard Darling, 1873-1942. 2. Inventors - United States - Biography. I. Title.

First Edition

10 9 8 7 6 5 4 3 2 1

Graphic production by Shannon Halverson and Dick Lewis

Printed in the U.S.A.

For Ruth Colman Tower

Contents

Illustrations

Invention is the opposite of reasoning, and whatever results from reasoning is not invention.

- Hollister and Benedict, U.S. Circuit Court of Appeals, 1885.

Preface

This is a book about the making of an inventor and the process of discovery that led to a number of novel concepts in the field of mechanical science. The book tells the story of a little-known figure in American manufacturing, Howard D. Colman (1873-1942), a gifted and original thinker who contributed to the technical development of industries as varied as textiles, machine tools, small motors, temperature controls, and telecommunications, and who combined his skills as an inventor with a remarkable sense of new market opportunities. Colman owned 149 U.S. patents and earned a great deal of money as a result of his researches, but he also shunned publicity and was so reserved in his personal affairs that few people, outside of his family and closest friends, knew very much about him. He was, if not exactly a recluse, a scientist with a passion for solitary investigations. Colman's story has never been told before at length because information about his work has hitherto been sketchy and incomplete, but the unexpected appearance in 1998 of hundreds of letters that he exchanged with his friend and business partner William Barber during the first decade of their relationship (roughly 1891-1900), including a large file of drawings, notes, and photographs, has given us fresh insight into Colman's professional life and laid the foundation for a study of his creativity. Out of his struggles to perfect his inventions during this period, the day-to-day routine of constructing and testing models, were forged the mental habits and practical mechanical skills that enabled him to make his mature discoveries.

It's difficult, if not impossible, to account for a phenomenon such as Colman. Highly creative people are *sui generis*, often emerging from environments that are radically different from those of their calling - Colman, for example, was reared by academic parents with a strong interest in ancient and classical languages - and thus behaving in ways that are unusual in these circumstances. We all respond to peculiar imaginative realities, but the more powerful our creative gifts, the more seductive these inner visions will tend to be. Colman revealed himself at an early age when he began fashioning his own hand tools and dreaming up fantastical devices; and his parents showed their wisdom by allowing him to pursue these interests more or less to his heart's content. He was fortunate that they appreciated his talents and indulged them to the extent that they did, since the world of mechanisms that he inhabited as a boy was as foreign to their way of thinking as the world of classical languages was to his. If it's a truism of psychology that creativity is rooted in the conceptions of childhood, then Colman's later scientific work may be viewed in a sense as a continuation of these youthful flights of fancy.

There are many lessons in Colman's story, but one of the most surprising is just how frustrating and debilitating a highly creative life can be. "I have found that 'the way of the inventor is hard'," Colman admitted in 1894, though he was not yet 21 and at the beginning of his career. For five years he had labored mightily on the design of a warp drawing-in machine for cotton production (D.I.M.), a machine that had failed to perform to his expectations, and eventually he had become bogged down in a cycle of testing and calibration that offered little hope of resolving his problems. Invention, for Colman, was a source of endless fascination, and the work that he did to formulate his various schemes provided his greatest satisfaction in life. The trouble was that each of his ideas had to be tested by experience, and in the complicated process of "proving up" an invention, a thousand things could go wrong. Colman liked to set up trials of his machines in as many locations as possible in order to gather the best experimental data, and he preferred the actual working conditions of a cotton mill to those of the laboratory. Typically, he immersed himself in his demonstrations, logging information on the operations, doing calculations, checking mechanisms, making adjustments. Thus engrossed, he sometimes continued for days with little or no sleep until the process had either been tested to his satisfaction or he quit from exhaustion. The emotional letdowns that he experienced at the end of the trials were inevitable and occasionally quite severe, but the worst thing of all was the feeling that his creativity was blocked and not being able to do anything about it.

When he started building the original model of his warp drawing-in machine (D.I.M.) in 1889, Colman had no money and little fabricating experience and only the vaguest notion of what it meant to take a new product to market; and it's doubtful that he would have been able to sustain himself for long in this effort without the timely assistance of a

Wayland Academy benefactor named William Barber. Introduced to Colman by his son, a Wayland classmate of Howard's, Barber offered to provide $100 for a half-interest in the project. While the loan failed to produce the desired result - Colman's scheme was far too ambitious for his limited fabricating resources at the time - the relationship between the two ripened into friendship, and Barber continued to invest in the business, as a means of keeping it going, over the course of the next decade.

Barber became a mentor as well as a partner. He was able to evaluate the progress of Colman's experiments from a purely practical standpoint, weigh their commercial possibilities, and make decisions on whether or not to go ahead with a promising line of inquiry. Frequently he served as a sounding board for Colman's theories and speculations, and provided the objectivity that the young inventor lacked in his eagerness to break new ground. He was also a willing listener whenever Colman ran into difficulty. Barber's experience as a financial investor, the many years that he had spent operating a land office and logging business in central Wisconsin, and his not inconsiderable working knowledge of tools and machines complemented Colman's much more intuitive sense of forces and motions and his understanding of their mathematical relationships. In purely personal terms, Colman needed Barber to give his blessing to the whole enterprise of scientific invention, help him justify in his mind the speculative habits and solitary work behaviors that were necessary for the pursuit of his chosen career. Before the advent of celebrity scientists and the gigantic research corporations of today, inventors were regarded by the public with a great deal of skepticism, and it was typical of Colman that he always referred to himself as a "manufacturer" outside of his circle of friends.

Colman is a classic example of the self-made man, for nearly everything that he learned as a scientist was the result of his own initiative. School had little value for him except in its broader social aspects; only at Wayland Academy, in fact, did he encounter anyone that significantly influenced his thinking - in this case, a teacher named Winfield Sweet, who helped to increase his knowledge of mathematics as a calculational tool. In the main, Colman charted the course of his intellectual development through countless small practical experiments, beginning with the woodworking projects of his boyhood that his parents and older sister Anna describe in their reminiscences, and continuing through his adult years as a research scientist, when he directed the activities of the Barber-Colman Experimental Department and oversaw the company's multi-million dollar business.

The goal of this book is to understand the personal and creative motivation that lay behind Colman's development as an inventor, identify some of the experiences that contributed to his growth in this respect, and provide an appropriate level of technical and biographical detail to enable us to judge his achievement. But what is *appropriate*? One of the challenges of writing a book on Colman is knowing how far to go into a description of his inventions and knowing what events to include (or exclude) in an account of his career. This is a story, after all, whose dramatic moments are mostly imaginative and inner-focused and whose principal conflicts involve the unraveling of mental puzzles of Colman's own devising. It is not the material of a conventional biography. In order to take the measure of this man, we need to recognize that his life's journey was fundamentally different from that of most people and attempt to put ourselves in his place not just by sharing his outlook on his own times but by adopting his sense of himself as a creative person. And this means considering many of the details of Colman's scientific work and examining his strategies for bringing his projects to a desired state of completion. It also means presenting a realistic picture of the frustrations and disappointments that are endemic in the life of an inventor.

This book is intended for a general audience and organized for different uses. While the chapters treat Colman's work in depth, there is a chronology and list of patents in the appendix for anyone merely interested in an overview of his career. (Along the same lines, casual readers may wish to browse through the book's illustrations, a list of which is provided on pages *ix-x*, or review examples of his patent designs, beginning on page 348.) I have tried to let Colman speak for himself as much as possible in these pages - no amount of secondhand description, after all, can match the immediacy of a person's conversation - and to this end I have quoted liberally from this letters and experimental notes in telling his story. I have also reproduced a number of extended passages from the same sources in a section of the appendix entitled "In Colman's Own Words" (see page 310 ff.). Among other things, this section reveals the inventor's thought processes in the development of new ideas, his descriptive powers and ear for conversation, and his sense of humor.

Many of Colman's letters and notes were composed in great haste, and I have exercised an editor's perogative to add punctuation and standardize spelling in some of these for the sake of clarity. Otherwise, Colman's writings appear here as they do in manuscript. I am conscious of how much Colman would have objected to having any of his personal correspondence published in book form, since none of it was intended to see the light of day, but I content myself in knowing that he valued many of his papers enough to preserve them in an office cabinet during his own lifetime, and that one of my reasons for printing them now is to honor his accomplishments.

Most of the materials that I used in reconstructing Colman's career, such as letters and notes, are in manuscript form, though I have also taken advantage of printed documents from the Barber-Colman Company and U.S. Patent Office in describing the commercialization of his inventions. Whenever I have quoted any of Colman's writings directly, I have identified the source with an abbreviated notation at the end of the sentence or paragraph. I have employed this method, rather than a conventional system of footnotes, to save the reader the trouble of looking back and forth.

At the start of this project, when I was first asked to write a book on Colman, I was troubled by the apparent lack of personal information that was available for my research. In the succeeding months, however, all this changed significantly, thanks in large part to the resourcefulness of Colman family members in turning up forgotten documents in various attics and basements; and the present Colman archival file, now encompassing several large storage boxes, has become a rich source of contemporary information on the inventor's life and times. It is only fitting that this file should be permanently housed in Rockford College's Howard D. Colman Library, which the inventor's four children established in 1967 in honor of their father's memory.

1

A Solitary Thinker

He (Colman) was a rarely-seen figure on the streets of Rockford.

- *Rockford Morning Star, 1942*

i

Howard Colman's career as an inventor and entrepreneur spanned more than a half century of American life. He grew up, in the 1880s, when there was still a strong handicraft tradition in this country and artisans did mechanical job-work as a way of making ends meet; and he died, during the Second World War, when the United States had become the largest urban industrial nation on earth, with an armaments program incorporating the advanced technologies of mass production and a highly-organized research community involved in the exploration of the new sciences of digital computing, jet propulsion, and applied atomic physics.

Colman himself reflected this kind of change, from self-taught journeyman mechanic to professional research scientist, in his own experimental work. As a boy, he made a scroll saw out of a hoop skirt and equipped his own wood shop with a homemade lathe. He used a knife and chisel to build a warp-drawing machine for the production of cotton cloth when he was sixteen; and he became so absorbed in the problems of warp preparation by the time he was a college student that he decided to quit his classes and concentrate all his efforts on ways to improve this device. He was always his best teacher. Throughout his life, his happiest moments seem to have been spent in the imaginary world of his own experiments. If other people saw his textile machines as combinations of pulleys, levers, and gears, Colman saw them as peculiar expressions of force and motion and the conversion of energy into solid forms. His mind could easily interpret complex mechanical actions, and he visualized the solutions to many engineering problems by building up a picture in his head of the most familiar elements and then rearranging them until new configurations presented themselves. He was able, his friends said, to think like a machine.

The experiments in warp preparation that Colman carried out in the early days of his company served him well in later life. Sales of his small, hand-operated mechanical knotter for yarn ends (patented in 1901) helped to stabilize the business and provided the necessary capital for an expansion of his experimental facilities. The knotter also anticipated the development of a warp-tying machine, which was put into production three years later, and a line of highly-successful warping and spooling devices, which were introduced at the time of the First World War. The kind of mental operations that Colman went through to design these products, the determination of speeds, motions, and mechanical relationships, provided the conceptual background for his innovations in other fields. He ventured into the production of milling cutters and, eventually, the manufacture of hobbing machines because of his inability to purchase commercial gears that were accurate enough to meet his standards. He experimented with radio frequencies and electrical current in the development of the first remote-controlled overhead garage door, and some of the by-products of his researches were a radically-improved shaded pole motor, a new line of temperature-control instruments and furnace regulators, and an extremely durable and quiet-running standard electric fan. In the 1920s, we know, he toyed briefly with the design of a jet engine and began a systematic inquiry into the memory technology of a device for storing messages. The binary system of coding that he employed in his machine, which was known at the time as a multiplex telegraph, looked forward to the development of the first digital computers. Two prototypes of these were actually developed by the Barber-Colman Company in the 1940s, after Colman's death, according to the machine logic that he originally explored.

Colman had a nose for business, and his experiments were usually conducted with the goal of making money. Although he was frustrated by existing patent restrictions and a lack of capital in the early years of his company, he never lost sight of the market for his inventions and was quick to take advantage of opportunities that appeared in the course of his experimental work. His hand-knotter, which he conceived more or less on

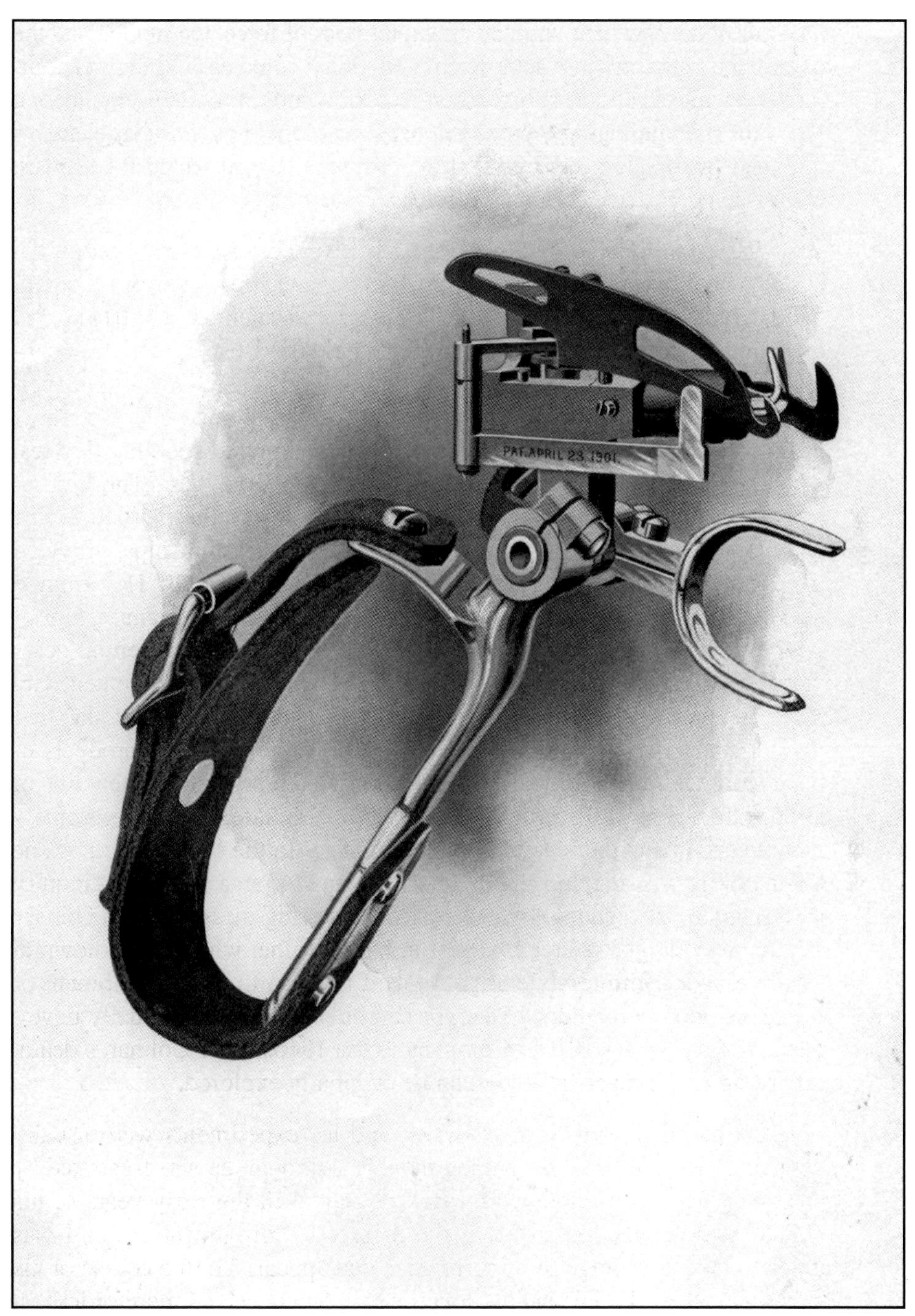

Howard Colman's hand-knotter.

the spur of the moment while testing another invention, was an immediate commercial success and led to the company's first overseas sales; the use of the device was so widespread in American textile mills before World War I that its brand name actually appeared under "knotter" in the *Century Dictionary.* His warp-tying machine proved to be equally popular with cotton manufacturers, attracting considerable industry interest during its preliminary field tests and forcing Colman to construct a new production facility to handle orders for the machine after it was put on the market. The president of the American Cotton Manufacturers Association described it as "one of the most important inventions of the present generation." Another industry expert said that it was "the first radical improvement in the textile art in over 100 years" and compared its impact on mill production to that of the Draper loom. Sales of the knotter and warp-tying machine helped to turn the Barber-Colman Company into a formidable competitor in an expanding market for textile equipment. Once his business was sufficiently capitalized, Colman established separate development groups for each of his product lines and relinquished responsibility for the company's daily operations. The decision freed him from the worries of production scheduling and allowed him to adopt a much broader experimental focus. He could look for new applications of his existing patents, explore opportunities in other commercial fields, and indulge a lifelong interest in the physical sciences without concerning himself about the immediate practical value of his investigations.

As president and majority shareholder, Colman structured the company to his advantage. He retained the rights to the patents when Barber-Colman was incorporated and then either licensed or sold them outright to the company in exchange for shares of stock. In the beginning, he also insisted on having a contract for his "services as an inventor" and was paid separately for these duties and his work as president. He made all the key decisions about investing, budgeting, and developing new products. He borrowed money from Barber-Colman to buy real estate near the main factory "at his discretion" (Corporate Minutes) and personally held the land in trust until it was needed by the company for expansion. When his colleagues were skeptical about his interest in temperature controls, he established his own subsidiary business to finance his experiments; and after the experiments were successful, he incorporated the business into the company as a new department. "Colman ran the whole cotton-picking place," a contemporary at Barber-Colman remarked. "If a serious problem came up - a machine broke down, some type of bottleneck in production - he'd go out there and ask the people: 'Are you going to fix this or shall I do it for you?' And he always knew exactly what to do." If he controlled the company because he owned most of the stock shares, he directed its strategic development because he understood the process of innovation better than any of his colleagues and had a knack for finding the solutions to problems that no one else could visualize.

Barber-Colman's rapid growth from a small job shop and experimental laboratory into a diversified global corporation made Colman a wealthy man, but money was important to him mainly as a means to an end. Work was his passion. He had very few compelling interests outside of his professional life. Like an anchorite, he walled himself off from the affairs of society. Even his meals and conversations with his family were scheduled to provide rest and refreshment during the intervals of his experimental work; he tried to use the same systematic approach to the conduct of his personal affairs that he did to the management of his business. While he was proud of his inventions and aggressive in defending his patent rights in the courts, he seems to have been genuinely unconcerned about any other kind of personal recognition. He named three of his best-known inventions, the check-pump, knotter, and warp-tying machine, after his partner William Barber, and he might well have continued to use Barber's name in similar promotions of new company products if the latter had not decided to liquidate his interests in the business. Colman's biggest honor was probably his selection by the Franklin Institute to receive the Longstreth Medal for his contributions to textile manufacturing. Most reports of this honor fail to mention that Colman skipped the award ceremony when it was held in Philadelphia (1935).

In general, Colman did what he wanted. He conducted his experiments inconspicuously among a small group of colleagues and let the results determine the pace of his work. He went out of his way to avoid attention. Few people really noticed him. On most days he arrived at the Barber-Colman factory early in the morning, before the start of the first shift, and used the stairway to go directly to his office on the top floor; at the end of the day he sometimes worked by himself when other employees went home. If he stayed late into the evening, he could retire to a small bedroom "penthouse" on the roof of the building that he had constructed adjacent to the Experimental Department. No one knew his schedule exactly, and no one tried to monitor it. In a creative business, freedom was as important as mental preparation, and Colman relished his ability to pursue ideas whenever they came to him and wherever they led him.

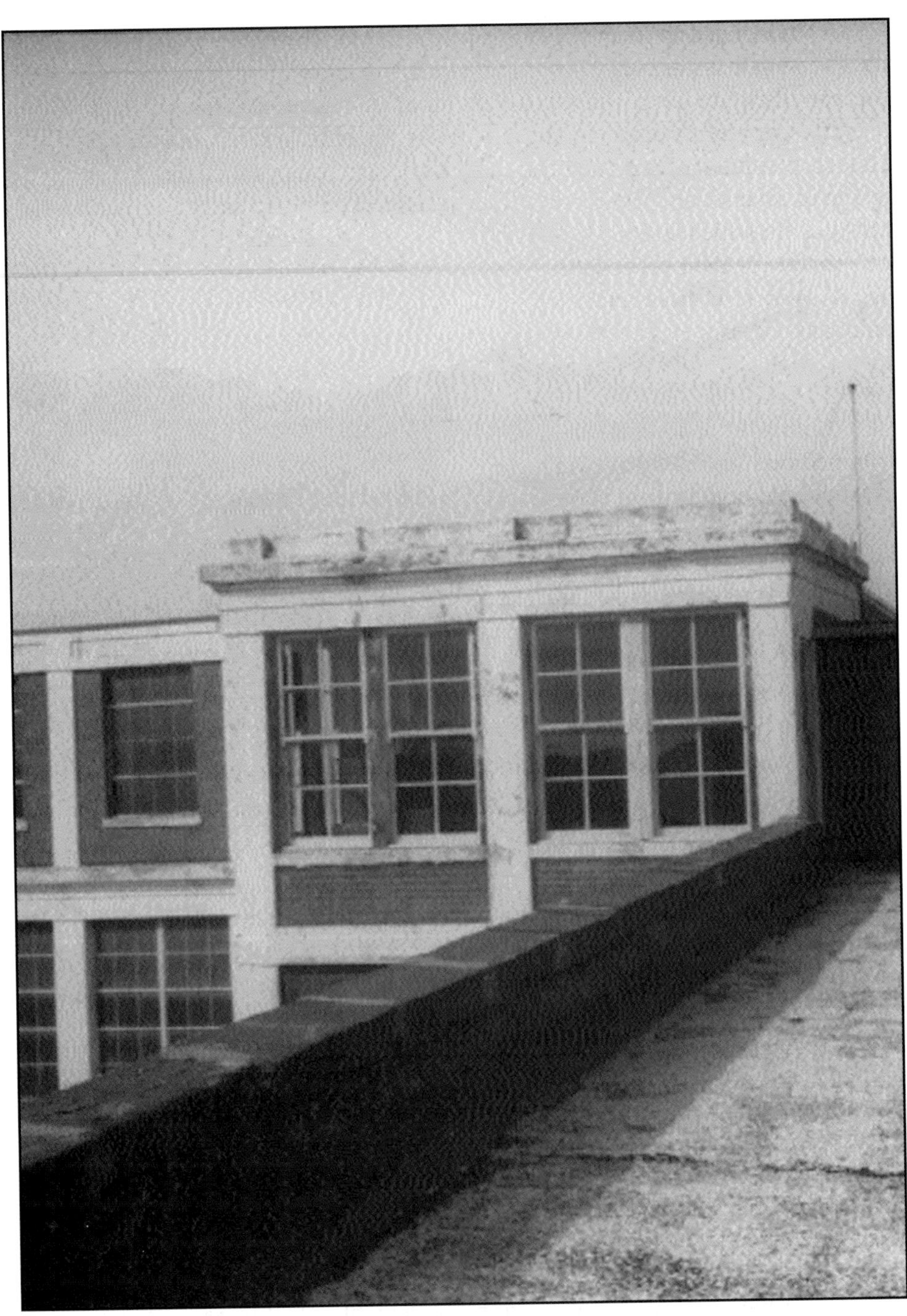

Colman's "penthouse" on the top floor of the Barber-Colman factory in Rockford, as it appeared in 2004.

A Solitary Thinker

Thus isolated from attention and absorbed in his own carefully-organized imaginative routines, Colman passed the majority of his adult life. As the company grew and its number of products increased, his visibility declined proportionately. Corporate research, by its nature, encouraged collective solutions; and what historians have sometimes called the "heroic age of invention" - the period of the late nineteenth and early twentieth centuries in which solitary workers, like the young Thomas Edison, were celebrated for their discoveries - had given way, by the eve of the First World War, to a more anonymous era in which the organized efforts of company experimental departments and the increasing sophistication of their technical problems made individual recognition less common and the results of their investigations far less comprehensible to the general public. Colman's hand-knotter, a small scissors-like device that tied and trimmed two strips of yarn in a single closing motion, was something that most people could relate to when it appeared at the turn of the century; warp preparation was still in its early stages of automation. A few years later, however, the invention was followed by Colman's motor-driven warp-tying machine, and the entire process of warp replenishment had become so complicated that few people outside of the industry could comprehend it. Judging from the amount of attention that the knotter and warp-tying machine attracted in trade publications and the popular press, Colman might have been able to sustain his reputation as an inventor if he had been willing to promote himself and encourage journalists to write about his experiments, as Edison did throughout his career; but these things were intolerable to Colman and beyond his ability even to contemplate.

Except for some friends in the textile industry and a handful of scientific colleagues, Colman was little-known personally outside of the Barber-Colman Company. People may have recognized his name on the business masthead and been aware of his success as an inventor, but mainly as an abstraction, a remote corporate presence. He lived in Rockford, Illinois from the end of the nineteenth century onwards, the majority of this time in a large Eastlake-styled Victorian house on one of the city's finest residential avenues and kept a membership in a local country club, while nevertheless remaining a stranger to most of his townspeople. His rigorous daily schedule, the sheer amount of time that he devoted to his experiments, limited the possibility of random personal contacts. Instead of participating in the social life of the country club, Colman used its golf course for walking, typically in the early morning before others were awake and often in the darkness; a habitual way of organizing his thoughts. Out of respect, his friends at Barber-Colman went through the motions of inviting him to weddings and birthday celebrations, and these would invariably produce the same punning reply when his wife mentioned the requests: "Presents, yes. Presence, no." What was Howard Colman really like? Most people in Rockford would not even have recognized his face, let alone been able to talk about him, and this confusion extended to the employees of his own company. According to his son Walter: "Father never allowed his picture to be taken by a professional or allowed his picture to appear in the newspaper." Reading through the company's old publications and product literature today, one is struck not only by the absence of Colman's photographs but by the limited number of references to the man himself. It's hard to believe that someone so important to the management of a corporation such as Barber-Colman - and thus so vital to the economic well-being of a middle-sized American community such as Rockford, Illinois - could have escaped notice to this extent, but the fact is borne out by a review of the newspapers and business periodicals of his day, and it is something that the people who knew him always emphasize in their reminiscences.

Nothing illustrates this better, perhaps, than a story that made the rounds at Barber-Colman about the inventor's spur-of-the-moment decision one day to use the company elevator instead of climbing the stairs to the Experimental Department. Upon approaching the elevator operator and asking to go to the fifth floor, Colman was told that the area was off-limits to the public. "Who are you?" the operator asked. "Howard Colman," he answered. "Oh, sure," she said, "and I'm Shirley Temple."

ii

Reconstructing the details of a man's life long after his death can be difficult, especially if that man, like Colman, was accustomed to working in private and to revealing as little of himself as possible to the people around him, including the members of his own family. So far as we know, the memorandum books that he kept of his experiments have been destroyed; and it seems unlikely, knowing his habitual reluctance to talk about his feelings, that he ever kept a diary or account of his activities that was not intended to be strictly a professional document. Some of Barber-Colman Company's "daily notes," the minutely-detailed records of the investigations that were carried out under his supervision in the Experimental Department, still exist in old filing cabinets in the company's former Rock Street factory, but the majority are so fragmentary and abstruse that trying to make sense of them seems hardly worth the effort. Colman's letters to his wife Bertha, the ones that remain, are similarly disappointing, mostly travelogues and chronicles of appointments that were composed without forethought and intended to fulfill his social obligations. Here, for example, he writes Bertha (then his fiancée) from Boston, in 1901, during his marketing of the hand-knotter:

> My dear Bertha;
>
> It was awfully good of you to write so soon and when the weather was so hot. The letter came yesterday morning, and I intended to take time in the afternoon to write you a respectable letter, but a man of some importance came in to make my acquaintance, and it took him three hours to do it, and when he was through, there was no afternoon left. Now I am going to Lowell and have only a short time, so I guess you won't get much of a letter. I am selfishly sorry that I couldn't write you yesterday for, if I had, there might have been time for an answer before I left here, but now I guess there isn't. My present plans are to leave here Tuesday evening and stay in Buffalo all day Wednesday until 10:45 in the evening. Reach Rkfd. Thursday evening. If the goodness of your heart extends to dropping me another line, address it c/o that hotel in Buffalo that I wrote you from - I forgot the name, but it begins with a "B."
>
> Everything is lovely here - a few hard knots to untie - but nothing at all to worry about. I must run for the train - no time even to read this over - quite a number of little things I would write about if I had time. Perhaps I will later.
>
> Devotedly,
> Howard

The letter is typical in its rambling manner, its focus on business, and its evasiveness. We never discover the identity of the man of "some importance." We never find out what Colman discussed with him, or what "knots" were left to be untied. Likewise, we assume, his fiancée never got the letter he hoped to write her "later," because he never found the time. That was simply the way he was. His work had a higher priority than anything else in his life. Friends and family learned to accept this, since there was little they could do to make him change. His daughters remember with both fondness and amusement the typed, formal greetings that he sent them at college, having dictated every word to his personal secretary and closed the messages in the same inimitable manner: "Your affectionate father, Howard D. Colman." For the most part, he made a point of avoiding discussions of work with his wife and children, of never mixing "business" and "pleasure" (though it was not always clear which one he really thought was which), and his family correspondence as a result has little to interest a biographer beyond the light that it throws on his personality.

It's unfortunate that not a single one of Colman's closest working associates saw fit to write down his impressions of the inventor or to provide us with behind-the-scenes accounts of the Barber-Colman Company because there were so few people that Colman included among his confidants. His mentor and original partner, William Barber, was more than thirty years his senior and the father of a schoolmate. He retired from the company in 1909, four years after it was incorporated. Colman leaned heavily on him for the financing of his early experiments and used him as both a counselor and technical advisor, especially, in the 1890s, when he was struggling with the designs of his warp-drawing machine; but there is no record of any Barber memoir of this period, and his involvement in the business declined after Colman hired professional managers to oversee the operation.

Luther Miller, who was Colman's patent attorney and a minor partner in the company in 1905, shared a great deal of Colman's time on and off the job and was undoubtedly privy to many of his thoughts. Before he was married, when he rented space in Rockford's Water Power District, Colman had the habit of unwinding in Miller's law office at the end of each work day and of discussing the progress of his experiments with him. Colman made Miller the best man in his wedding, and they took a trip together to the Panama Canal at the time of the First World War; but the two eventually had a falling out, and Miller liquidated his shares in Barber-Colman and moved to California.

Another partner and long-term colleague of Colman's was Harry Severson, who was recruited from the University of Wisconsin in 1901 as the company's first regular employee. Colman was impressed enough with Severson to turn over the management of the business to him not long after this, and he later made him the executor and trustee of his estate, giving him certain discretionary powers over the terms of his bequest. No one was a more conscientious administrator and faithful family friend than this man, whom Colman's children called "Uncle Harry" with their father's encouragement. The fact that he was a civil rather than a mechanical engineer, however, limited his usefulness to Colman in the actual development of his inventions. And for no very good reason - at least for no very good reason that was apparent to anyone else - Colman had the habit of addressing him by his last name, leaving Severson in the quandary of knowing how to reply, preferring to use Colman's first name and hesitating to seem too familiar and usually, in the end, saying ... nothing. This quirky habit was probably insignificant and indicative of little more than Colman's reserve, but it illustrates the way that he held himself back from even his closest friends, and it points out the difficulty that others sometimes had in

Howard Colman (left) in a rare public appearance at the time of the First World War (1915). The photograph was discovered in a scrapbook belonging to Fannie Severson, the wife of Colman's close friend and business partner, Harry Severson, who is shown on the right. A penciled inscription in the scrapbook identifies the event as a "World War I Preparedness Parade."

understanding him. Severson would have made an interesting expert witness in the reconstruction of Colman's career. He would have been able to pull together the different threads of the company's business history and explain how Colman took advantage of market opportunities in the evolution of his experiments. And he would have had a lot to say about the integrity of his friend's creative work, the peculiar way that one product evolved from another, even while possibly admitting that he was not always able to make the best sense out of everything his friend did. Unfortunately, so far as we know, Severson left behind no written record or chronicle of his years at Barber-Colman, only two loose-leaf scrapbooks of photographs and company articles that were clipped from the employee association magazine and compiled by his third wife, Fannie.

Besides the three original partners, Barber, Miller, and Severson, there were probably only a handful of people that Colman trusted enough to share his confidences. One was Martin Noling, the head of his Experimental Department, who helped to launch the company's European operations and worked closely with him on his early patent litigation. Others were his neighbor and protégé Duncan Stewart, a later president of Barber-Colman (1952-63), and his personal physician, Archibald Church, a Chicago neurologist who treated him for his chronic severe headaches and bouts of depression. Still another was his private legal counsel, Emmet Richardson of Milwaukee. What these men knew about him personally and professionally has never been disclosed, though it's hard to imagine that they would have been any more inclined than his business partners to record their impressions for posterity or that, in the case of Church and Richardson, they would have been willing to breach a confidential relationship by saying much about him.

Colman was always an object of interest among his own employees; his remoteness seems to have increased his stature in this respect and embellished the accounts of his inventions, and stories about him circulated in the company for many years after his death. "When I came to Barber-Colman in 1949," Bill Paulson, an engineer, recalled, "he was no longer here, but his presence was still felt and existed in almost every product." Walter Colman, who became chairman of the Barber-Colman board of directors in the 1960s, regularly mentioned his father in his addresses to employees; and various testimonials to the company founder were included in its publications. A small pocket-sized booklet with a facsimile of the Franklin Medal on the back cover was even printed by Barber-Colman in honor of Colman's work (1942). This contained a reminiscence by his colleague Bert Peterson which attempted to put his achievement as an inventor into perspective:

> He started business alone with an idea, and left behind an organization employing approximately 3,000 men and women, engaged in the manufacture of textile machinery, machine tools and cutters, electrical equipment, and molded plastics. Space is too short to give a list of his inventions, but they covered many fields outside of the textile art. He found his greatest pleasure in experimental work and has left behind research departments in every branch to carry on his developments.

If the company appreciated Colman's achievements, however, it allowed many of his papers and artifacts to be destroyed in the years following the Second World War. No one ever tried to preserve his notebooks, apparently, or to set aside an area for his experimental prototypes. The company records that have come down to us, the articles of incorporation, the early corporate minutes, the file folders of random product literature, and the employee association magazines, seem to have survived because of neglect. They were put away in a safe or file drawer and simply forgotten. Like most companies, Barber-Colman was much more concerned about its immediate business future than its past, and if it dealt at all with the remnants of its early corporate history, it was usually to get rid of them.

Roger Schuette, who started working at Barber-Colman as an electrical engineer during the last years of Colman's life, remembered being asked in the 1940s to help clear out a warehouse near the company's Rock Street plant in order to make room for inventory. To his amazement, he found the building "just filled with the study models of Colman's inventions, including some very early radio-controlled door operators, typewriters and receiving printers for the multiplex telegraph." On his supervisor's orders, "everything was scrapped." Schuette was particularly interested in the drawing of a jet engine, which was "torpedo-shaped with a combustion chamber" and signed with Colman's name (it was dated "1921"). The discovery made an impression on him at the time, he said, because jet technology was still in its comparative infancy, the first turbojet designs in the world having only appeared a decade earlier.

Colman once told his daughter Dorothy that he'd had hundreds of ideas for every one that ended up as a patent application. This is supported by contemporary accounts of the many different prototypes and concept drawings in his experimental area at Barber-Colman, and we may well wonder now what other things, besides the sketch of the jet engine, were being stored in the warehouse that Schuette and his co-workers cleared out, and what preliminary models of future inventions might have been discovered there if the contents had been saved. The trouble was, of course, that the key to deciphering these things was Colman himself. He had everything in his head. Even a simple coupling mechanism was associated in his mind with a larger complex of experimental ideas; a drawing of a rotating shaft would have been linked to other drawings of treadles and sprocket wheels, whose precise relationships and importance were only known to him. His Barber-Colman colleagues were aware of this, and they were willing to discard his study models for this reason.

iii

Inevitably perhaps, with the passing of time, Colman's achievements ceased to be important to anyone but his family. It was his children who kept his memory alive and made an effort to preserve the records and documents of his professional career. His letters to his wife Bertha from 1900-02 were stored by Ruth Colman Tower in an old candle box. Family photographs, a few formal portraits from his 1902 wedding and his early years at Barber-Colman, and an assortment of factory views and mechanical studies, including an interesting sequence of his warp-drawing machine (1895), were kept in manila envelopes. Copies of various speeches on Colman, which were delivered posthumously, were filed with at least one speech from his own lifetime: his father's semi-humorous presentation to the company's athletic association on his son's first experiments ("A Peep into the Early History of the Barber-Colman Company," 1914). His children collected articles from newspapers and magazines, ranging from English journals, such as the *Manchester Guardian* and *Evening Chronicle*, to American textile trade publications and Rockford newspapers; these covered the entire 20th Century. They also preserved the autobiographical monographs of Colman's father ("Sketch of the Life of Henry Colman," 1923) and mother ("Memory Pictures," 1929), and a reminiscence written by his sister Laura ("Episodes in the Life of Howard Colman," 1942).

The family became a natural repository for documents from Colman's colleagues and friends, especially product brochures, commemorative publications, and records of patent litigation. From 1904 onwards, Colman spent a good deal of time either defending his patents or initiating lawsuits as a result of their infringement, and the surviving transcripts of these court proceedings help us understand the progress of his experiments between 1893-1919.

When the legal arguments in favor of an inventor's "pioneering rights" are as meticulously documented as Colman's were over the course

Colman's residence at 929 N. Main Street, Rockford, Illinois in the 1920s.

of a long career, the courtroom records become a rich source of information about the man himself. There are thousands of pages in the 20-odd legal briefs and transcripts of record in the possession of the Colman family, many of them concerned with procedural issues and complex interpretations of the law, and the testimony is often so technically-complex and comprehensive on both sides of the issue that it's hard to follow the course of the proceedings. (During one Barber-Colman lawsuit before the U.S. Patent Court of Appeals, a lawyer observed that he had seldom encountered a case "more carefully and exhaustively tried and considered.") Yet there are diamonds among the sawdust, and the volumes pay re-reading. Barber-Colman's 515-page "rebuttal testimony" from a lawsuit against the American Warp Drawing Machine Company (1920), for instance, contains the transcripts of 122 letters that Barber and Colman exchanged between 1894-1903. The letters were read into the trial record as "contemporaneous proof" of Colman's financial situation and "mental point of view" while working on his inventions.

According to his own court testimony, Colman took great pains in the composition of these letters, sometimes preparing rough drafts or study copies before putting them in the mail. Compared to the correspondence with his fiancée, which is limited by a kind of conventional politeness, his letters to Barber are forthright, thoughtful, and articulate. They give us a feeling for his aspirations as an inventor, his sacrifices in pursuing his experiments, his negotiating skills, his doubts and financial worries. His relationship with Barber was much closer and much more critical to his growth as a businessman and experimental scientist than has generally been acknowledged in the histories of the company. (Colman himself always honored Barber's contributions, even to the extent of minimizing his own, as in his decision to name three of his earliest inventions after his partner.) The letters show the many ways that Colman benefitted from his relationship with Barber during the long period of solitary experimentation (1891-1903) that led to his first successful commercial inventions.

In preparing for a patent trial in the U.S. District Court of Massachusetts in 1916, Colman assembled several boxes of documents relating to his earliest scientific work: cash books, cancelled checks, photographs, engineering drawings, and old letters that he had exchanged with Luther Miller, Fred Barber, William Barber, and other business associates between 1891-96. These boxes, because of their importance to the company, were delivered personally by Martin Noling to W. Orison Underwood, the Barber-Colman legal counsel in Boston, and after relevant portions were introduced into evidence at the trial, the materials were returned to Rockford and kept in different locations in the Rock Street factory, including a safe in what was known at the time as the "Tower Room" and a steel strongbox that was locked up, according to an old inventory sheet, in "H.D. Colman's personal filing cabinet and case." In the 1940s, after Colman's death, his son Walter evidently went through the contents of the safe and strongbox and removed many of these documents, along with other papers belonging to his father, to his own residence in Rockford. (Among the documents was a large pasteboard transfer file containing the copies of more than 250 letters and notes that Colman exchanged with William Barber between January 4, 1896 - December 4, 1900 on the subject of the check pump invention, apparently their *entire* correspondence in 1896-97, and a major portion of their correspondence during the following three years.) The documents ended up in an attic over Walter's garage on Spring Creek Road in Rockford and, after his death in 1983, were more or less forgotten by the family. They did not see the light of day again until 1998, when a great-grandson discovered them while rummaging through the attic.

Still another collection of Colman's letters, written to his daughter Dorothy between 1934-42, surfaced after her death at the turn of the century (2000). The letters, which are self-reflective to an unusual degree, offer a rare glimpse of Colman's private affairs: his social contacts and routines at home, his horseback riding, his delight in nature, his fascination with cameras, his flippancy in conversation. Considered alongside the manuscripts from the safe and strongbox, particularly those written between 1891-1903, they add an important dimension to our sense of him as a creative personality.

In the end, the definitive record of Colman's inventions is the four-volume set of his Letters Patent (U.S. Patent Office) that was compiled by Leydig, Voit and Mayer, the successor to the original Rockford firm of Morrison and Miller that Colman engaged in the 1890s to do his legal work. The volumes were presented to Ruth Colman Tower at the time of the sale of the Barber-Colman Company (1987) as a means of commemorating the law firm's long relationship with the manufacturer. Containing specifications for each of his 149 patents, with detailed technical drawings illustrating the mechanisms' operations, the books establish the basic framework for our assessment of Colman's technical achievement.

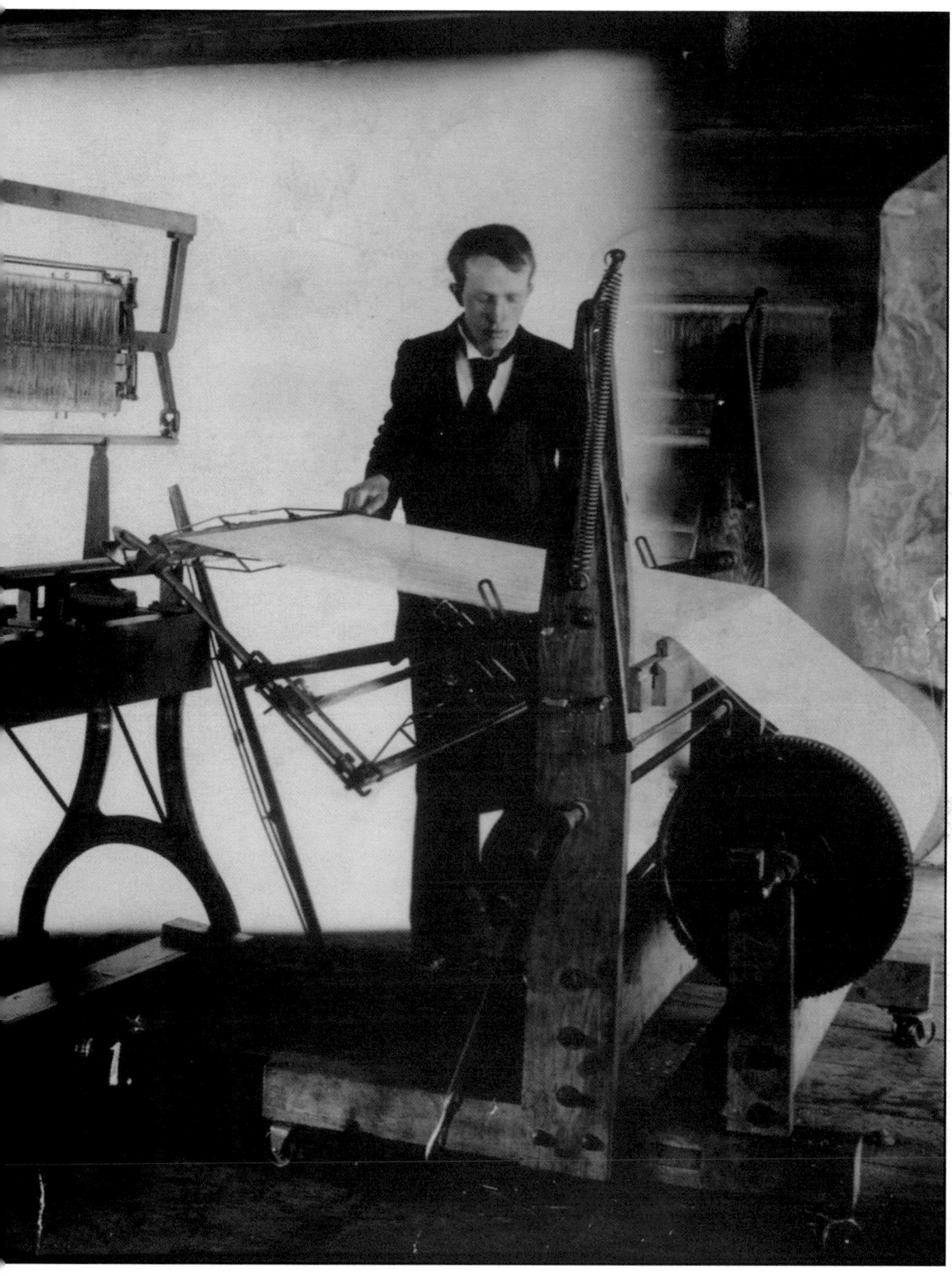

n and his warp drawing-in machine (D.I.M.) in the 1890s. The photograph was taken in the inventor's second-floor hop in the Spengler Brothers' building in Rockford. A white sheet was used as a backdrop.

2
Memory Pictures

Her son Howard, the youngest of her four children, is known to have believed that he owed to her much of what he was able to accomplish in his lifetime.

- Article on Howard Colman's mother, Lucinda Colman, in the Barber-Colman News, 1951

i

Howard Colman's gift for invention was unprecedented in his family. None of his ancestors, so far as we know, ever engaged in manufacturing or showed much interest in tinkering with mechanisms, and none achieved a fraction of his business success. Both his father, Henry Colman, and grandfather, Henry Root Colman, were Methodist ministers, bookish men whose talents inclined more to writing and public speaking than to the kinds of abstract thinking that are usually associated with experimental science. On the surface, Henry Colman was unlike his son, actively promoting his political views through journals and lectures, advocating for social reforms, and enjoying his status as an elected official of his church's annual conference. In middle age he is said to have resembled the founder of Methodism, John Wesley, and he apparently encouraged this association by wearing his hair in a bob, in the 18th Century fashion. "I sent each of the children my picture," he wrote in his diary (1907). "I confess I would like to hear and see from the curtains all of them as they open my picture. And I would be pleased to hear Anna's [his daughter's] exclamation as she gets the first view ..." It's hard to imagine his son Howard ever saying this or allowing himself to be photographed for a similar purpose.

While Howard respected his father and went out of his way to please him, he looked elsewhere for his earliest mentors. Henry Colman had little evident mechanical ability. There are few references in his diaries to tools, crafts, and labor-saving devices, and there's nothing to suggest even a passing interest in the kinds of things that his son found immediately appealing as a child: wheels, gears, couplings, the effects of gravity, and the nature of power transmission. The elder Colman's concerns were academic rather than practical. For the most part, he spent his time on issues of temperance and social justice, and when he used his hands, it was mainly to write in his journals, cultivate flowers, and do the family laundry. An unusual aversion to getting dirty limited his range of activities. "He was most careful in his personal habits," the *Milwaukee Journal* noted in his obituary (1927). "His cleanness of person and clothing seemed almost a part of his religion." In Henry Colman's eyes, nothing was nobler than a "*clean*, genuine man" (emphasis added) and nothing more inspiring than a person who devoted himself to others in the spirit of "good will" (Address of Welcome, Barber-Colman Association, 1917).

The life that Howard Colman led was fundamentally different from this, for he seemed to have had as little interest in social issues as his father did in technical ones (Howard was absorbed by the challenges of his experimental work to the exclusion of almost all outside pursuits). His machining was a noisy and messy affair, full of the sounds of cutting metals and permeated by the smell of oils and lubricants. It was an environment, one suspects, that his father found immediately disagreeable.

Howard Colman's relationship to his mother appears to have been more complicated, if only because he openly acknowledged her influence on his development and shared many of her characteristic mental habits. Both enjoyed word games and demonstrated a remarkable visualizing capacity: she in her storytelling and recitation of Biblical parables; he in his ability to understand the sequences of an experiment by picturing the forces and motions of its mechanical elements. Lucinda (Darling) Colman may have lacked a scientific background, but she was a lively conversationalist who impressed others with detailed accounts of her past experiences - even remembering her impressions, as a five year old, of arriving in Chicago for the first time:

> I can see the tavern that father takes us to, a white frame building. As we go up the stairs we land in a sort of lobby, furnished with a couch and chairs. There is a long hall running to the north, with many doors on either side ... I can see my mother sitting on the couch and a woman acquaintance she made on the boat sitting near her. Mother is helping her to trim a new bonnet. I can see her rolling the ribbon over the top of the bonnet and making a large bow ...

She kept these images, she said, in the "attic" of her brain like old photographs and recalled them more or less at will. In her nineties, at her children's urging, she drew upon them extensively in the composition of a 30,000-word autobiography. The book used the images as cues in the reconstruction of her experiences and employed a stream-of-consciousness narrative to collect her impressions. As she admitted, the finished manuscript was mostly "a long rambling" through her "memory gallery," a series of chronological captions for pictures that were invisible:

> The pictures keep well even if we do not turn them to the light very often (Memory Pictures, 1932).

Howard's own powers of memorization, sustained by an acute visual-spatial intelligence, were vital to his inventive work, and one assumes that much of this ability was inherited from his mother.

Lucinda (Darling) Colman, it should be added, was no more mechanically-inclined than her husband and much less interested in the kinds of "curiosities" - unusual aspects of science, history, and geography - that he routinely noted in his "Omnibus Book" (1854-1906). Both considered scholarship to be the highest form of human endeavor. Both graduated in the first class of Lawrence College (1857), and both taught Latin and Greek in an Evansville, Wisconsin academy for several years after they were married. Lucinda was the first woman to earn a master's degree from Lawrence, and Henry the first person of either sex to receive an honorary doctorate in divinity from the college. They were well-matched in tastes and temperament. Lucinda became one of the pioneers in the state of Wisconsin in early-childhood education, the head of the WCTU in Milwaukee, and the secretary of the state's Methodist Missionary Conference. She was her husband's equal as a scholar and social reformer, but somewhat more unorthodox in her thinking and less personally ambitious. Her self-effacing behavior, in certain ways, was suggestive of her son's, even though it expressed a different imaginative world and different intellectual concerns.

It's always interesting to speculate on the ways that heredity and environment contribute to the development of an exceptional creative gift. Howard Colman certainly reflected the talents of both parents, and he was fortunate to grow up in a family that honored learning and personal achievement to the extent that it did. The elder Colmans expected their children to excel academically, and they hoped that Howard would one day enroll at Lawrence College and answer a call to the ministry, like his father and grandfather. They assumed that he would play an active role in the

Lucinda Darling (right) as she appeared in 1857 at the time of her graduation from Lawrence College.

Methodist Church in some capacity, even as a layman, and that his formal education would more or less follow their own. The fact that he was attracted to the sciences at an early age and pursued these interests into adulthood as an inventor must have been as surprising to them as it is today to anyone who considers Colman's achievements in the light of his family background.

Where did this creativity come from? Why was a minister's son born with such a prodigious talent for mechanical invention when no one else in his family - parents, siblings, and children - ever demonstrated a fraction of the same ability? His daughter Dorothy considered his inventiveness to be the result of a variation in genetic type similar to that of a sport in biology, a result of random changes in cellular structure; and certainly it's hard to account for the appearance of his talent in any other way.

Notwithstanding his choice of a scientific career, Colman modeled his behavior on his parents and internalized their values. He obviously appreciated their companionship because he remained in regular, close contact with them throughout his adulthood. After the Barber and Colman Company was successfully established, he subsidized their monthly income. He also purchased cars for them, bought them a house, and otherwise provided for their welfare. In the entire written record of the Colman family, there is not a single instance of him having been anything but a dutiful son. "If the commandment 'Honor thy father and thy mother that thy days may be long' [can be interpreted literally] ...," his father noted in his diary (1917), "then he [Howard] shall have two centuries." Colman never practiced religion as an adult, but he remained an observant Methodist in everything except theology.

ii

Henry Colman was a descendant of English Puritans who emigrated to North America in the seventeenth century. Records show that his American ancestors were farmers in Massachusetts and Connecticut, and that Henry's father, Henry Root Colman, who combined farming and preaching, moved from the East in 1840 to become a missionary to the Oneida Indians of northeast Wisconsin. Young Henry attended his father's mission school and spent several years of his childhood in a crude log parsonage in the vicinity of Green Bay. As an adolescent, he worked on his brother Charles' farm and hired himself out to a neighboring family where his "business" was to tend "a little garden," take care of a cow, "feed and trim the horse ... [and] especially ... please the baby" (Sketch of the Life of Henry Colman).

After his father was reassigned by the Methodist Church to a district near Appleton and chosen as a trustee of the new Lawrence College there, Henry devoted more of his time to academic work. He learned Latin and Greek from his father's "dictations" (Sketch); and in 1853 he enrolled in the College's classical program, joined a debating society known as the Philalethaeans, and taught in a local preparatory school as a means of supporting himself. It was at Lawrence that Henry met his future wife, Lucinda Darling, a classmate from Racine. The two were married in 1860, and a year later Henry entered the ministry.

Because of the Methodist policy in the nineteenth century of rotating preachers among the churches of a region, Henry and Lucinda moved sixteen times in the course of his career, serving both rural and urban Wisconsin congregations, and bringing his children up in parsonages that usually were furnished with donated articles from the members of the local church. He estimated that he traveled 5,000 miles a year while receiving an average of $1400 in wages, the use of a parsonage, and free rail service. An entry from his 1887 diary indicates how he spent his days:

> I read some, turned out two weeks washing, cut some wood, prepared a sermon, read more, went to Springfield in the stage, walked 3 miles, made 5 calls, talked new churches ..., preached a sermon prepared last week, ... took two more probationers, and walked near 3-1/2 miles, reaching home at 9:35.

In 1897 he organized the Wisconsin Anti-Saloon League and campaigned throughout the state "to help secure law enforcement and stir up public sentiment" (Sketch). He accepted his last pastorate the following year in Milwaukee, and he retired in 1909, at the age of 75, after spending more than a half century in the ministry. He continued to take an active interest in politics and church affairs until his death in 1927.

If Henry Colman's career was distinguished by its longevity, his private life - as revealed in his Omnibus Book and diaries - was remarkable for the range of his intellectual interests. He was a compulsive note-taker who recorded everything that caught his fancy: facts on climate and the ocean depths, an outline of nebular theory, 170 common words among the languages of different continents, predictions of future "Great Events," household remedies for colds, statistics on the world's religions, burial sites of English sovereigns, descriptions of the sunrise by famous authors, names of "Great Men Believers" and "Great Men Skeptics," and ideas for intellectual improvement. In the back of his Omnibus Book, he listed the

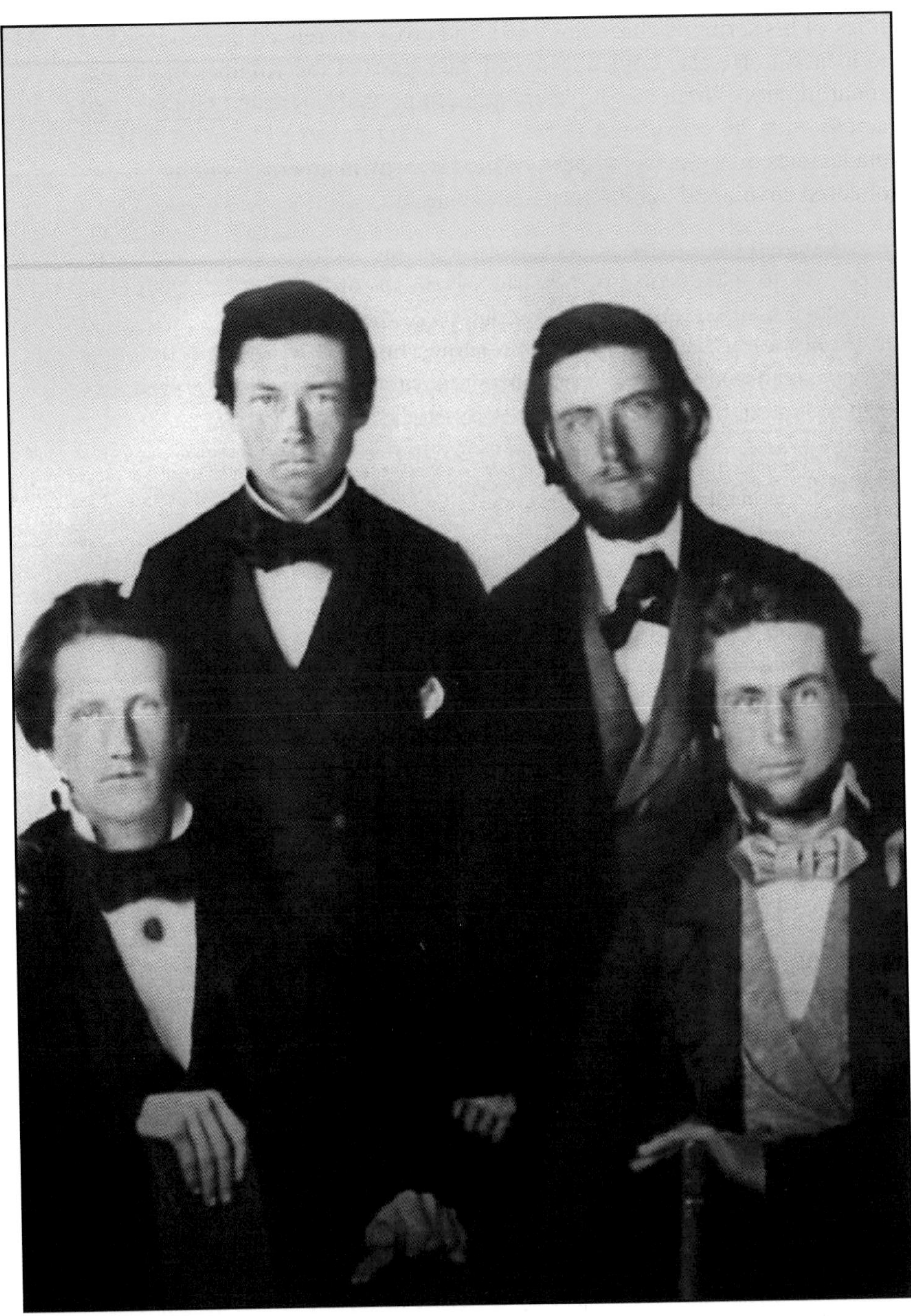

The male members of the first graduating class of Lawrence College in 1857. Henry Colman appears, left, in the front row.

titles of his sermons chronologically and cross-referenced them according to location. He also copied down all the names of the volumes in his personal library. Whenever he heard something that interested him or came across what he considered to be an important passage in his reading, he made notes on a piece of paper and filed it away in an envelope; his "index of scrap envelopes" had 83 different subjects.

Colman used these notes for sermons and lectures, but a larger purpose was to make sense of a world whose scientific "facts" appeared to challenge many traditional interpretations of the Scriptures. He struggled to bring the information from his readings into accord with his religious views, and he sometimes found himself as much at odds with the members of his own church as he did with the scientific community:

> Ever since the Renaissance, word war has waged between those who saw, or thought they saw, new revelations of God's ways in the great worlds without us and within us, and those who had devoutly harmonized the older science and the Word ... When I began [preaching], the war, at times bloody, concerning astronomy and Scripture had become history, and already astronomy had given new meaning to the Psalmist's "The heavens declare the glory of God." Then it was geology and the Bible. How we young fellows from college fought to prove that the day periods of the Bible were also the long cataclysmic periods of geology. Later we wrestled with the slimy serpent of Evolution. Often did the monster lie dead on the field. Nine lives! He had ninety and nine lives ...

Colman was generally regarded by his Methodist colleagues as having an "open mind toward the new in science and theology" (*Milwaukee Journal,* 1927). He realized that researchers would continue to discover important "truths" about the natural world - truths, in turn, that would help to shape an understanding of its fundamental purpose and reality - and he thought that one of the critical tasks of Methodism was to reconcile these experimental "facts" with the teachings of the Bible. Could a rational science coexist with religion? Were the only real explanations of the world mathematical and empirical? Did the observable phenomena in nature provide evidence of a Supreme Being? Or did they indicate an evolutionary process which was merely random and purposeless? Colman thought that the evidence of modern science, when broadly interpreted, reinforced a system of religious belief. Science proved that all things originated from the same matter and were shaped by the same laws, and it was hard to conceive of this happening "without an originator." He saw evidence of a unitary process at work in different living objects, serpents that "appeared to possess in an undeveloped form the limbs of other animals" and "animals, in embryo, pass[ing] through the lower orders of life:"

> Serpents' ribs are legs; elephant's snout is a hand; some breath[e] with lungs, some with gills. Gills and teeth [resemble each other] in embryonic form.

The human foetus itself, when "imperfectly developed," resembled that of a "fish or reptile." Was it impossible to imagine reptilian orders, in the earlier stages of evolutionary development, giving rise to mammalian features? Was this any harder to believe than some of the anthropological oddities that appeared in the popular press?

> Sewell, when traveling in Germany, found a man who had in his laboratory all kinds of cold-blooded animals reduced to a state of torpidity; also a young woman that had been a convict, who had been thus preserved 12 years & whom the man had no doubt he could restore ... [and] a young woman in Canada who had done her regular business for 15 months without eating.

Colman liked to reflect on the relationship between "Scientific Faiths and Religious Facts." If imagination and intuition were too little valued in scientific research, it was likewise true that most religious thinkers were unwilling to use logic to explain the phenomena of the natural world. He found it strangely reassuring to think that the flux around him could be interpreted by abstract, mathematical analysis. "All the planets move in one plane and with their satellites in one direction from west to east," he wrote. "Had these matters been left to chance, the chances against this uniformity would have been at millions of [a] million to one." He was fascinated by statistics, calculating the numbers of "Spiritualists," "Materialists," "Nominalists," and "Conceptualists" in the world. He worked out the approximate numbers of births and deaths in the nineteenth century, the populations of different age groupings, and ratios of missionaries and missionary preachers to the total population. On the basis of this, he estimated that it would take at least 50,000 years to make everyone in the world a "Nominal Christian." He collected statistics on ocean depths, elevations of table lands in Asia, long and short slopes in the Old and New Worlds (" ... in each world, there is a minor law corresponding with the major of the other"), distances in the solar system, and planetary temperatures and masses. He was intrigued by the notion of a fundamental substance in the universe, a tasteless, weightless, intangible ether that permeated everything and provided a medium for the transmission of light. He could not look at a sunset without thinking about its deeper religious significance, and a brilliant evening sky occasionally moved him to eloquence:

> Stretching across the western sky was a huge bank of saffire. Above, rubies would be pale. Mountains of fire were rolling and heaving. Yet how easily would an aeroplane float through ether, nor would the occupants' vision be dimmed. To me, it seems two vast walls impenetrable. Yet vapory and nearly nothing as it all is, it reflects the blazing glory of the sun and moves through the world of ether, more dense than the solid rocks, so dense that gold and lead are but as finest gossamer, the densest of all known substances.
>
> That ether brings to us the brightest of the sun, nor does it leave the heat of that vast orb. All power known to earth or known on earth is from the sun, and the ether brings it all. Men experiment on the power of radium to stimulate plant life and tell us that radium to the value of one thousand dollars does not give as much energy to an acre as the sun gives to a foot square in thirty minutes. Ether is power and life. With[out] it, the universe would collapse. In it, we live and move and have our being. Is it God? I hesitate. It is cold matter, yet it may not be.

Henry Colman was an uncommon man, a linguist and classical scholar, a social reformer, and a philosopher of science. He had a wide-ranging curiosity and appetite for information that complicated his sense of a religious calling. Although different from Howard in personality, he resembled him in certain fundamental ways. He had the same capacity for disciplined inquiry and sustained introspection. He had the same reserves of energy. Like Howard, he enjoyed statistics and methodical proofs, and he had a similar habit of challenging himself with mental puzzles as a means of stimulating his imagination. He was also a perfectionist who became unhappy when his work bogged down or failed to meet his expectations:

> I am not pleased that all thru my life, my spiritual self has found so little expression in my diary. These columns have dealt almost wholly with the outward facts of life, with very little note or comment. This is not the better way to develop either spiritual or intellectual growth.
>
> Should any one be so foolish as to read my diary, he would not know that I claim to have spiritual life. And what have I to record? That I pray so many times daily and search the Scriptures daily? All true, but of what interest? I must confess that I have difficulty in fixing my thoughts when I kneel.

The note of despondency in these "self-examinations" will be heard again in his son Howard's correspondence, particularly in the accounts of experiments gone awry. His frustrated accounts of experiments with textile machines, in particular, are reminiscent of his father's diaries.

iii

Lucinda Colman's ancestors came to this country from northern Ireland in the eighteenth century. The earliest immigrant family was Scots Presbyterian and headed by a shipbuilder named Andrew Hunter, who settled in Connecticut. A grandson of Hunter's served as a captain in the American Army of Independence and established a homestead in New York state at the conclusion of the Revolutionary War. He was Lucinda's great-grandfather; and she eventually became the owner of one of the seven silver spoons that he fashioned from the hilt of his Army sword.

She was born near Lake Ontario in upstate New York in 1835 and moved with her parents to a farm outside of the village of Racine, Wisconsin five years later. As it happened, her trip to the Midwest coincided with that of her future husband, whose family pulled up stakes on its own New York farm in the same year and followed the same route through the Erie Canal and the Great Lakes to Wisconsin. She and Henry would not actually meet until their first year at Lawrence (1853), but in the interval their lives followed similar paths. She lived in a "log house with one large room" and rode with her parents in a wagon hitched to a pair of steers (Memory Pictures). Her mother, a former schoolteacher, supplemented Lucinda's early education with home lessons and seems to have been at least partially responsible for the child's rapid academic advancement. In 1848, at the age of thirteen, Lucinda was certified by the Caledonia School District as an instructor in its summer school, a significant achievement even considering the likely shortage of teachers in the region. She wrote easily and well and was known both for her extensive vocabulary and habit of punning. It's interesting that one of the things she remembered most clearly from her childhood was the times she learned new words and expressions.

Contemporaries described her as "spirited" and "independent," though they noted that she was never deliberately provocative and always tried to accommodate herself to the social conventions of the day. While many Wisconsin churches in the nineteenth century encouraged their members to dress plainly and avoid any appearance of self-indulgence, Lucinda wore a bustle and hoop skirt, put flowers and ribbons in her hair, and regularly enjoyed herself at dances. She did what was reasonable and consistent with her beliefs. The bylaws of coeducational colleges like Lawrence offended her because of their "numerous and explicit" rules on the relations between the sexes. During her four years there, young men and women were not allowed to associate outside of classes unless they were attending church or sharing umbrellas. (After meeting Lucinda, Henry Colman carried an umbrella with him wherever he went and secretly referred to himself as her "rain beau," a name that may well have originated with Lucinda herself.)

She considered Lawrence's bylaws to be a "joke" since they ended up suggesting "activities and transgressions that would never be thought of without them." In her opinion, the prominent public notices of the bylaws in the college merely tempted people to break the rules. At her graduation, Lucinda and the other female members of her class were prevented by college protocol from sitting on the platform, causing her later to observe ironically that it seemed "more *dignified* on commencement day to have only men on the rostrum" (emphasis added).

Reading Lucinda Colman's memoirs now, one is impressed not just by her fluency and good humor but by the peculiar way she viewed the world. She made an effort to "see something beautiful everyday," and she controlled her emotions by holding cold water in her mouth whenever she started to get angry and by recalling pleasant "pictures." Her imaginative life seems to have been vivid enough to buffer even the most debilitating thoughts. However she used her meditations, we know that they were unusually attractive to her, and that the longer and harder she dwelled on them, the more difficult it was to let them go. Once, on a trip to California, when her clothing trunk was misplaced, she went through the process of visualizing its contents and mourning the disappearance of each garment in turn. Her memories of the clothes added to her sense of loss, and the shock of the loss fixed them in her mind.

Then the trunk was unexpectedly recovered:

> This is an interesting picture. Home again! What do we see standing in our dining room? Our trunk that we had checked to San Francisco. We doubted our ever seeing it again. My memory pictures of the garments I would like - and of those I must have - and of those I must do without - are immediately thrown into the waste basket.

What is curious about this is that, in composing her memoirs, she thought first of her feelings in losing the "mental pictures of the garments" rather than her relief in getting the actual trunk back.

Lucinda Colman in her eighties. The photograph was used as the frontispiece of her book of reminiscences.

Memory Pictures

Lucinda's reflections took on an independent life in her mind and existed for her in a kind of virtual spatio-temporal reality. They were treasured for their significance as well as for the vividness of their imagery ("This picture is now one of the dear memories that will often be recalled ... "), though she also recognized that all the pictures would become dimmer in the course of time ("While we are looking at a picture, it begins to grow old".) If Henry Colman was intrigued by the theory of a celestial ether as the fundamental substance of the universe, his wife was instinctively drawn to an even older neo-platonic notion of ideas that are eternally present. Minds, like radio receivers, she thought, simply picked these things up:

> We spend two days with daughter Anna and her husband in Omaha. Again they are hearing the call of the West. *"Seattle" is on the air this time* (emphasis added).

It was more than a metaphor. Whatever existed in nature could also be discovered in the realm of ideas ("Automobiles keep up with our thinking, sometimes get a little ahead..."), and such thoughts eventually transformed themselves into the elements they were contemplating:

> This picture shows us listening in - The radio, by my side - is picking up wonderful things on the air - Lovely Music, College Lectures - Literature - History - Ancient and Modern. I wonder if some time in the great future - the very words - spoken by Adam and Eve - may not be caught - floating around in space - by the radio and broadcast to us who are listening in!

iv

Howard Colman was fortunate in his birth, growing up in a highly-educated and civilized family that recognized his precociousness, supported him financially while he conducted his earliest experiments, and set an example for him of patient scholarship. He was given special treatment as a child and permitted to explore his mechanical interests to his heart's content. Every Colman parsonage had a de facto shop or laboratory area reserved exclusively for him. His parents gave him tools and materials at an early age and marveled at his handiwork. If the religious environment of the house, with its Bible readings and formal prayers, sometimes seemed oppressive to him, it nevertheless was one in which learning was highly valued, and Howard could benefit from thoughtful family discussions on a variety of subjects in addition to religion. His father was a student of six languages, an omnivorous reader, and an amateur statistician who had more in common with his son intellectually than either of them was willing to admit. His mother, whom he idolized, had the same sort of literary interests as her husband, but she also possessed a rare capacity for visualization that evidently was passed on to her son and later distinguished his experimental career.

3

Early Years

I had no mechanical education except what I picked up myself, what I studied myself. I had no formal education. But I began from my early childhood to interest myself in things mechanical, and to work with tools and build machines.

- From Howard Colman's court testimony, 1919

i

Wisconsin was Howard Colman's home for the first twenty-one years of his life. He was born, on July 9, 1873, in the small southeastern town of Waukesha, and he afterwards lived in four other southern and lakeshore communities, including Milwaukee, while his father fulfilled assignments to different Methodist churches. He received his formal education in Wisconsin schools and academies, and completed his freshman year at Beloit College before dropping out to devote himself to his inventions. As someone who learned to do mechanical work on his own, he modeled himself on the tradesmen and jobbers that he encountered while growing up and internalized much of Wisconsin's older handicraft tradition. He acquired a knack for construction by watching carpenters cut and join pieces of wood and by working with tools he fashioned himself. He learned the elements of machine design, the relation between weight and displacement, and the effects of linear and rotary motion from his visits to factories such as the Beaver Dam Cotton Mills, where he was first inspired to build a device to solve the problem of warp replenishment during his days at Wayland Academy. He filled his head with images of waterwheels, drivelines, and gear trains transmitting power to other mechanisms. He knew the weight and feel of different woods and metals because he learned instinctively through his hands and body, as well as, more logically,

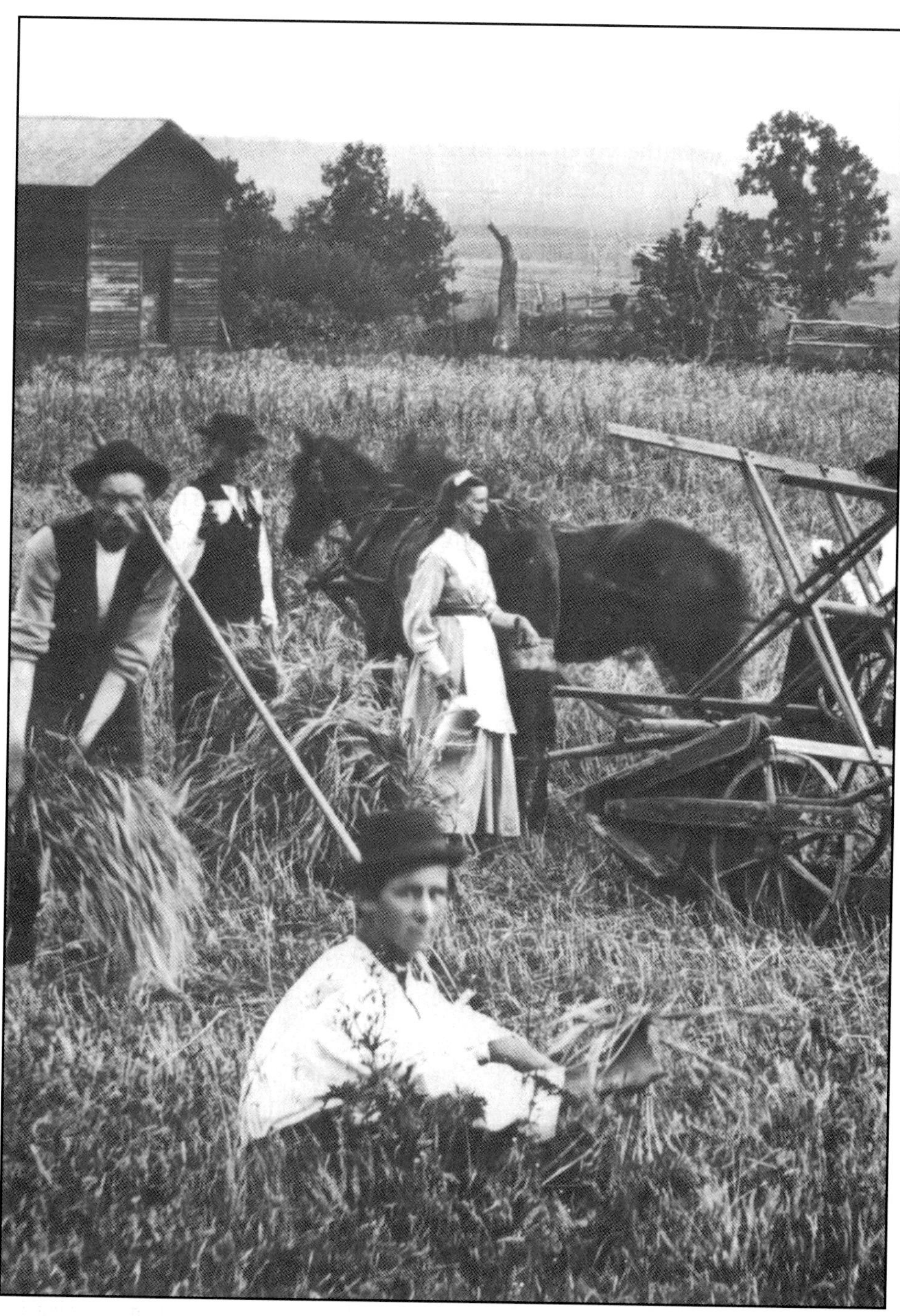

In the 1870s, homesteads such as this in Dane County were the heart of southern Wisconsin's rural economy and an important source of the farmer-mechanics who established the region's first mills, forges, and machine shops (Courtesy, State Historical Society of Wisconsin).

through the abstractions of mathematics; and if he had no one to guide his youthful experiments, he had the considerable creative advantage of an intelligence that was able to shape itself from the beginning by free play.

Wisconsin was still largely a timbered wilderness at the end of the Civil War, its vast northern pine forests giving way to hardwoods and conifers, scattered bogs, marshes, and prairie openings in the south, where the majority of its population resided. After the end of hostilities, railroad construction accelerated. More than 2,000 miles of track were laid down in the 1870s, and many remote areas, hitherto inaccessible, were opened to development, spurring a general logging boom. Saw mills and paper factories appeared on the banks of rivers and streams, and new farms were established in the cutover regions left behind by the logging trade. Cities such as Sheboygan, Racine, and Milwaukee emerged as important industrial centers in the lakeshore counties during this period, as immigrants from Europe, primarily Germans and Scandinavians, poured into Wisconsin to fill the jobs created by the postwar expansion. Between 1875-95 the state's population more than doubled, with a second wave of German immigrants settling in Milwaukee and the southcentral counties in the last decade of the century.

The rural Wisconsin society that Howard Colman grew up in was supported by an informal market network of home industries and small family farms, whose principal crop, in the 1870s, was wheat. Dairying, as a large-scale enterprise in the state, was still more than a decade away. The first cheese factory in Wisconsin had been built in 1864; and dairy products, for the most part, had limited commercial value because of the threat of bovine tuberculosis and the practical difficulties of separating milk and butter fat, a problem that Colman himself would one day address with his invention of a spiral separator. At the time it was common to find gardens and livestock pens behind the houses of Wisconsin's merchants, and woodshops and mechanical areas in the outbuildings of its farms. Many people, not only farmers, made handicrafts and did job-work in metals and hardwoods as a means of supplementing their incomes. A knowledge of tools was considered to be as important to a man's livelihood as experience in planting and harvesting. Using an axe and hammer, operating a forge, drilling, turning, and grinding, taking measurements and forming parts were the stock-in-trade of most persons with ambitions to improve their lot in life. In many rural communities, this kind of versatility was also a matter of economic necessity, since there was seldom enough demand for any craft to allow a worker to specialize.

We are fortunate to have several excellent first-hand accounts of Colman's Wisconsin childhood, but the specific nature of his mechanical education - the people he met, the things he saw that inspired him, the places he visited - remains largely a matter of conjecture. We know that his father traveled widely within the districts assigned to him by the Methodist Church, calling at the homes and businesses of the members of his congregation; and it's reasonable to assume that he was exposed to many different examples of manufacturing in the course of these visits. Did his family, his son in particular, sometimes accompany him on these trips? Was Howard introduced to mechanical work through his father's contacts? The superintendent of the Beaver Dam Cotton Mills, we know, was a Methodist and close family friend, and it was this relationship that made it possible for Howard to go inside the factory and study its weaving operations. Were other members of the Beaver Dam congregation receptive to requests for admission to their places of work? Certainly the boy needed no special entrée to the town's millpond, race, and waterpower sites; its smiths and harness makers; its coopers, tanners, and carpentry shops; and its railroad. There was a lot of commercial activity in the market towns of southern Wisconsin that took place in the open, much that would have made an impression on a young boy with an interest in handicrafts and mechanical devices. That Howard Colman observed such things and learned their processes is proved by his own rapid technical development. From his earliest childhood, his days even as a toddler, his manual, manipulative instincts expressed themselves strongly and almost irresistibly.

ii

Howard was the youngest child of Henry and Lucinda Colman, having been preceded by two sisters, Anna and Laura, and a brother, Harry, who had died in infancy from whooping cough. Harry's real name was Henry Abner Colman, and his birthday (July 6) each year was remembered by his parents with sadness. The natural excitement surrounding Lucinda's pregnancy in 1873, the hopes and expectations that eventually attended the arrival of another son - someone to carry on the Colman name, someone perhaps to continue in the Methodist ministry - and the near coincidence of Howard's birthday (July 9) with that of his dead brother gave the occasion a special poignancy. Forty years afterwards, Henry Colman would recall in his diary how his wife's labor began:

> As we retired the night before, he [Howard] seemed to rise in the womb and *turn a somersault*. I immediately rose, dressed, and put a bed in the parlor, where she lay in pain during the night (emphasis added).

A midwife or "English nurse" in Waukesha was brought to the Colman house, and at 6:15 pm the following day Howard "gladdened all hearts at the parsonage by putting in an appearance" (Sketch). When the nurse carried the baby from the parlor in a flannel blanket and placed him on the floor next to the kitchen stove, it was both to keep him warm and to acknowledge an old superstition: "She thought the lower he was put, the higher he would rise in life" (Diary).

The baby was nine-and-a-half pounds, a surprising weight perhaps in view of Colman's physical stature as an adult - he grew to only five feet, eight inches and, like his sisters, was slight in bearing - but some of his birth weight was probably attributable to an unusually large cranium. According to his sister Laura, his head "became a problem in hats and caps, as well as a mix-up with older boys who wore the same" (Episodes), and we know from other family accounts that his haberdasher later credited him with the second-largest hat size in Rockford, Illinois. Colman's head was one of the things that people tended to remember about him from his childhood, along with his red hair, and the fact that, in the words of an acquaintance, "he was always thinking." His expanding cranium seemed to be evidence of a burgeoning interior life.

Howard and his sisters were given regular courses of religious instruction by their parents, and the earliest language lessons that the children received were based on the Scriptures and religious homilies. There were formal prayers at meals and bedtime. Other parts of the day were set aside for Bible studies, the singing of psalms, and moral teachings. The children were encouraged to memorize sacred passages and to use religious analogies in explaining human behavior. Howard seems to have tolerated this, even though his native intelligence inclined him towards a view of the world that was practical rather than spiritual, and his curiosity normally expressed itself through the manipulation of tangible objects. He was accustomed to accepting very little on faith. His boyish intuitions, the flights of fancy that gave him an expanding sense of the experimental possibilities around him, were valuable mainly as starting points in a sequence of logical inquiry. They had to be demonstrated to his satisfaction before he could accept them as true. The religious environment he grew up in was plainly foreign to his way of thinking, so he learned to withdraw into a world of mechanisms, into himself, as a means of freeing his ideas.

By all accounts, Howard was an active boy with a variety of friends and exploratory interests. What few people realized - what he successfully concealed throughout his life from everyone outside of his family - was the fact that he was virtually blind in one eye, the result of a freakish incident in his early childhood when his sister Laura threw a toy that struck his left cornea. (This impairment was revealed by his sister at the time of his death and seldom, if ever, discussed during his lifetime.) Colman seems to have been able to compensate for his weakness and to live a normal life, but one wonders how much of his seriousness and meditative bent was influenced by the loss of vision.

Several incidents from his childhood reveal the tenor of the Colman household in the 1870s. At three months Howard was christened in LaCrosse, Wisconsin by his paternal grandfather, Henry Root Colman, though the ceremony itself was delayed so long by the elder Colman's golden wedding anniversary celebration on the same day that the boy had to be put to bed and then awakened over his mother's objections. At ten months, he took his first step, "a sign of precociousness" (Episodes). At almost the same time he spoke his first words:

> Now I am trying to help this baby repeat a sentence - God is love. It is a little too much for him. He looks bewildered. Then he looks up into my face and says, " 'ove Mama!" I'll never forget that " 'ove Mama." What mother would? (Memory Pictures)

Lucinda remembered the child sitting on her lap in the evening, his attention fixed on something outside the window: "I lean forward and look up to discover what is attracting his attention. Behold! It is the moon in the clear sky ..." For all his parents' efforts to direct his learning, Howard preferred his own activities, the more unstructured the better:

> We discover that a baby boy is best pleased with playthings that he can take apart and readjust according to his own ideas. So we give him material and do not tell him how much we grow as we watch him grow (Memory Pictures).

In 1874 the Colman family moved to Ft. Atkinson, Wisconsin, forty miles west of Waukesha, where Henry was given the pastorate of the largest congregation that he had served to that time. The five family members, who crowded into a single-seat buggy for the trip westward, found a "fair frame parsonage" that was "near the railway station," two blocks from the Methodist Church. The location proved to be a fortunate one for Howard, who was fascinated by the sound and motion of the locomotives; and his father recalled that "we closely watched our boy lest the trains carry him off, not to return him" (Sketch).

Howard Colman at three years of age.

But the trains carried him off in other ways. By the time he was three, Howard was building houses out of furniture and tying dining room chairs together to make his own steam engines. After the Colmans moved to Milwaukee in 1876 and Henry was assigned to what was then considered to be "the strongest and best [congregation] in the Conference," the Spring Street Church (Sketch), the family provided Howard with a miniature "train of wooden cars, hooked into from the top, a hack to take the passengers to the train, and an express wagon for the baggage - the last two of metal with which he spent many thoughtful hours" (Episodes).

It was not long before Howard was asking for tools, beginning with an old family chopping knife whose blade had been discovered many years before in the field of his maternal grandparents' New York homestead and passed on to his mother as an heirloom. The boy, when he learned its history, "emphatically claimed it as his inheritance" (Memory Pictures). Then there was a hatchet, which his father supplied, and a saw, whose teeth "ached to show their sharpness on the table legs or the chair legs" of the parsonage. When Howard was four, according to his father, he conceived the idea of a machine to wash dishes and apparently went through the motions of fashioning some kind of hypothetical contraption. At seven the boy not only had his own workshop in the house, a room, in his father's words, "as essential to our parsonage as the kitchen," but also a collection of hand tools, including a primitive jigsaw that he put together himself with "nothing from the store except nails and screws" and a piece of metal from an old hoop skirt:

> This bit of steel, with teeth carefully filed into its side had been mechanically adjusted, and it worked. At Confidential's [Lucinda Colman's] suggestion, the merchant provided that shop with a new scroll saw. I did not take measurements of the inches Company [Howard] grew that month, but I do know that the home still possess[es] mementoes of the good work done by that new saw (Peep).

Some of the "mementoes," his sister Laura remembered, were wooden letter openers, corner brackets, and picture frames (Episodes). The calculations and measurements that went into the creation of these objects and the adjustments that were made to improve the jigsaw's performance were things Howard learned by trial and error. His inventiveness was spontaneous, like a child's knack for language.

The analogy to language may be worth pursuing here. The linguist Noam Chomsky has argued, for instance, that a child's ability to speak cannot be understood solely in terms of parental teaching and environmental influences; that it is also due to a kind of genetic coding, a natural feeling for meaning and syntax which occurs as the result of our evolutionary development. Cognitive scientists tell us that we carry genetic plans in our heads that have a lot to do with the way we experience the world, and that these are as different from one another as human fingerprints. Thus when we talk about Colman's "inventiveness," we are really talking about a set of neuromuscular tendencies and predispositions that worked themselves out over time in response to his life activities. Why did his gifts lead him in the direction they did? His youthful explorations, his speculative steam engines and washing machines, his improvised jigsaw and other handtools, were his means of discovering who he was (and who he could become), and these were guided by an extraordinary capacity for understanding mechanical process. His creativity as an adult seems to have been rooted in this playfulness as a child. Or put another way: he seems to have been successful as an inventor precisely because, in one important respect, he never lost his sense of wonder. He was unwilling to limit his thinking by the acceptance of received wisdom, and from his earliest childhood onwards, he demonstrated a remarkable independence of mind. His work areas - in the different parsonages his family occupied and, later, in the Barber-Colman factory itself - were always his safety zones, the places where he was freest to be himself.

iii

"Little Company," in his father's words, kept "enlarging" throughout his boyhood. After the jigsaw came a foot-powered lathe, set up in a corner of the parsonage woodhouse, and "created somehow without cash." Its principal feature was a balance wheel that had been "made of a large cheesebox [and] filled with sand from a nearby lake shore" (Peep). There were also water-wings fashioned from a rubber pillow, which he used to teach himself to swim, and an "old huge family umbrella," which was hoisted as a sail on the family rowboat (Episodes). During "one sultry Fourth [of July]," his father found him working on the design of an "ice boat," the "sweat dropping down," though the first opportunity to test the vessel was at least half a year away. Henry considered the incident to be an example of both his son's "foresight" and a desire to stay cool by filling his head with "thoughts of ice" (Peep). Ever the improviser, Howard did things on his own, too impatient to wait for others to help him and confident enough in his own skills to be able to conquer any uncertainties. "He never bothered his mother," Laura wrote of Howard's youthful projects, and thus the things that he devised were "always a surprise" (Episodes).

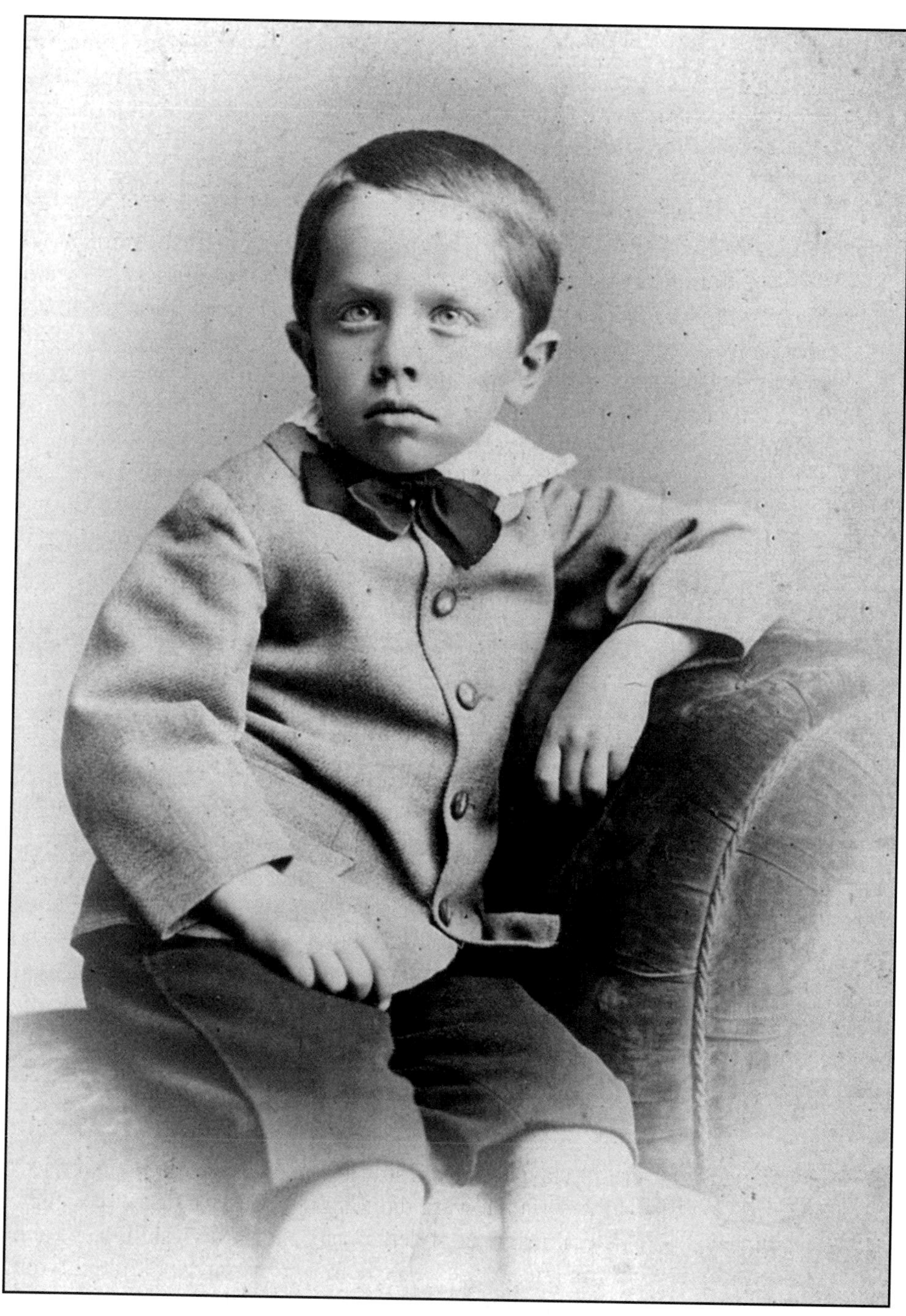

Howard Colman at five years of age.

Colman's formal education began in Milwaukee's Fourth Ward Public School, in 1880, when he was seven years old. Everything he had learned to that point was either self-taught or the result of his parents' home instruction. The decision to send him to school seems to have been made haphazardly, as his father later recalled in his autobiographical "Sketch:"

> One day at dinner ... Laura asked, "Why not let Howard go with me to school?" Howard ... seconded the suggestion, I nodded assent, and mother consented. He was put into the primary department and was delighted. The teacher captivated him. It was soon found that he could read, so he was changed to the first grade, but the teacher did not suit him. One day he came home and announced that he had been "sent up." His mother said "promoted." He replied, "I knew that, but I was afraid that you would laugh at me if I said 'promoted'." He was put into the second grade and soon became "dead in love with that teacher." But it was the kind of "dead" that gives new life.

The boy was "very apt to learn," Henry Colman observed, his "intelligence .... a matter of general remark" (Diary). From all accounts, Howard found school easy, with the exception of Latin and Greek, which his parents, because of their own classical backgrounds, encouraged him to study. The requirement of learning the ancient languages, of applying himself to subjects for which he seemed to have had no special aptitude, was new to him, and the lessons that this experience taught him, in discipline and endurance, were never forgotten. "In later life he often said [that] the real value of his schooling was [in] studying these two subjects," Laura wrote, "upon which he had to concentrate to get them, and that is the important part of an education" (Episodes). Like most people, Colman distinguished in his mind between the subjects that interested him, such as science and mathematics, and the ones that did not; but unlike many people, he valued the latter because they challenged him intellectually.

Both Henry and Laura Colman could attest to Howard's early "habit of private study," which manifested itself not only in the the projects that he pursued behind the doors of his workshop, but also in the amount of time that he spent lying on his back, on a bed or sofa, absorbed by his fancies. If he thought all the time, he also seems to have thought best *horizontally*. As he got older, this habit of quiet meditation increased in regularity and became a source of amusement to other members of his family:

Lucinda Colman as she appeared in 1882, when Howard was nine.

> Often the bedroom door was locked for hours. Not a sound was heard. When Confidential [Lucinda Colman] became sure that sickness was compelling quiet and would rap on the door, the reply was not ever in lovely accents. Interruption was taboo (Peep).

On one occasion, his sister Anna saw him lying on the sofa and tried to cheer him up, assuming that he was unhappy. "Stop trying to raise my spirits!" he growled, and the phrase, almost immediately, "became a family byword" (Episodes).

Noise and interruption, Colman believed, were the enemies of concentration, and when he reached adulthood, whenever it was within his power to enforce, he insisted on quiet surroundings. There was an unspoken rule among his closest associates in the Barber-Colman Experimental Department that no one was to speak to him unless spoken to first; to do otherwise was to risk breaking his train of thought and incurring his displeasure. His brother-in-law Beach Maguire prepared for Colman's visits by putting the family parakeet in the closet; and Howard's own children were forced to content themselves with rabbits as pets, instead of dogs or cats, because rabbits were the quieter creatures. As soon as he came home in the evening, as soon as the front door slammed, his children knew that they had to stop making noise. The next few hours were part of a regular routine, with Colman reading, thinking on his back on the library sofa, and, later, working at his drafting board in an upstairs study, and except for the dinner hour and a brief period spent chatting with his family, the house was virtually silent.

Colman's attitude towards interruption was well-known to his employees, and no one wanted to provoke him. Yet there was also a standing joke at the Barber-Colman Company that such precautions were unnecessary. He was so engrossed in his schemes, it was said, so preoccupied much of the time, that he could have been hit over the head with a baseball bat and never noticed a thing.

On a personal level, Colman's life had a remarkable consistency. As a boy he was unusually serious-minded, distinguished from his peers by his intelligence and passion for work. His sister Laura noted that a "wise father and mother knew that it was best that he be kept busy" and therefore tried to keep him supplied with tools and materials to the limits of their ability. This was often difficult, given the challenges that Henry and Lucinda Colman faced in trying to rear three children on a marginal income. In one sense, however, there was little need for concern: "He [Howard] was so interested in what he was doing and planning, that he had no time to think up mischief, whereby he could learn the deception of Father and Mother" (Episodes). To characterize him as antisocial would be unfair. He enjoyed the company of people his age and relished being the center of attention. "His many friends were always boys who were interested in what he was doing" (Episodes). He knew that he possessed an unusual mechanical aptitude and had a strong sense of his individuality, but he needed to be in control of his surroundings to express himself fully. This meant finding a quiet area in each of his dwellings, away from distractions, where he could reflect on things that interested him.

Colman spent one academic year (1880-81) at the Milwaukee Fourth Ward School and then moved with his family to Whitewater (1882-84), Lake Geneva (1885-87), and Beaver Dam (1888-89), as his father accepted new church assignments. During this period Anna entered Northwestern University and Laura graduated from high school. The frequent changes and upheavals in the family's living patterns, the necessity of leaving old friends and making new ones, and the difficulties of becoming adjusted to strange locales seem to have had little noticeable effect on the academic progress of any of the Colman children, but such things may have reinforced the importance of Howard's imaginary projects, which, besides his family, were among the few sources of continuity in his life.

Sometimes, if he were lucky, his projects bore fruit in school, as in the case of a "miniature derrick" that he constructed for a physics class in Lake Geneva (Diary), a forerunner perhaps of the check-pump for skim milk that would become his first successful commercial invention. But usually there was little crossover between his experiments and academic studies, and he continued to pursue the former in isolation, stimulated by the devices and manufacturing processes that he observed in the places in which he lived.

iv

When the Methodist Conference sent Henry Colman to Beaver Dam in 1888, the assignment was welcomed by the family because of the location there of Wayland Academy, a small coeducational Baptist school with a reputation for classical studies. Howard was approaching the age of graduation - he was fifteen at the time - and his parents wanted to find a program that would prepare him properly for enrollment in a college or university. Ordinarily, the Colmans would not have been able to afford to pay the tuition of a private academy on a minister's salary, but it was Wayland's policy to waive these costs for members of the clergy.

Howard' s parents thus found themselves in a fortunate situation in Beaver Dam, with a new church and parsonage, and a highly-regarded preparatory school for their only remaining child at home.

Although Wayland offered a variety of electives - history, philosophy, French, German, bookkeeping, commercial law, and the classics - there can be little doubt that Colman enrolled in the last program and spent his school days reading and translating Latin and Greek. Wayland's archival files contain no record of his actual electives, but the classics were the heart of the Academy's principal college-preparatory program, and it's hard to imagine his parents allowing him to choose another course. We know that he spoke approvingly in later years of his mathematical studies at Wayland; and this subject, in the tradition of the older New England grammar schools, was part of the Academy's classical curriculum. ("ANCIENT CLASSICAL. - A thorough drill is given in mathematics and in the ancient languages." Wayland Greetings, Vol. III.) Mathematics included aspects of the natural sciences, such as the problems of motion and the properties of energy and matter, which Aristotle described in the Physica. If Colman was a classicist who diligently completed his translations and textual exercises according to Academy standards, he was also an analytical thinker who would have welcomed an opportunity to explore the ancient treatises on science and mathematics under the direction of a qualified teacher. Since most of his youthful experiments were random and prompted by happenstance, he would have found a good deal in these writings to help organize his thinking.

The mathematics teacher that he worked under at Wayland was Winfield Sweet, a native of Sauk County, Wisconsin, who appears in his only surviving Academy photograph as a person in his mid-thirties, with close-cropped hair and an abundant handlebar mustache giving him the aspect of a gentleman. According to Wayland records, Sweet started teaching at the age of fifteen and pursued a dual career as a public school instructor and Baptist minister in Richland Center, Wisconsin, before going to Wayland in 1886. He spent five years at the Academy, three of them while Colman was enrolled there. In 1891 Sweet resigned to accept the ministry of a Baptist church in LaCrosse. Two years later he went to China to establish a Baptist missionary school in Hanchow - he eventually gave it the name of "Wayland Academy" - and remained abroad until his death in 1917. These facts, basically all that we know of his career, tell us nothing of his character, his academic interests, or his relationship with Colman. We are left only with the Colman family story, recounted by both of his daughters, that Howard believed his mathematical education at Wayland was much more advanced than anything he received in college, and that when he later

The Wayland Academy faculty (c. 1887). Howard Colman's mathematics instructor, Winfield Sweet, is shown at the right end of the middle row.

withdrew from Beloit to devote himself to his inventions, he mentioned the superiority of the Academy program in justifying his decision.

Wayland had been founded in 1855 as a "university" mainly in response to the need of Wisconsin's Baptists for an institution of higher learning to prepare young men for the ministry. Although it never realized this objective and later was reorganized as a "collegiate institute" to appeal to a school-age population, it maintained its religious focus. Wayland's goal was not only to teach its students to think but to support their development as Christians. ("No man is prepared for life's work and responsibilities until he has a strong will, a good conscience, and an inflexible devotion to righteousness" - Wayland Greetings). Daily chapel services and Tuesday morning Bible classes were required of every student. Evangelists conducted revival meetings in Beaver Dam throughout Colman's years at Wayland, and the school's quarterly newspaper printed the names of students who underwent religious conversions at these events.

Given the fact that Colman was already required by his parents to attend at least four church services on Sundays with them and to participate regularly in the religious life of the Beaver Dam English Methodist Church, he reached a point in his sixteenth year where these activities became intolerable. He could do nothing to change Wayland policies, short of withdrawing from the Academy. But the Methodist services were another matter. Summoning his courage, he told his parents that he did not intend to go to church again, that he simply *would not go.* It was a rare instance of the boy's rebelliousness and a decision that his father, in particular, mourned for the rest of his life. Henry Colman's diaries show that he always blamed himself for Howard's decision to leave the Methodist Church, though at the time he did not try to overrule him. He may have sensed in Howard's otherwise dutiful behavior, his continuing thoughtfulness and concern for his parents, how strong his feelings were.

Wayland was both a boarding and day school, and many students, especially those from families of modest means, enrolled in the latter, the majority of these from Beaver Dam. Howard, who lived at home with his parents in the English Methodist Church parsonage, had to walk more than a mile to school each day along Beaver Dam's main commercial thoroughfare up a slowly ascending gradient to the city's eastern edge. It's evident that he had less free time at Wayland for his mechanical projects than in previous years, considering the demands of his classical studies and the other programs, religious and academic, that he was expected to attend. Every student at the Academy, for example, participated in a literary organization and contributed to a weekly program of readings, orations, and political debates. A photograph of one of these groups, the Longfellow Society, shows Colman in a jacket, tie, and waistcoat at the center of the front row, looking away from the camera.

Despite the demands on his time, Colman's mechanical experiments continued, and there was a steady procession of young men into the parsonage workshop throughout his Wayland years. In the beginning visitors were attracted by stories of his gadgetry, the homemade devices that he contrived out of discarded materials and used for his woodworking schemes; but after his first year in Beaver Dam, they were drawn by the news of another apparatus that was under construction, a machine for automatically replenishing the warp of a commercial textile loom. In terms of its complexity and range of operation, Colman's new machine was vastly different from anything that he had previously attempted to build - the kind of device, in fact, that no one had successfully developed. It was only a prototype and had not yet fulfilled Colman's expectations, but it had shown enough promise and was radical enough in concept to encourage him to go further. Clearly, it represented a considerable accomplishment for a sixteen-year-old schoolboy. Before this, he seems to have occupied himself with the development of homemade devices that were loosely modeled on existing woodworking tools, such as planers and jig saws, and other mechanical implements that he had observed in the community. His new machine, however, had charted a new direction. Now he had begun to explore the possibilities of an entirely theoretical device, an invention without an existing standard model, and had undertaken the slow, painstaking process of testing his ideas through the construction of a prototype.

V

The inspiration for Colman's machine was the Beaver Dam Cotton Mills, the largest employer and most prominent business on the city's millrace. The factory, known to locals as the "lakeside plant" because of its proximity to the Beaver Dam Lake, had been constructed in 1882 adjacent to a dam at the head of the raceway. The building was three-stories high and powered by a 5,000 pound iron turbine in its basement, an underground flume carrying water from the dam directly to the mechanism and then discharging it into the Beaver Dam River. Visitors to the Mills could feel the building vibrate and hear the rushing water, the hum of the shafts, belts, and pulleys that conducted power upwards from the basement "engine room," even though they were unable to see the turbine and left to wonder about its operation. Colman lived only a few blocks

Howard Colman as a member of Wayland Academy's Longfellow Society in 1889.

from the factory, and we know that he sometimes went through it in the company of his parents. As his father remembered:

> Beaver Dam was proud to have a cotton mill. Mr. [Alex] Kingsbury, its superintendent, was an attendant at our church, and his wife and daughters were members. We often visited the mill, especially when friends from other places were visiting us. Howard was a frequent visitor. He noticed the girls drawing in each one of the many threads of cloth through two loops and a reed of the harness with their fingers, which was a slow task (Sketch).

The process that Colman observed was called "hand-drawing," and it was extremely laborious, in marked contrast to the efficiency of the Mills' automated weaving operations. Whenever a warp beam ran out of thread, the loom had to be stopped and a full beam hung from brackets at the side of the machine. The thread-ends of the new beam, held together by metal combs, would then be lifted over the top of the loom and dropped down on the other side, so that they were close to the ends of the old warp. Women, known in the trade as "drawing girls," would use long hooks to reach through the openings of the harness eyes and draw back, one by one, the threads of the old and new beams. These were then tied together to "renew" the warp. Though the drawing process was often as fascinating to visitors as the mechanized weaving, it was a nuisance to mill operators like Kingsbury, who hated the interruption and continually struggled to find people who were willing do the work.

Kingsbury told Colman that the person who eventually figured out how to automate the drawing process would revolutionize the industry. "It was about the only one of the operations in the manufacture of cotton which still had to be done entirely by hand," he remembered Kingsbury saying, and the statement had "made a very considerable impression."

According to Colman's own "Brief History of My Drawing-In Machine," which he prepared as evidence in a 1906 patent-infringement lawsuit, his initial tour of the Beaver Dam factory had been prompted by the visit of an aunt, Mrs. Elihu Colman, in 1889. During the summer, while a new Methodist parsonage was being constructed, the Colmans had moved into temporary quarters next-door to the Kingsburys. The two families had become close friends, and Alex Kingsbury had apparently offered to show the Colmans and their visitor through the Mills as a way of being hospitable.

Colman weighed the idea of a drawing-in device for several months after the tour and began exploring the possibilities in earnest in September. He borrowed a reed and harness from Kingsbury to experiment with and,

The Beaver Dam Cotton Mills (c. 1885) where Howard Colman was introduced to the concept of warp replenishment.

by the middle of October, had a "general conception" of a drawing-in machine "pretty well in mind." He met with Kingsbury to discuss his ideas and get advice, and shortly afterward began building a full-sized wooden model of a controller mechanism for manipulating a loom harness. This feature was judged to be the principal obstacle to the success of any machine for warp replenishment, and it was the key to the coordinated action of all its mechanisms. Colman's model held a single harness and no reed or warp. It was, by all accounts, a crude contrivance, having been put together entirely by hand with the help of a pocket knife and chisel, and incorporating materials such as hazel nuts for the bodies of the cams.

Nevertheless, it worked. A week before Thanksgiving and four months after his sixteenth birthday, Colman exhibited his invention for his father and Kingsbury. Placing it on the dining room table of the parsonage, he turned a drive wheel at the end of the machine and held up a harness with his other hand. Kingsbury and Henry Colman stood facing the middle of the machine. They saw a hook-like mechanism at the end of a metal rod rise and catch a strand of the harness and carry it to a waiting needle, which penetrated a small opening or loop in the line with a darting motion.

Kingsbury was astonished. Whatever skepticism he may have had about the drawing-in project vanished instantly. After examining the machine in detail, he told Henry Colman that he had "been studying that [the problem of warp replenishment] for twenty years" and was "not as far along" as the boy was "after six months" (Peep). Questioned by Kingsbury about his plans for the remainder of the device - a reed and second harness still needed to be attached to it to demonstrate the machine's effectiveness - Howard said that he already had the additional features worked out in his head. He produced a preliminary design for a complete drawing-in machine (D.I.M.) and explained how the new elements would work in conjunction with his existing controller mechanism.

After the exhibition, Colman started building a new machine to accommodate the harnesses and reed, and salvaged as many parts from his original model as possible. A month later he was finished. The date was associated in his mind with his sister Anna, he later wrote, because she had returned to Beaver Dam for Christmas around this time and proceeded to annoy him by asking questions about the new project. Drawing-in was a complicated business, he knew, and hard to explain.

> In this machine the needle took the threads directly from the sheet of warp, without any intervening selector. It was so arranged that, if the needle failed to take a thread, the harness mechanism would stop, and the

> needle try again - the warp, meanwhile, being fed ahead a slight amount. If the needle took only one thread, it passed it through the harness and reed, and the warp in that case also fed forward a slight amount, the harness mechanism continuing. If the needle took more than one thread, these threads were replaced in the sheet, and the warp was fed backward a slight amount and the needle tried again, the harness mechanism, meanwhile, stopping.

Impressed by Kingsbury's high opinion of the device and eager to support his son's experiments, Henry Colman eventually agreed to pay for the costs of a new model that would be fashioned primarily from metal; and Howard plunged into the task of making the patterns and machining the parts, even though his previous fabricating experience had been limited entirely to wood. The most difficult cuts were done for him by Kingsbury, and it's possible that much, if not all, of the shop work was carried out in the Beaver Dam factory itself.

Because of his studies at Wayland, Colman was only able to devote part of his time to the drawing-in machine (D.I.M.) during the winter months. His lack of metalworking experience also hampered his progress, and it was not until the spring of 1890 that the new device was fully machined and assembled. By then he was in his last semester at the Academy and preparing for graduation.

In the summer Colman returned to his invention full-time and experimented with the designs of a new selector mechanism. When the warp threads were separated in the drawing-in process, he realized, a complex sequence of mechanical motions was required to drive a thread end through the appropriate harness (heddle) eye and dent of the reed. Colman fashioned a tiny oscillating rod with fork-like prongs to hold the openings in place prior to the approach of the drawing-in needle. Provided that the harness eyes were uniform in size, the needle would strike the openings rapidly and precisely.

Yet the warps seldom cooperated. The minute spacings needed to ensure the operation of a drawing-in machine could be thrown off by crossed threads, changes of tension in the threads, different thicknesses, a build-up of loose fibers, and high levels of static electricity. Threads sometimes broke. They also frequently stuck together, and the prongs would pick up two strands at once and cause the needle to enter the wrong opening or miss the eyes completely. Colman's description of the selector device in his 1890 machine shows how approximate the interconnections were between the elements:

> One of the devices consisted of a pair of rubber bands, driven by pulleys and held against each other, during a certain portion of their length, in such a way that the warp threads were fed between the bands and clamped thereby, and as the bands travelled they became stretched, thereby separating the warp threads.

The mechanism only worked, he realized, if sufficient attention were paid to the adjustment of the parts, and if it ran at low speeds; and this was highly impractical from a commercial point of view. It needed to be tested in actual mill conditions.

After a summer of experimentation, Colman completed the designs of a new selector device and "sensitive feed" and incorporated these features into his machine. He re-enrolled in Wayland for a postgraduate term during the fall, apparently at his parents' urging, but then "stayed out" during the winter of 1891 in order to "push the work on the drawing-in machine," hiring a Milwaukee machinist and pattern-maker named George Barnard to help him with "improvements." When the spring semester started, he once again enrolled at Wayland "because my family thought I should not neglect my education, and also because my father had expended all the money in the machine that he felt he could afford to." The practical education that Howard was receiving in mechanical design was far less important to the Colmans than their son's readiness for college. He had been accepted by Northwestern University for the fall semester, and his parents considered it academically prudent, and much less of a drain on the family finances, to keep him in school.

For the first time in his young career as an inventor, Colman's work was halted because of a lack of money. He had gone as far as he could go by using his improvisational skills, and the D.I.M., in its latest configuration, would now require more precisely-machined parts to become a "practical device." These would have to be jobbed out to journeymen metalworkers. One of his Wayland classmates, Fred Barber, who was a regular visitor at his workshop, offered to ask his own father for assistance. He said that his father had a history of helping promising Wayland graduates with college tuition and other expenses, and he thought that he might be persuaded to provide some kind of limited financial support for Colman's experiments. His father would be coming to Beaver Dam in the spring for a meeting of the Academy's board of trustees and the annual graduation, Barber said, and it would be an ideal time to show him the machine.

Howard Colman's 1891 drawing-in machine (D.I.M.). Photograph by Fred Barber.

In June Henry Colman was surprised to see his son, Barber, and "an older gentleman" climbing the stairs of the parsonage to the second-floor workshop:

> Like the little boy who wants to see what is doing, I went up also and was introduced to Mr. [William] Barber, who was in town for the Academy trustee meeting. After studying the machine for an hour, Mr. Barber quietly remarked: "Go ahead, and I will furnish the money." No contract was made. No understanding as to division of profits was attempted. I have always believed that he was interested not in money returns but in helping a young man. Years later I met in Berkeley its leading Baptist pastor, whose church was near the great University of California. He was of the same Academy class and had been aided through college by Mr. Barber (Peep).

Because Howard was a minor, his father assumed the responsibility of negotiating the details of the agreement with Barber. He wrote to propose an equal sharing of risks and rewards:

> Had someone furnished the money from the beginning, he would have been entitled to one-half interest in Howard's drawing-in machine for cotton mills. I have put in $100, besides all Howard's time. We thought that, as the machine is now so near a demonstrated success, a half-interest might be worth $100, and whatever funds may be necessary to demonstrate its utility and protect [its] rights. I am, however, perfectly satisfied to receive from you $100, await developments, and do all the honorable later. The one hundred dollars will be used in perfecting the machine, we submitting to you a careful account of its expenditures. I may be absent when your letter comes, but whatever Howard pledges in this matter, will bind me (6/27/91).

William Barber did not reply until the middle of the next month (July 12). "My young friend," he began his letter:

> The few days delay to send was from being more than occupied with other matters to which this was only secondary in urgency. It gives me pleasure to thus cooperate with you, and we will hope to also obtain something substantial in the way of financial results. Just returned home, I find letter from your father, the tangible evidence of what I fully believed all along.

Thus on a little more than a handshake began a professional relationship that endured for more than two decades. If the D.I.M. was not as close to a "demonstrated success" as the partners believed in the summer of 1891 and the road ahead not nearly as straightforward as they might have hoped, the eventual return on their $200 investment would turn prove to be greater than either could then have imagined.

4
William Barber

I do not wonder you are quite elated with hope in the measure of success thus far attained ... Still, as Samantha Allen says, "Let us set down on the calm height of philosophy" - or words to that effect - and "not expect too much." Sometimes it costs more to get what belongs to one already than to overcome the first difficulties of production.

- Letter from William Barber to Howard Colman, 1892

i

William Barber is usually remembered as the man who gave Howard Colman his start in business but whose involvement in the partnership did not extend much beyond his initial investment of $100. His importance was strategic: he appeared at a critical juncture in Colman's early career and helped to pay for improvements to the D.I.M. when the inventor had run out of money, and this generosity was honored by the inclusion of his name on the company masthead. Barber lived in west-central Wisconsin in the tiny crossroads community of Warrens,* ninety miles from Beaver Dam, and the majority of his time was occupied by the operation of a creamery, general store, land office, and logging business there, seldom allowing him to visit Colman or to keep abreast of his experimental work. A self-described "conscientious Baptist" who was thirty years Colman's senior, Barber figures in his development mainly as a benefactor.

This, at least, is the traditional account of the Barber and Colman relationship. Some of the evidence for it appears to be anecdotal, based on the recollections of Colman's business associates and the shop lore that was passed along in newspaper articles and corporate publications in the stories of the Barber-Colman Company's founding. Until recently, in fact, only a few contemporary records of Barber's involvement in Colman's personal and professional life were known to exist. Old photographs

* Also known at the time as Warren's Mills.

William A. Barber (1848-1912), as he appeared in his sixties. This photograph is reproduced from Knots, the 1917 Barber-Colman Association publication.

show him occasionally in the background of Colman family gatherings, once in the rumble seat of a roadster, another time on horseback; and the Barber-Colman Employee Association yearbook, *Knots* (1917), includes a full-page formal studio portrait taken in his late sixties. According to the yearbook, Barber had grown up in Saratoga County, New York, and settled in Wisconsin as a young man on the eve of the Civil War, joining the state infantry after the outbreak of hostilities. His military service included several battles in the vicinity of Petersburg, Virginia, and participation in the siege of Richmond. He is also said to have been present at the Appomattox Court House when Lee surrendered the Army of Northern Virginia. Upon his return to Wisconsin in 1865, Barber joined his uncle in the management of George Warren and Company, which prospered during the statewide logging boom of the 1870s and 1880s. In 1882 Barber was elected to the Wisconsin State Assembly as a Republican for a single term.

Wayland Academy records suggest that Barber's interest in the school was the result of his search for a suitable college-preparatory program for his own children. (His son Fred graduated from Wayland at the same time as Howard Colman; his daughter Edith followed several years behind them in the school.) By the late 1880s, Barber had become one of the Academy's most important philanthropists, leading a capital campaign for the construction of a new girls' dormitory and accompanying the president of Wayland on his travels throughout the state to raise money. These and other acts of service led to his nomination to the Wayland board of trustees, where, at different times, he was elected president, vice president, and faculty-committee member.

Our knowledge of Barber would have been limited to these simple facts were it not for the discovery, in 1998, of a manuscript collection in the Walter Colman residence in Rockford. The majority of the documents in the collection relate to Howard Colman's dealings with Barber during the years of their partnership and range in time from the original check for $100 that Barber gave Colman for D.I.M. improvements in July 1891 to a letter that Colman mailed to Barber from Greensboro, North Carolina, in January 1903, during a visit to a local cotton mill. Taken in its entirety, the Barber-Colman correspondence is a revelation, completely exploding the notion of Barber as an absentee investor and demonstrating his not inconsiderable skills in nurturing Colman's talents. The letters show him offering technical suggestions, evaluating business options, and advising on negotiations. They prove conclusively that

Barber was involved in every aspect of Colman's experimental work, even from afar, and that his counsel, particularly his knack for countering his partner's occasional bouts of depression, was as important to the development of the company as any kind of monetary assistance. They also demonstrate that Barber's financial contributions to the partnership, rather than trailing off after 1891 as commonly assumed, continued for more than a decade, occasionally taxing his resources. Even so, he always answered Colman's requests for help and placed new bets on likely experimental projects. "I enclose the fifty dollars as suggested," he would write Colman in a typical letter of support, "and will merely say in brief that I am still willing to put some cash against your genius and perseverance" (10/26/92).

ii

In the summer of 1891, Howard Colman's immediate challenge was to rebuild the D.I.M with more rigid and precise metal components and to demonstrate its reliability at higher speeds. Whether or not he actually tested the machine in the Beaver Dam Mills in July and August, we know that he used all but $6.08 of the money Barber gave him to "improve some of the parts" (9/18/91), with much of it going to a Milwaukee jobber who redid the cams in brass and iron. Yet as Henry Colman noted in his diary, apparently in August (the actual entry is undated), the new mechanism did not measure up to his son's expectations: "Howard's cotton machine has failed … and Thursday Howard gave up." On August 28, the young man wrote a short letter to Barber, returning the unused portion of the $100 and admitting that he had run into problems that would require more time and effort than he was then able to devote to the project:

> … I have tried the machine. It will miss occasionally and at present I see no way to prevent it. I am very sorry that you should lose any money in it, and if I were in a position to do so, would rather refund the money than have it so. Perhaps after resting from it a year, I may be able to straighten it out after all.

Colman was less than two weeks away from entering Northwestern University, and he anticipated spending most of his time on academic coursework in the year ahead. Acceding to his parents' wishes, he was moving to Evanston, Illinois and mothballing the D.I.M. project for the immediate future. On September 12, his father got him "well-rigged up - [with] two good suits - and sent him off with $50," while reflecting on the significance of his son's departure:

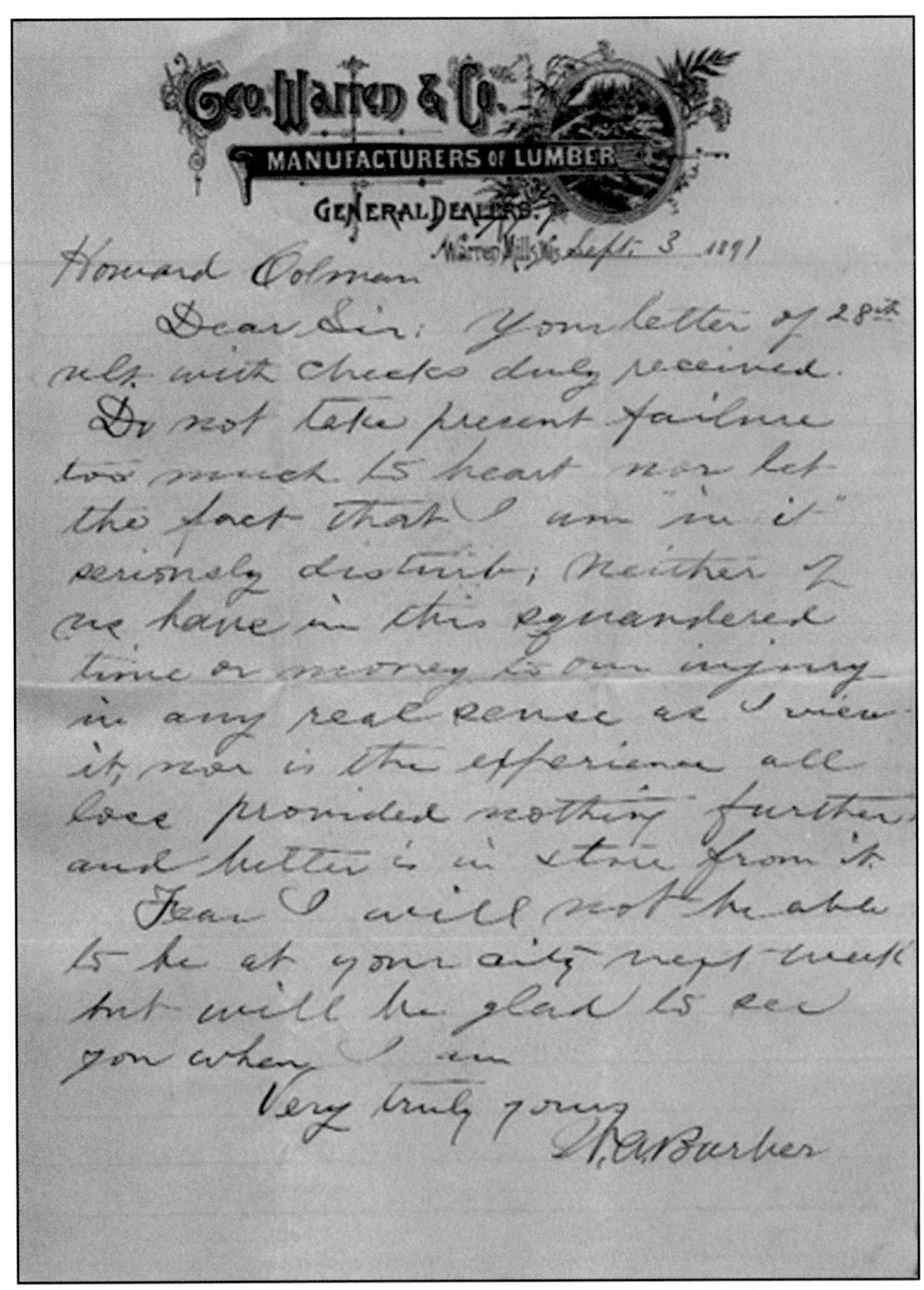

William Barber's letter to Howard Colman of September 3, 1891 acknowledged the receipt of the inventor's check for $6.08 (the unused portion of the $100 advance). Barber advised his young friend: "Do not take present failure too much to heart nor let the fact that I am in it seriously disturb; neither of us have [sic]in this squandered time or money to our injury in any real sense as I view it, nor is the experience all loss provided nothing further and better is in store from it."

> I am lonesome. Howard and I have grown together very much of late. My heart yearns for him. I do not fear that he will fall into vicious habits, but I do so much wish he wd yield his young heart to Jesus. But for the desire to have him hear another preacher, I would try to be sent to Beloit [Wisconsin] and so send him there to college, but it is better that he be [away] from home …, hard as it is and hard to say.

Earlier in the year, Henry had given serious thought to leaving the Methodist ministry and taking a job as a "traveling representative," a change that would have allowed him to move with his family to Evanston while Howard was in college. Howard's rejection of the Church was uppermost in his father's mind, who blamed himself for his son's apostasy, and the "desire to have him hear another preacher" seems to have been paramount in the decision to send him to Northwestern (undated diary entries).

There is a gap of 42 days in Colman's letters to William Barber during the fall of 1891. When Howard wrote again, he had dropped out of Northwestern and gone to live with his parents in Beloit (11/9/91), where his father was assigned to a new Methodist church. Although Howard enrolled in Beloit College soon after arriving in Wisconsin, he told Barber that he had also gone back to work on the D.I.M. and needed money to continue his experiments. He wondered if Barber would be willing to return the $6.08 that had been left at the end of the Beaver Dam experiments in August and perhaps risk an additional $25 on the project:

> Owing to the irregularities of the Methodist itinerary, this place is now my home. My studies in the college are light, and I have had considerable time to devote to the machine. I believe I see my way clear now. At least I have, without any intricate or expensive additions, overcome the difficulty which floored me at B[eaver]. D[am].

If the details of Colman's brief stay in Evanston are unknown, the reason for his move to Beloit clearly had less to do with the "irregularities of the Methodist itinerary" than it did with his father's efforts to save money. As Henry confided to his journal, he was unwilling to "bear so much expense" at Northwestern when a more economical alternative was available closer to home. Unbeknownst to his parents, however, Howard chose to enroll in the "philosophical course" at Beloit College instead of the classics, and then announced to his father that this would be "his last year in college" (undated entries).

Henry noted in his journal that Howard attended the Methodist Epworth League on one of his first Sundays in Beloit in the company of a young woman named Pearl Peterson, and that he went to a social function at a local Baptist church on another occasion "largely to see Pearl Peterson." Peterson's mother, who became suspicious of Howard's intentions, proceeded to give him a lecture on personal integrity. According to Henry, she thought that

> people would consider him a fraud, attending ch[urch] socials, etc., yet absenting himself from ch[urch], and that he ought to have more respect for his father. I had a talk with him, but he seemed so set against going [to church] that I did not insist (undated entry).

Howard thereafter refused to attend all church functions, social and otherwise, extending this restriction even to friends' weddings and funerals.

iii

In the fall of 1891, Colman's immediate goal was to give the D.I.M. a "severe test" in actual warp production; and he was successful in persuading the superintendent of the closest textile factory, the Janesville Cotton Mills, to install his device there, probably with the understanding - this would have been standard procedure for drawing-in trials at the time - that any warp beams produced would be donated to the company in exchange for mill privileges. Because the Janesville facility was located nine miles north of Beloit, Colman decided to set the D.I.M. up first in a woodshed behind his house and attempt to correct any obvious operating problems in advance of the move. "Would probably want to spend some weeks more in experiments," he told Barber, "so as to make as sure as possible before incurring the trouble and expense of going to J[anesville]" (11/9/91). On Christmas Day, he wrote Barber again to say that the D.I.M. was performing satisfactorily and ready for shipment:

> Since the receipt of your check, I have been at work on "our machine" as steadily as school and the numerous delays attendant upon this sort of work would allow. Have been very successful so far. Tho' some details are not yet perfected to my satisfaction, I have very little doubt but that experience and experiment will enable me to produce an efficient machine.
>
> Am going to take it to Janesville next week. Don't expect it will work well enough at first for anybody else to run it, but do hope to make it work myself. Succeeding in that, course I hope to make a machine which anybody can run.

He suggested meeting Barber in Janesville so that the latter could "see the machine work" and satisfy himself "as to its value." Barber responded promptly, on January 6, with a willingness to meet Colman anywhere that he wished. "I like your perseverance," he declared, "and think *we may yet win.*"

William Barber

By the time that Colman received Barber's letter, however, he had concluded his experiments and returned to Beloit. From the very beginning of the Janesville trials, it had been apparent that the D.I.M was too unwieldy at high speeds for the delicate work of the feeler fingers, causing them to clamp the warp threads haphazardly (Brief History); and he had halted his experiments, shipped the D.I.M. back to Beloit, and re-installed it in his woodshed. As was often his habit, he dealt with disappointment by refocusing his attention. The Wisconsin winter offered a legitimate excuse:

> My shop here is not as good as the one I had in B[eaver]. D[am]., and it is impossible to keep it warm in the very cold weather we've been having, and besides, I feel the need of a rest from invention. But will be at it again before [a] very great while (1/23/92)

Colman "kept at it," in his words, as best he could in the following weeks, hiring a Beloit jeweler to fashion "a new selector and selector mechanism" for the D.I.M.; and this man subsequently loaned Colman a Barnes foot lathe for use in the development of other machine parts (Brief History). During the winter and spring, Beloit College classes generally took precedence over Colman's mechanical investigations. He seems to have been weighing several options for the future, including the possibility of taking a job in Illinois, since we know from his father's diary that Howard "had an offer to go into an engineer's office in Ch[icago] and went down, but found that the work was not such as he needed …" This intriguing little entry, undated but evidently from either April or May 1892, suggests that Colman may have had some doubts about the long-term feasibility of the D.I.M. project.

Nevertheless, at the beginning of June, he wrote William Barber once again to determine his friend's interest in the D.I.M. and to state his readiness to resume experiments, if Barber agreed.

> I would like to know what you wish to do about the machine. It does not work perfectly yet, but I firmly believe that it can be made to do so. I have so little time to spend on it now that progress is very slow. This summer I feel that I must do something which will be more immediately profitable. But it seems a great pity to abandon it when success seems so near. I feel almost certain that with $20, besides the $10 of yours which I have still have, and with, say, a month's time, I could make it do actual

> work in a mill myself, and after that it would not be long before we could produce a machine which an ordinary mill-hand could manage (6/1/92).

Barber replied immediately, enclosing a check for $25 to emphasize his commitment to the project; and Colman, as soon as his Beloit classes were finished on June 23, used some of the money to purchase a fly wheel and foot treadle for the D.I.M., giving him a crude power source to carry out experiments. In August, while his family went on a camping trip in Lake Geneva, Wisconsin, Howard stayed behind in Beloit to build a new steel warp frame, replacing the original one of wood that had been constructed in Beaver Dam. "The machine is nearly completed," he told Barber on September 1, " - near enough so that I have succeeded in making it go very satisfactory." What this meant, in practical terms, was that the D.I.M. was working as well as could be expected under the circumstances, with its patchwork of wooden and metal parts and assemblage of older harnesses. "I have used them so much in experimenting when the machine was not in the shape it is now," he complained to Barber about the latter, "that they are in bad shape and really do not afford a fair test ..." Therefore:

> The only way to really test it [i.e., the D.I.M.] is to set it up in a mill, and I think, aside from the matter [of the] harnesses, that it would be much more safe and satisfactory to run it in a mill awhile before making any application for patents or anything of that sort.

This is the first reference to a possible patent application that we encounter in Colman's letters, though we know from another source that he had used his limited time in Evanston, in the fall of 1891, to do research at the Chicago Public Library into existing American warp-drawing patents, and that his work on the D.I.M., within the context of what he had learned from this research, was intended to produce an entirely original mechanism (Brief History). His existing limitations were both technical and financial. If he had yet to develop a satisfactory D.I.M. model and demonstrate its effectiveness in mill conditions because of mechanical problems, his chances of doing so were hampered by a nearly-depleted treasury:

> I have about $5 of your money left, and this will be nearly used up in making the further improvements which I wish to make before taking the machine to Janesville ... You doubtless notice that it has taken more time and money than I anticipated at the beginning of the summer. This has been caused in part by the delay in getting material which I mentioned in my previous letter and in part by my making over in a more thorough and workmanlike manner many details which did not absolutely fail to do their work but which were most provokingly liable to get "out of fix" at just the wrong moment ...

> Should be glad to hear from you at your earliest convenience, as it will make a sad difference in my plans if you don't wish to advance any more money (9/1/92).

Implicit in the letter was Colman's intention to withdraw from college. As he had earlier told his father, he did not plan to return to Beloit after his freshman year, feeling that the D.I.M. project was too important to delay his decision to become a full-time inventor any longer. In his view, his machine was close to being a demonstrated success; and he worried about losing Barber's financial backing if he interrupted his experiments a second time. An entry in Henry Colman's diary for "September 1892" thus provides a valediction for his son's formal education:

> Howard & College. Howard said that he did not desire to attend col[lege] here but wished to work on his machine, which seems nearing success. So I consented, and he will probably not attend college this year ... May the good Lord lead him.

After Barber sent him another $25 on September 5, Howard resumed his work in Janesville and made considerable headway in drawing in warps that could be put to use in the factory. While the results were far from perfect, Colman was encouraged by the comments of H.I. Witham, the Janesville superintendent, who considered the D.I.M. to be "a great deal better" than other warp-building mechanisms he had seen. Even the "boss weaver," an initial skeptic, had been forced to admit: "Well, I guess it runs as well as the first locomotive." But this success also brought the inevitable - and seemingly relentless - demands on Barber's pocketbook:

> Have about $8 of your money left. Will probably have to ask you for another $25 before I get through here, tho' I won't need it for another week (10/7/92).

After additional tests, Colman reported that he had discovered a cure for his harness problem that promised to "make the machine somewhat simpler and enable it to run faster." The remedy, regrettably, depended on a fresh infusion of Barber's money:

> It doesn't require any very radical changes, but still I should not like to undertake it without at least fifty dollars for that and some other minor improvements I want to make, and very likely I should have to ask for more before I get thro[ugh] ... Mr. Witham, superintendent of the Janesville Cotton Mills, is very confident of my success and freely consents to my referring you to him. There will be plenty of time for you to write him, as my health and especially the muddled condition of my thinking apparatus require that I rest for a week or so ... I have one dollar of your money left (10/11/92).

A close-up of Colman's early D.I.M. shows the wooden warping frame, gears, and cotton threads. The device was photographed on a table in the dining room of the Colman parsonage.

This pattern of experimenting, redesigning, and refinancing, with intervals of "rest from invention" when Colman steadied his nerves and cleared his head for yet another round of experimentation, was to recur throughout the entire D.I.M. project. His improvements to the mechanism were always incremental, based on hard-won insights from his shop and mill trials, and leading to a whole new set of operating variables that needed to be explored in turn. The work was like splitting hairs. To address all the aspects of warp replenishment - to anticipate, in particular, the minute changes in the alignment of the threads and feeler fingers when they were " 'out of fix' at just the wrong moment" - required unusual habits of patience, concentration, and attention to detail.

But Colman was nothing if not resilient. His days of rest were often followed by periods of intense activity, and many of his most important technical breakthroughs occurred after long spells of emotional and physical exhaustion. On November 11 he had been down to his last dollar and ready to stop experimenting. Less than a month later he was bursting with excitement in a letter to Barber and calculating the profits from the sale of the D.I.M., profits that he estimated to be in the millions:

> I believe that I have now overcome the last real difficulty in the way of our machine and that there is now absolutely no room for a reasonable doubt of its ultimate success ... The present machine, having undergone so many changes, is a rather patched-up affair and will never be a really practical machine, but I believe that it has already accomplished its principal object - i.e. it has proved the possibility of a thoroughly practical machine.

He went on to say that he had researched the existing patents for "machines of this character" and was convinced that the "field" for their own D.I.M. design was "clear." From his conversations with a mill machinery salesman, moreover, he had begun to ascertain the full dimensions of the market they were entering:

> I had estimated the number of mills in the world at about 5,000. He thought there were more than twice that number. Many mills would need ten or more machines. He considered \$30 to \$50 a fair royalty for such a machine. Supposing only 5,000 machines sold at only \$25 royalty, we would get \$125,000. Supposing 10,000 machines sold at \$50 royalty, it would be \$500,000. These figures do not consider the fact that machines wear out and have to be replaced, that we would doubtless make improvements and displace our first machines by better ones, and that we could in all probability so modify the machine as to adapt it to flax, silk, and wool.

And there was more. If Barber would invest "any considerable amount of capital" in the enterprise, there was the possibility of yearly D.I.M. rentals to mill owners. A hypothetical target in this case might be 5,000 installations at $100 per annum, "amounting to, in the 17 years a patent lasts, $8,500,000." The installation fees alone would cover the costs of manufacturing the machines. But why stop there?

> If you wish to go on with it yourself, wouldn't [it] be a good idea to build a new machine as perfect as the best machinists obtainable can make it, regardless of expense, and place it on exhibition at the World's Fair?

Though Colman was admittedly still wrestling with "difficulties" that had arisen from his latest mechanical "arrangements," he felt that the D.I.M. could be prepared for exhibition in "two weeks or so," if he worked continually at it. A face-to-face meeting between the partners, in either Beloit or Warrens, was becoming a matter of practical necessity:

> The expense of such a trip seems utterly insignificant, if there is the slightest possibility of millions depending on it (12/5/92).

On the same day that he mailed his letter to Barber, Colman discussed the D.I.M. with Witham, who offered to invest his own money in the project. If Barber were unable to furnish the capital for a new model, he told Colman, he himself would be willing to put up $20,000 for a half interest in the business. Witham advised him, in any case, to begin preparing applications for patents in the U.S., Canada, England, France, Germany, Austria, and India, and then proposed to "throw up his job as superintendent" at the Mills and go on the road to drum up business. As an Englishman who had spent many years in the textile industry abroad, he felt that he could do the most good for Colman by selling the D.I.M. in Europe. In writing Barber a second excited letter in the space of a few hours, Colman was now inclined to reduce his estimate of the time required to finish the D.I.M. from "two weeks or so," as earlier stated, to a matter of a few days. "I can get the machine ready to show you by next week," he told Barber, "if you can come down then" (12/5/92).

The idea of exhibiting the D.I.M. at the World's Fair, which was scheduled to open in Chicago in the summer of 1893, was enormously appealing to Colman. He gathered his notes and drawings on existing American warp-drawing patents and left for Warrens to make his case in person. There he discussed with Barber the uniqueness of the D.I.M.'s design in terms of the state of the art and outlined specific plans for the machine's reconstruction, eventually obtaining a pledge of $500. The two then traveled together to Rockford, Illinois, an industrial community twelve miles south of Beloit, to find a metalworking jobber to undertake the project. After an extensive search, they chose the Spengler Brothers Company, a highly-regarded manufacturer of dies and special machinery in the city's Water Power District. While in Rockford, they also engaged the services of a patent lawyer named Jacob Behel and took him back to Janesville to see the D.I.M. in operation.

Within a few months, Barber and Colman (in the latter's mind at least) had gone from being partners in an experimental project of uncertain value to the owners of a machine design with the potential to earn a small fortune. While moving forward with the rapid reconstruction of the device, one of their first priorities was to obtain legal protection: specifically, to identify the D.I.M.'s essential elements and document their originality in a patent application. They planned to organize for mass-production after the machine's exhibition at the Chicago World's Fair and the expected sales orders. Barber began drawing up formal partnership papers and wondered if his agreement with Colman should not extend to countries outside the United States, such as England, in light of the D.I.M.'s expected worldwide sales. He also contacted R.G. Dun and Company to establish credit for the business (he referred to it as "Colman and Barber" in his application), anticipating the need for additional capital if things went according to plan.

Not even Henry Colman, who had been disappointed in Howard's decision to pursue experimental work full-time instead of college, was unaffected by the excitement. Writing in his journal in early December, he reflected on the part that higher powers were now apparently playing in his son's good fortunes as an inventor:

> Affairs seem to work providentially, tho' not exactly as we prefer.
>
> We did not like the way Mr. Kingsbury treated the machine in Beaver Dam (tho' at first he greatly encouraged Howard). In Sept. '91 we sent H[owar]d to Evanston to school. Had he remained there, he probably would have dropped the machine, except in vacation. But after considerable hesitation, we were sent here [Beloit], and H[oward]., not liking the school [Beloit College], devoted much time to his machine and was near the cotton mill in Janesville, where he has been afforded every possible facility [and] allowed [to use] the machine shop without cost, and aided by engineers and [the] sup[erintendent]. In the fall, H[oward]. did not wish to continue in col[lege], and I consented to his working at the machine, tho' I greatly preferred that he attend school.

> Now he seems likely to have a machine worth hundreds of thousands to the world, if not to him … So all things work. Providence seems to be in it all.

iv

Anyone who questions William Barber's value to the Barber and Colman Company, his mechanical expertise, or his level of involvement in Colman's experimental work should read Barber's letter to the inventor of December 15, 1892, regarding a possible design for the D.I.M.'s cams:

> Dear Friend;
>
> On the way home I studied the cam question and submit sketch showing a way I would like opinion upon. You see it involves a feather shaft or equivalent, but is that materially objectionable?
>
> Fig. 1. Body of cam with a hub (H) caused to move laterally on shaft by cam groove on roller attached to Base B. If admissible, of course, the shaft could move in bearings, avoiding feather shaft. Fig. 2 is a thick disc to fit over hub of fig. 1 and given right relation by adjustment with set screw, as indicated. In face of disc (fig. 2) is to be cut groove to give the motion at right angles with shaft & portion of a groove indicated at G, and having a hub also to equal space required between faces of the two parts.
>
> Fig. 3 is end of arm to be operated by the cams, and is provided with two rollers. Of course, the principle is all I try to show. Possibly there is objection to this that does not occur to me. Your remark about shape of rollers on principle of bevel gear, which would be necessary in the plan thought of, led me to think more about it and try to find how to use rollers at every cam bearing surface and have the rollers run at exact (or nearly so) right angles with the track on which traveling. In case of roller in base indicated to be absolutely perfect would require both roller + groove to slightly taper.

Here we get the flavor of an early Barber and Colman technical conversation. We may well suppose that other exchanges at the time were conducted in a similar vein, as the two evaluated the D.I.M.'s mechanical systems before preparing a formal patent application. Barber had visited Colman in Janesville during the week of December 8 and watched several D.I.M. demonstrations at the Cotton Mills. Both were concerned about the irregularity of the rollers' motions; and Barber had outlined his idea of a new cam configuration in a series of pencil sketches (see illustrations on page 75 opposite).

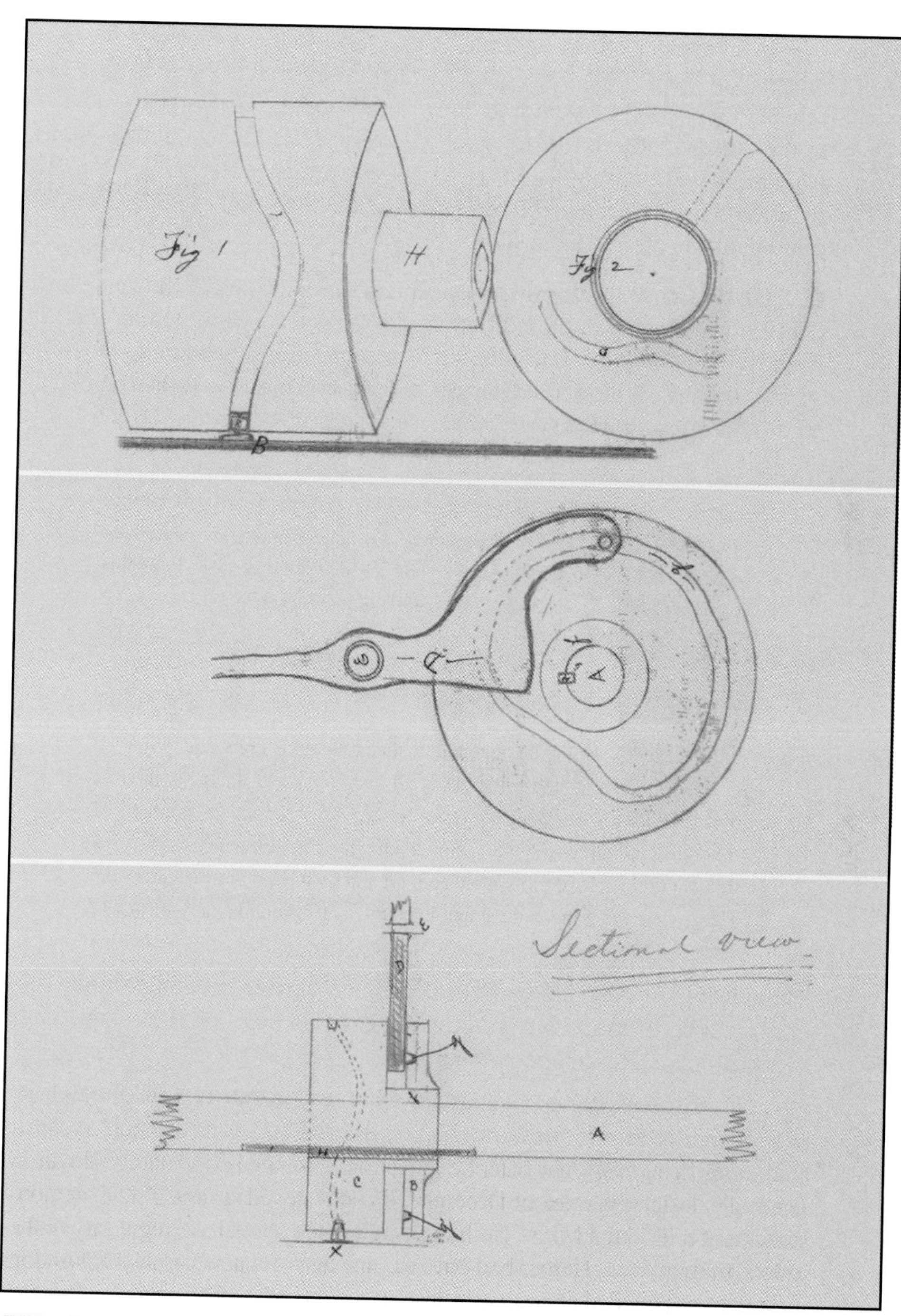

William Barber's sketch of a possible D.I.M. cam configuration (top) was intended to illustrate principles outlined in his letter to Colman of December 15, 1892. By way of comparison, Barber enclosed in the same letter two other drawings of a cam "scheme" from an existing U.S. patent, including top (middle) and sectional views (bottom).

In his reply, Colman said that he was "gratified" by Barber's "deep ... interest" in the D.I.M. He hoped that his criticisms of the proposed cam scheme would not cause him to "lose the advantage of [Barber's] advice" in the future. Indeed, if Barber felt strongly about his recommendations, Colman hoped that he would try to convince him anew (12/17/92). He returned Barber's sketch with several modifications and offered a detailed critique of the points in question.

Barber wrote back on December 19, agreeing that Colman's stated "objections" were "ample" on most of the points, while hoping that his friend would still give consideration to a suggestion for widening the roller surface tracks. He said that Colman would never lose his support by being forthright in his opinions:

> You need not suspect misunderstanding of motive or judgment on our * part, as one who has given so much special thought as to produce what you have. [You] must have explored mechanical principles pretty thoroughly and ... [be] possessed of a good stock of patience to give so much attention to the objectionable features of crude suggestion.

He went on:

> However, to show you are not in danger of losing our cooperation by candid rejection of of immature plans, [I] will say that your expression about "endwise motion of rock shaft that will limit speed" leads me to think that possibly there may be a good way to avoid this. If motion in arc of circle admissible cam groove, could [it] be cut with opposite eccentricity and amount reduced in proportion of leverage and pivot to a top on rock-shaft? ... It would give reciprocating motion to least weight of metal possible, I think.

These were not the opinions of a mechanical novice, a dabbler in the sciences, but someone with a mature and reasoned point of view shaped by years of practical problem-solving.

Nevertheless, Barber conceded technical authority to Colman. He was plainly in awe of his partner's talents, and he was willing to invest in the warp-drawing venture, at least in part, because of an interest in supporting his personal development. At the same time he recognized the importance of clarifying ideas through discussion and debate. He understood mechanical systems well enough to propose alternative arrangements,

* Barber is evidently referring here to himself and his son Fred, Colman's Wayland classmate, who was working in Warren and Company and interested in the D.I.M.

even to question the feasibility of certain changes from an operating perspective. Because he enjoyed Colman's trust, he felt an obligation to keep him on an emotional even-keel, to provide the right balance of encouragement and objective criticism. He needed to help him anticipate pitfalls, overcome doldrums, and complete the "improvements" to the machine in a timely fashion. In "trying to get everything on a perfect plan at first," he warned Colman, "we may unconsciously be aiming at too much, forestalling improvement later on" (12/19/92).

One of the difficulties that Barber and Colman faced was in deciding how far to go in refining the D.I.M., in knowing how much time and money to devote to the project before applying for a patent. It was obviously to their advantage to include as many claims as possible in their application, to present a comprehensive mechanical design; but they also knew that their claims would have to be proved up, reduced to commercial practice, before they were legally binding, and Colman still had not demonstrated the "practicality" of the device to his complete satisfaction. He had, after all, set himself the task of building a device to draw a perfect warp, and the idea of perfection exercised a peculiar seductive power. The closer he came to realizing his goal - the fewer mistakes he made in drawing in a warp - the more design alternatives he seemed to conceive. He found himself absorbed in a process of continuous refinement, with one idea generating another, and variations suggesting themselves in the course of finishing even a simple modification. Colman recognized his predicament somewhat belatedly:

> I have been thinking over the field of possible improvement, and I find that the number of different arrangements which might prove advantageous is very large. To determine absolutely which is best, it would be necessary to try them all and compare results. Of course this would require a great expenditure ..., which it seems to me is unadvisable at this stage (12/20/92).

He told Barber that he intended "to use in the machine we are now going to build only such schemes as we have good reasons to suppose will work satisfactorily" and to postpone other changes. Much more would be learned from the D.I.M.'s commercial operation, once it was mass-produced, than from any amount of preliminary testing. His goal in rebuilding was to simplify the design by reducing the number of parts and making them easily adjustable: "When the mill men have discovered that they can't do without our machines ..., we can go in for the fine points."

Spengler Brothers started building a new D.I.M. on January 7, working from the existing model and various sketches that Colman provided. On January 12 he moved to Rockford to oversee the construction and took a temporary room at the Madison Street YMCA. Progress was slow. A broken water wheel at the factory shut down production and required more than a week to fix. The plaster-paris patterns for the cams cracked, and work was delayed while these were repaired. Each new cast required several days to set, at least one to finish, and one-two more for the iron to be poured and shaped. Colman could only watch the work, estimate the cost of the delays, modify his plans, and attempt to control his impatience. He was not always successful. His dream of exhibiting the device at the Chicago World's Fair soon vanished, and his new hope, expressed in a letter to Fred Barber of February 22, was to have it ready for testing in Janesville by the first of April ("but am not making any promises about it"). This, too, had to be altered. We know from Henry Colman's diary that Howard's health suffered during the winter and that he sought the help of a specialist in Milwaukee to treat his illness. No longer concerned just with the costs of his experiments, Colman had become responsible for regular payments to the Spenglers and other jobbers, for his living expenses away from home, and for transportation between Beloit and Rockford. When his account with the Spenglers was $200 in arrears and the expected payment from William Barber late in arriving, Colman expressed his frustration to Fred Barber in an uncharacteristically angry letter:

> What's the matter? Didn't you receive the letter I wrote you last Sat. stating that $200 on Spengler's acct. was overdue? ... I'd like to know "how the land lies," what you expect to do, and where your father is, etc. The protracted nervous strain of the work of this machine is more than I am used to and is, I'm afraid, making me impatient and ill-natured ... (3/23/93).

For most of the year, Colman lived hand-to-mouth in a kind of experimental limbo, chronically short of funds, frustrated by the Spenglers' delays, embarrassed to ask Barber for more money, and annoyed when the payments were late. Both he and Barber began to have serious second-thoughts about the wisdom of retaining Jacob Behel as a patent lawyer, since they had heard several stories from acquaintances in Beloit about his questionable business ethics. Behel's advice to them to delay their request for a patent until the new machine was finished now made them anxious to draw up an application. They decided to select a new lawyer, L.I. Morrison of Rockford, to do their legal work.

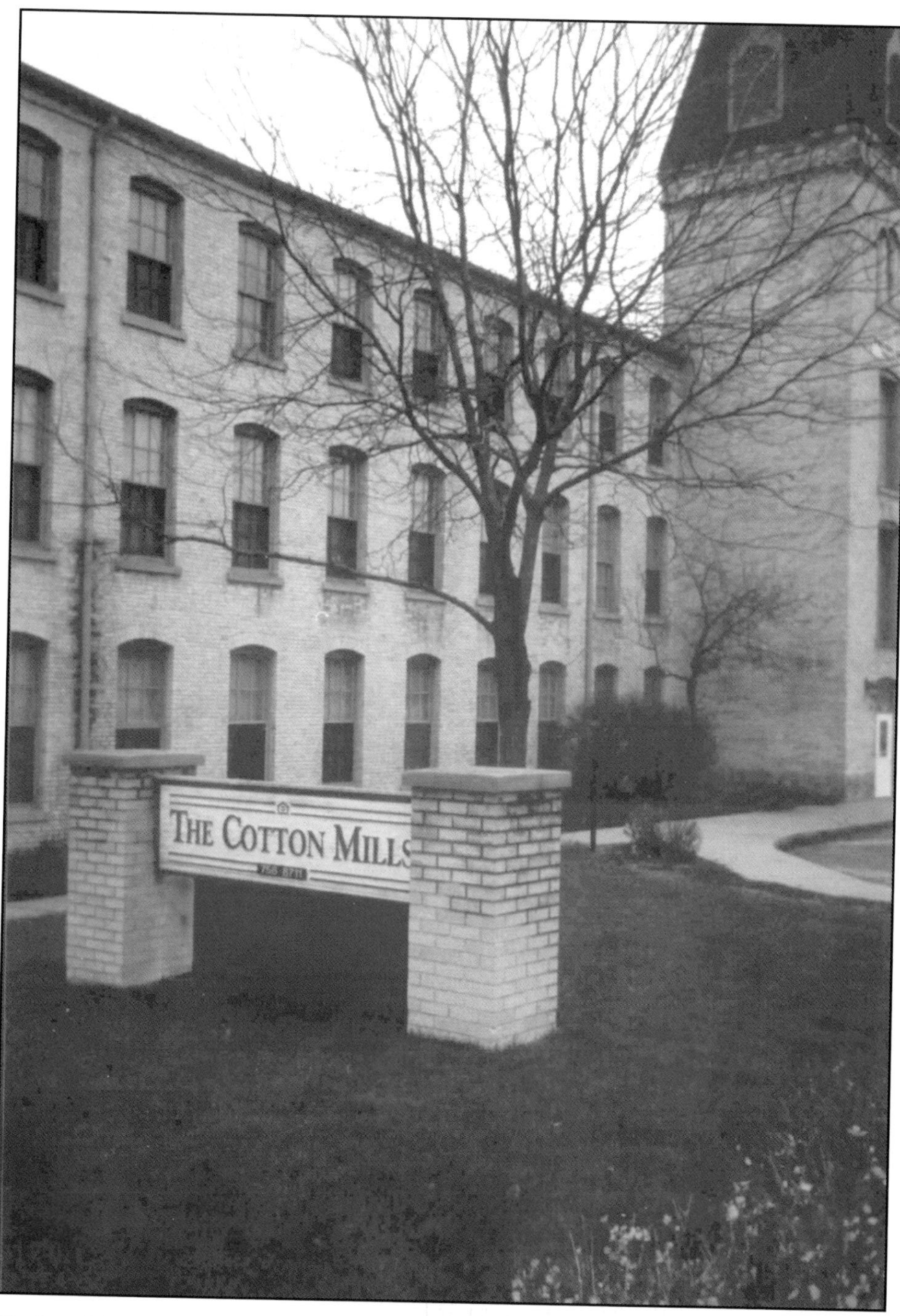

The Janesville Cotton Mills, where Colman conducted his D.I.M. experiments, was the first manufacturer of cotton goods in the state of Wisconsin. The building survives today as an apartment complex.

On April 25 Colman notified William Barber that the drawing-in project was "progressing - but very slowly." Eight days later he admitted to Fred Barber that he had "given up guessing" when the machine would be done. He had learned from the boss weaver in Janesville that a strange man had been asking questions there about his invention, and the stranger turned out to be George Sutherland, the Mills vice president, who said that he wanted to form a stock company for Colman and manufacture the device in Janesville. "In fact, he talked just a trifle as if he owned the whole concern already." Colman's suspicions were further aroused when his friend Witham told him privately to be wary of Sutherland, that he would "cinch" Colman if given the opportunity (5/12/93). The Janesville Cotton Mills no longer seemed like the best place to test his machine. As a result, he made a trip to Aurora, Illinois to investigate a cotton mill there (its harnesses were, unfortunately, non-standard) and even gave some thought to setting up again in Beaver Dam.

Colman's worries about the D.I.M. were compounded by a series of almost comic misadventures. He wrote Barber repeatedly about the Spenglers' delinquent account but received no reply because the latter mailed his check to the Spengler Brothers in care of Janesville, Wisconsin. Another time their letters crossed in the mail, Colman's asking for money, Barber's enclosing an amount that was never requested. Colman wrote a cover letter to go with a list of expenses, then neglected to enclose the list. He visited the World's Fair in Chicago in June and came back "so completely 'broke' " that he hadn't the "wherewith" even to pay for his board (such were the "distressing results of trips to the World's Fair when rashly indulged in by impecunious inventors"); he asked Barber for an advance of $25 against the amount that Barber expected to pay at the conclusion of their contract (6/6/93). "Opening this pad to write," he informed Barber on July 14, "I found the enclosed sheet, so I judge you didn't get the whole of my last letter. Please excuse the blunder." When Colman went to the Fair again in August, Barber's letter to him was forwarded to Beloit, instead of to Chicago. When Colman returned to Beloit, he was "compelled to acknowledge" to Barber that he was no longer worthy of "trust and confidence." He had lost his account book at the Fair, after packing it in his satchel at the start of the trip. Thus he had no way of knowing his actual expenses to date:

> … I cannot in the least find fault if you decline to trust me with any more money after what has happened. But if you should conclude to do so, I

> would suggest that you insist on at least a monthly report of expenditures in detail. It would at any rate be a kindness to me to do so, for I realize that I must learn to be more systematic and businesslike in my methods (9/4/93).

Colman did the best he could with limited resources. He tested the rebuilt machine in the Spengler Brothers factory, carefully evaluating each modification in relation to the number of threads that could be drawn per minute, checking the accuracy of the parts acting on the eyes of the heddles, comparing his results to earlier trials; but he was left to wonder about the reliability of these tests since nothing could be "positively proved" without going to a mill. Did he have enough data to proceed with a patent application? When he drew in a beam, he had no way of knowing if it had been done accurately or not without putting it into a loom and weaving. It was impossible to tell by watching it being drawn because the mechanism ran at high speeds. And it was hardly feasible to inspect the beam afterwards by hand. This normally took a day to do, and even then the results were open to question (5/12/93). He confessed to Barber that he sometimes had difficulty making sense of the experimental data: the variables related to the operation of the machine, the many issues of design and construction.

The longer Colman worked on the problem of warp replenishment, the more he found himself distrusting the results. The machine seemed to obey its own eccentric logic. When he increased its speed, it broke fewer threads. Yet the motion of the needle became more erratic. When he adjusted the needle mechanism, it picked up "doublers" (two eyes with a single thread). When he tried it the next time, the situation was reversed. The needle hit the eyes cleanly, but the threads started crossing, and the machine's speed declined. "The process of perfecting it," he wrote Barber with characteristic resolve, "is, I confess, very much slower than I expected, but we are always able to improve it a little, and we are coming nearer and nearer to perfection, so I see no cause for discouragement" (7/5/93).

A month later Barber sounded his own discordant note. His financial position had significantly worsened, he told Colman, and common sense now dictated a "curtailment of every expense not fully warranted." Colman was to "desist from adding materially to the cost" of the machine other than to help "secure [a] patent on what we have now." The demands on Barber's money were such that there was little left for the drawing-in project. A nationwide financial panic, which President Grover Cleveland blamed on the Silver Purchase Act of 1890 and his political opponents attributed to the government's own restrictive money policies, had set off a wave of falling prices, job layoffs, and credit difficulties. Earlier, on May 16, Colman had appealed to Barber to help settle the account with George Spengler because of the latter's cash problems ("Spengler's principal customers - the furniture companies here - are on the verge of bankruptcy and are owing him a great deal ..."), but their correspondence otherwise has few references to the nation's deteriorating economy. Barber normally limited his business discussions in the letters to the details of the drawing-in venture itself and tried to avoid burdening Colman with financial concerns. If "business conditions were the same as a year ago," he wrote on August 10, he would not have hesitated "to go on as we have for a month or so" while waiting for things to get better. As it was, he was forced to ask Colman to "drop all 'side shows' " immediately and to attend to the matters at hand "in prudent lines and manner." Colman's notions for improving the machine, the peripheral speculations that normally occurred to him in the course of his investigations and enlarged his field of inquiry, had to be completely restrained and any action on them delayed until more favorable times. In suggesting that Colman take a break from his experiments, Barber showed that he clearly knew his man: "I think ... you will be yourself benefited by a little relaxation from *such close application to the one thing*" (emphasis added).

Colman's letters to Barber of August 18 and 25 make no reference to Barber's request for a "curtailment of expense," and in fact continue as before, with discussions of the costs of machining, transportation, and room and board. On September 4, after acknowledging his debts and chiding himself for a lack of organization in his business affairs, Colman wondered whether Barber would still be willing to provide any money for testing the D.I.M. at a cotton mill once the patent application was finished. He did not believe that the mechanism, in its current shape, would have much value "without working on it six months or so in a mill - perhaps more." He had been thinking of an improvement which would help to eliminate some of the most troublesome problems, and for $30 or $40, he could incorporate this feature into the machine and add it to the patent application.

Barber responded, on September 16, with the suggestion that Colman consider setting the machine up in a mill and using it to prepare new warp beams there; he could run it at whatever speed was necessary to "work it successfully" and earn some money from the beams that were drawn. It was a way to sustain the project and keep body and soul together. The cost of the improvement that Colman proposed was actually so modest that Barber said he was ready to approve it if he thought it had any chance of bringing the experiments to a close, but the fact was that the costs of the venture had already surpassed what he hoped to get back from the invention, and the likelihood of having to absorb even more expenses in relation to the patent work made him content to "await the outcome" of the project as it was currently budgeted. He enclosed a check for $100 and said that he hoped to be able to send more money in the future: "This lack of ready funds is unexpected and not pleasant."

V

"Howard is on the sick list today - nothing serious," Henry Colman wrote Barber on September 18, and it is apparent that the young inventor spent the next seven days recuperating at his parents' home in Beloit. But he gradually regained his strength. "As I was confined to the house all that week," he reported to Barber on October 9, "I had plenty of time for meditation, and I concluded that it was very important to try the improvement I spoke of ..." It was important enough, he said, to have actually gone ahead and asked George Spengler to do the work, and to have stayed a week in Rockford overseeing its completion. If Barber objected to this, Colman said that he would stand the expenses himself. He wanted to report, however, that the new feature had proved to be successful in later tests, and that it added significantly to the value of the invention. And there was more to report. He confessed that he had also gone to Chicago, without consulting Barber, in order to explain his modification to L.T. Mann, the draftsman who was working on their patent drawings. He had ended up staying there an entire week in order to make sure that Mann depicted the changes accurately. The cost of everything had turned out to be $34.37, including $20 for "Spengler's work." But since Colman had "exceeded" his authority "in incurring it," Colman did not plan to charge it to Barber without his "special consent."

Colman was confident enough in his relationship with Barber to be willing, occasionally, to circumvent his authority. But he did so in subtle ways, and he always exercised his inventor's prerogative to determine what was best for the project at each stage of development. If he could demonstrate the value of a change to the machine, prove it in repeated tests, and if he were afterwards willing to pay for the costs of doing this himself, he felt that he had the freedom to pursue a promising idea into fabrication without having to ask first for Barber's approval.

Colman pointed out in his letter that the improvement had left him with just one problem, the occasional picking-up of doublers, and he believed that this could be overcome with a few weeks of work in the Janesville Cotton Mills. The cost of doing this would not be much more than "carefare and hotel." The end of the drawing-in venture seemed once again in sight, and his earlier estimate of six months of testing was apparently forgotten. "Perhaps the decided success I met with last time makes me over-sanguine now," he wrote Barber, "but I have nothing else to do for the two weeks it will probably take before the draftsman finishes, and I shall be much pleased if you find the expense justifiable" (9/4/93).

True to form, Barber agreed to reimburse Colman for the "improvement" and said nothing more about his own pressing financial issues. "Am willing to stand the expense you have been to and glad you went on with all of it; especially glad of the success referred to" (10/11/93). The "success" was based on trials in Spengler's factory, not mill operations, however, and Colman knew that there was a world of difference. According to his notes on the D.I.M. project, he made preparations to ship the machine to Janesville again sometime after the first of November. The device was lowered through the upper-story window of the Spenglers' factory onto a wagon and taken to the nearby Rockford railroad freight depot. Colman admitted to encountering "various botherations" in the process of installing the machine in Janesville, and he delayed writing Barber until November 20 in order to be able to offer "some positive facts of encouragement instead of promises." A new idea for picking up the harness eyes, a "very simple contrivance," had been incorporated into the machine before its shipment to Janesville, and as far as he could tell, this had solved the doubler problem. He had not finished weaving all the beams that were drawn, "not yet got all the facts," but considering what he had seen, he was "encouraged rather than otherwise."

Three days later Colman reported that the Janesville trials were a failure:

> I've got my facts, and they [are] embodied in this - our machine is a beautiful mechanism which isn't worth its room for practical use. It will work when all the conditions are favorable, and if the greatest care is used in handling it. Otherwise, it will smash and skip harness eyes most recklessly. In fact, the element of unreliability is still present, and if it were a tenth as large an element as it is, it would be sufficient to render the machine impractical.

The letter to Barber is uncharacteristically cynical and detached, all the more so for its reasonable tone. Colman said he was sure that he could improve the machine's reliability if he had a fabricating shop and a cotton mill in the same location. He could at least save the time it took to travel between Rockford and Janesville, and prevent himself from wasting so much money and effort on changes to the machine that turned out to be impractical in mill tests. He admitted, however, that "the expense would [still] be considerable and the result doubtful." The only remaining option - "not a very good one, perhaps, but still the only one unless we go in much deeper than we are now" - seemed to be to sell the rights to the machine in its present stage of development. His 1891 researches in the Chicago Public Library had turned up several drawing-in patents from the 1880s belonging to two Maine inventors, Lewis Sherman and Richmond Ingersoll; and he thought that these men might be interested in acquiring the D.I.M. Why waste money on a patent application when the device was still unproven? "Please do not think that I have written in this tone merely because I happen to feel a little 'blue.' I have purposely waited until I don't feel particularly that way ..." (11/23/93).

Barber answered two days later:

> Can't say I was just expecting this exactly, but am not prostrated with surprise, and sympathize with you in view of the struggle this conclusion must have cost you ...There are considerations as to effect of negotiations before obtaining a patent that I am not decided upon, but it seems to me that our chance to sell would be much better with than without a patent.

He planned to write to L.I. Morrison to ask him to stop working on the current application. Barber could only guess now at their chances of actually getting a patent, and this had to be considered, along with the costs of future negotiations for the sale of their rights (11/25/93).

In the meantime Colman had his own conversation with Morrison, who wondered if the inventors that Colman had identified in Maine would not be inclined simply to steal his ideas and apply for a patent themselves. But Colman wondered if they would even be interested in discussing a sale. Wasn't it worth the risk to find out, to offer them the rights to the D.I.M. before a patent was obtained so that they could incorporate the best features from it into their own mechanism and apply for a patent on an improved design? If the negotiations fell through, then he and Barber should either "call it a dead loss and quit" or else put the project aside for a few years until Colman could develop a new scheme. He was otherwise completely "without any practicable ideas," though "quite decidedly of the opinion that anything more spent in patent [work] at present is not much better than thrown away" (11/27/93).

· one-time Methodist parsonage in Beloit, Wisconsin (628 Broad Street), where Howard Colman lived with his parents and two ·ers in the 1890s, may be seen in the background of this photograph from the early 20th Century. By a remarkable coincidence, Henry Tower family pictured here would later become related to the Colmans through the marriage of the boy in the front row ·), Richard Tower, to Howard's older daughter, Ruth. The Broad Street building was a duplex, and the Colman and Tower ·ilies occupied the same apartment at different times.

5

Trial and Error

I have often thought that there are few men who would have trusted any one so young and inexperienced as I am ... I am sincerely grateful for it and only hope that in the end you will have no cause to regret it.

- Letter from Howard Colman to William Barber, 1893

i

Howard Colman's early struggles to perfect the D.I.M. are painstakingly chronicled in his letters to William Barber, even though the technical details sometimes prevent us from understanding his intentions and tracing his progress in improving the mechanism. Like every inventor, Colman had to feel his way forward, relying on instincts and imagination to guide him through a conceptual maze of D.I.M. design problems. His endless fiddling with the warp-drawing apparatus in the Spenglers' shop and Janesville Mills was paralleled by an interior process of questioning and self-doubt. His impatience with the project increased as he came to realize how many experimental variables were actually out of his control and beyond his ability even to influence.

It may be well to try to summarize here the years from 1889-93. As we have seen, Colman's earliest letters describe his efforts to build a warp drawing-in machine out of makeshift elements, refine its operations with more precisely-fabricated parts, redesign the cams to increase the operating speed, and improve its reliability in mill conditions. They document his worries about financing, his eagerness to test new schemes, and his frustrations when his ideas prove to be wide of the mark. We sense his growing reluctance to ask Barber for money, as well as his uncertainty about the time needed to carry out changes to the machine; and we witness his continued determination to make the D.I.M. a success in spite of setbacks.

Statement of Account.

Warrens, Wis. Oct 11 1893

Mr. H. Colman Dr.

Drawing in Mach

In Account With Geo. Warren Company.

W. W. Barber

For amounts furnished

1891			
July	1	Cash	100 00
Nov.	25	[illegible] returned	25 00
1892			
June	2	Cash	25 00
Aug.	3	"	25 00
Oct.	24	"	50 00
Dec	14	" (at Beloit)	25 00
"	17	"	150 00
1893			
Jan	25	"	100 00
"	7	" Jones & L. [illegible]	3 96
"	25	"	4 85
Feb.	14	"	100 00
"	20	"	100 00
Mar.	11	" [illegible]	200 00
Apr	21	"	250 00
May	15	"	200 00
June	6	"	25 00
"	20	"	200 00
July	10	"	75 00
"	27	" at Rockford	250 00
Sept.	16	"	100 00
			$2,008 81

The cost of Howard Colman's D.I.M. experiments rose steadily throughout the early 1890s, as this statement of account graphically illustrates. From July 1, 1891- September 16, 1893, William Barber invested $2,008.81 in the "Drawing in Mach[ine]" project. Over one five-month period in 1893 (March-July) alone, he sent Colman $1,300, a considerable sum in an era when a $1.25 a day was considered a living wage.

In the fall of 1891, when he drops out of Northwestern University, Colman expresses his confidence in the future of the invention and his expectation of substantial domestic sales once the mechanism has been perfected. Although he goes through periods of depression during this time because of stress and overwork, his attitude is largely upbeat and assured. This phase of his experiments lasts until the winter months of 1893, when his mood begins to change. Worries about the costs of fabrication now give way to concerns about the efficacy of the D.I.M. design. He considers making extensive modifications to the machine, and he weighs the difficulties of doing this - patent complications, delays in construction, more expense - against the risks of proceeding without them. Increasingly, he senses that he is losing control of the drawing-in venture. He realizes that his ideas are of little consequence without Barber's money and Spengler's jobbing skills. He is at the mercy of lawyers and draftsmen in developing a qualified patent application. His mill privileges depend on Witham's continued good will. Colman's confidence in his ability to solve the D.I.M. puzzle is undermined by his failure to make much headway in eliminating simple errors in the drawing-in process. Not yet 21 and already accustomed to months of close, exacting investigative work, he ends the year thoroughly disillusioned with the D.I.M. project and questioning the value of a device that only a short time before had seemed to him to be unlimited in its earning potential.

Reading Colman's early letters, one becomes aware of a regular pattern of experimental activity: initially, a feeling of excitement about the possibilities of a new idea or concept; then a much more circumspect and deliberative stage of investigation in which the idea is tested and refined; eventually, a period of mental and physical exhaustion in which his activities are either curtailed or temporarily interrupted; and finally a phase in which he recovers his strength, resumes his experiments, and becomes productive again.

Colman's recuperative powers, like his stamina, were out of the ordinary. Working for days with limited sleep and refreshing himself with catnaps, often taking breaks only for meals, he amazed his contemporaries with his energy. Even in the doldrums, he continued to turn over problems in his head and think of ways to improve his schemes. Because of the time he devoted to the intricacies of cotton manufacturing, he had an almost visceral awareness of its mechanical elements. His understanding of the relationships between the various forces and motions enabled him to re-create, imaginatively, the drawing-in process in depth. He sensed it kinesthetically. Sometimes, when he felt himself limited by circumstances, unable to proceed with his experiments because of factors beyond his control or simply at a technical impasse, he would let his thoughts wander into peripheral interests, puzzle out the configurations of a new model, say, and occupy himself with the mental images of its possible operations. One of the spin-offs of his textile experiments was something called an "automatic self-registering speed indicator" (3/20/94), a little device for gauging the rapidity of a warp beam's revolutions that he gave a good deal of thought to during tests at the Janesville Cotton Mills. The idea occurred to him as a sidelight to his main investigations, almost incidentally, and although he seems to have done little afterwards to develop the mechanism or market it to mill owners, the speed indicator provided an outlet for his experimental interests at a time when he was questioning his ability to make the D.I.M. work.

By the winter of 1893-94, Colman had reconciled himself to a fairly limited course of action. He realized that Barber's enthusiasm for the venture had waned as a result of his financial problems and the ever-rising costs of the experiments. Colman also knew that he was a long way from getting the D.I.M. ready for commercial production. After arranging to put the machine into temporary storage at the Janesville Cotton Mills, he asked Barber for a "final" loan of $350 to tie up loose ends and see what he could still make of the invention, a request that Barber somewhat surprisingly granted. "I suspected you had not run out of 'ideas' or lost faith in them either," Barber wrote him on December 8. To which Colman responded:

> I certainly shall do all in my power to succeed, but I can't say that I feel absolutely certain - my experience during the past year has bred in me too much distrust of appearances for that (12/23/93).

Like other plans for addressing the machine's flaws, this, too, proved to be unsuccessful. In January Colman announced that his "new scheme" did not "go anything as well as the old one." Since the cost of making changes in the original design would be $2,500 or more, he could not in good conscience recommend going forward, even supposing Barber's willingness to support the project financially. Thus he needed to consider some sort of "remunerative employment":

> I am "out of a job" now, and if you know of any vacant situation which you think I could fill, you will be adding to my indebtedness to you, by remembering me (1/25/94).

But Colman was actually a long way from giving up. He does not seem to have looked for a job very actively or, at least, to have been successful in finding one, since nine days later he reported that he had devised yet another plan to address deficiencies in the D.I.M. He advised Barber that he believed himself justified in exploring the new scheme because of Barber's earlier agreement to provide him with $350, an amount he had so far barely used. The changes he had in mind involved "additional safeguards on the old scheme," something which could hardly make the machine "work any worse than it did" and which might well improve it (2/6/94). In his next two letters, with a new feeling of optimism, he addressed himself to "misapprehensions" that Barber might have had concerning "the difficulties of the case." It was really not as hopeless as he had previously let on, he said, and for this he blamed himself:

> I judge that the last letter you received from me was the one announcing the failure of the scheme for which I sent you drawings. I confess that I was rather despondent then, but I have recovered from that now and am perhaps a little inclined the other way.

He pointed out that some of his recent D.I.M. modifications - a new mechanism for preventing doublers, another for handling the harness eyes - seemed to be working surprisingly well. He had not picked up a doubler since making the adjustment. Moreover, he had been able to draw in an average of two-three beams a day that the mill could use for weaving. And the "new scheme completely remedied the breaking of the eyes" (2/16/94).

The real difficulty, Colman suggested, was his own lack of experience in working with metals. The theoretical basis of the D.I.M. was sound. He simply could not determine the kinds of adjustments that were needed to compensate for the stresses and vibrations. If greater rigidity was required in some of the joints and connections, and greater flexibility in others, he was at a loss to say which ones. He did not have enough confidence in his diagnostic skills to make the corrections, and he had been unable to keep the components in continuous alignment after the machine started its rapid rhythmic pulsing. Nevertheless, he told Barber, he felt that he was "making very satisfactory progress" and had gone to Rockford to enlist Spengler's help:

> The last changes succeeded completely in the points aimed at, and if the changes I am now here to have made do as well, I think the machine will be as good a success from a mechanical standpoint as we need to strive for at present. Of course these "improvements" may not prove to be such, and even if they do, I may see other things which need changing before Morrison takes his turn at it (3/6/94).

True to the pattern of his previous experiments, Colman soon ran into a number of roadblocks. The mechanism that Spengler made for him worked beautifully at first, and he had high hopes when he tested it in Janesville:

> But in one beam the revolving knife got caught and stopped, so that about a couple hundred threads were broken out, and I had to start over. In another the hook which catches the threads when the needle has pushed them through the reed got loose and failed to catch a large number of threads, and so on from one thing to another for 3 or 6 beams. At last I did get one that was pretty good, but in the next the thing began to draw doublers. As I wrote you, this had not bothered at all since sometime last fall, so I was much surprised, especially as I couldn't discover what was the matter. But after only half a day, I found what might have caused it, but am not sure yet whether that was the only trouble. When I tried to draw in some more beams, the device for bringing over the eyes began to fail again more outrageously, and now my arm is getting so sore from vaccination that I can't work for a while.

However, the trials were not a complete waste of effort. Colman told Barber that, despite the many operational headaches, he doubted that any "further changes of importance to the patent" would "be necessary to make it work," given the likelihood of them being able to construct a much more rigid model in the future. Thus he intended to ask Morrison to begin writing up a patent application, to "proceed in that direction," if Barber were in agreement (3/20/94). Colman was determined to stay the course in any event and believed that they would both be compensated one day for their Sisyphean labors: "Feel certain that if we only 'keep everlastingly at it' we will be rewarded with ample returns" (5/8/94). He was no longer aiming at perfection, he said, merely at a standard that the patent examiners would accept.

ii

In the spring and summer of 1894, Colman spent much of his time working with Morrison and L.T. Mann on the D.I.M. patent application, as well as mulling over the designs of the two Maine inventors, Lewis Sherman and Richmond Ingersoll, who held the existing American rights to a pioneering drawing-in machine, a device that had yet to be manufactured commercially. During a visit to Morrison's office in January, Colman had read a notice in the *Patent Office Gazette* of three new patents that had been issued to these men, and although the brief description of the mechanisms did not give him much cause for concern at the time, he had taken the precaution of sending for the drawings and specifications and adding them to his patent library. Colman had pointed out to Barber, perhaps in an attempt to place his own experimental difficulties in perspective, that the "eastern concern" had certainly not "run out of money or confidence" in the fourteen years since it secured its first patent. If Sherman and Ingersoll had failed to "put anything on the market" during this period, they had beaten Barber and Colman "all hollow" in terms of "perseverance" (1/15/94).

Nevertheless, after additional study of the Sherman and Ingersoll designs, Colman discovered that a few features of the D.I.M. infringed on the pioneering patent, and he began to look for ways to modify these parts so that he could avoid future legal problems. He also made arrangements to ship the machine back to Rockford to help Morrison draw up his specifications for a patent application. Having the model at hand, he knew, would enable the lawyer to understand the principles of the warp drawing-in process far better than any amount of secondhand description. Colman wanted "to push the patent work as rapidly as possible" now and "to leave the question of building [a] new machine" until a later date, after the Patent Office had ruled on the application. He would no longer interrupt Morrison with last-minute "ideas for improvement" and cause delays in the formulation of the D.I.M.'s legal description. Instead, he planned to begin compiling a separate file of "variations" and "corrected designs" that could be used for future experiments. It was nearly impossible for him to do otherwise, he told Barber, because new ideas kept coming to mind whether he willed them or not:

> I have ... been revolving in my mind every possible scheme for simplifying the machine. Have found some places where it can be done and others where it might be done but where is doubtful without experiment. There are points in connection with picking up the threads which cannot very well be determined even by experiment with the old machine, and so I think *I will design that portion of the machine in two or three different ways* and perhaps try them all when we build again (emphasis added: 7/31/94).

Rather than relying on a single approach, Colman would explore several options in parallel. He intended to develop alpha, beta, and gamma variations of the same mechanical "scheme" as a means of hedging his bets.

On October 4, 1894, after more than four years of experimental work, Colman filed his application for a D.I.M. patent. He also wrote to Barber with the news that Henry Colman had been reassigned to a Methodist Church in Milwaukee. Colman anticipated that his parents' income there

L.T. Mann holds up a white bedsheet as a backdrop for a photograph of the D.I.M. Colman later remembered him as "the best draftsman I ever heard of for artistic work. He did it in a wonderfully short time when he got at it" (Warp Drawing-In Machine Court Testimony, 1919).

would be less than in Beloit and the household expenses somewhat greater, and he said that he was no longer willing to be a financial "burden" to them. Having reached the age of 21, he felt that he should be living on his own. His investigative work in Rockford, in any event, prevented him from moving permanently to Milwaukee. Since he had previously struggled to support himself even with his parents' help, he now found himself in an awkward personal situation. "You promised me your advice as a friend in this contingency," he wrote Barber, "and I certainly need it now."

Choosing his words carefully and summoning all the diplomatic skills at his command, Colman outlined a proposal to restructure the partnership agreement. There was an aspect of the "present arrangement" which had probably not occurred to Barber, he said, and which he now took the "liberty of mentioning," knowing that Barber would consider the issue with his customary fairness and objectivity. In any experimental project, Colman pointed out, there were a number of "legitimate expenses:" the inventor's work; the costs of fabricating a model; and the expenses associated with drawing up the specifications. Usually an inventor had to hire others to do both the prototyping work and preliminary mechanical drawings:

> It seems to me that my inventive ability fully balances your investment, for judging by the few other cases I know of, it would be impossible to hire done what I have done for anything like the sum you have invested. I did not mention this at the start because I believed that the expense of the blunders I would make through inexperience would balance the value of my services as draftsman and designer, but it has been the universal testimony of those who have had experience in experimental work that I have got along with remarkable economy.

Since he and Barber had considered themselves "even" before he began working on the new set of D.I.M. drawings, Colman thought it was unfair for him to have "to bear the whole burden of the present work." He proposed to split these expenses with Barber: to charge him $10 a week until the drawings were done and then to submit the finished documents to impartial judges to decide their actual value. The weekly payments would apply to the final settlement. If it turned out that Barber had overpaid him, he would expect to refund the difference.

> Then if we sell, we will be even, at least I will be willing to call it so, altho' it would perhaps be fair to say that the inventive ability I am investing fully balances all expenses, including payment for drawings

> and building [the] new machine, thus making me entitled to full payment for drawings in any case.

Colman may have sensed that this was too strong. He tried to be nonchalant:

> But please understand that I consider your judgment of what is right and fair in the case as better than my own, and that I make these remarks merely to call your attention to a phase of the case which you may not have thought of.

After he had signed the letter, he made a final appeal for help. Both the message and logic were familiar:

> Please reply as soon as possible, for I fear I must seek remunerative employment unless you and I can make some such arrangement as above ...

When the letter reached Barber on October 5, he sat down immediately to draft a reply. Just as Colman had been assertive in making his case, Barber was forthright in countering it. After acknowledging the letter and mentioning his plans to attend the upcoming Baptist State Convention in Janesville, Barber reminded his young friend that the entire drawing-in project, with its changing focus and long history of financial investments on Barber's part, was something that Colman himself had solely determined:

> I have thought much of your position as well as my own in reference to our interests in the drawing-in machine. For some time I have felt desirous of getting out of the entanglement but saw no place or way except ahead that did not seem the wrong one, but the amount and kind of investment we have each put in, you have all along practically decided; the relative value of our stakes in this game of chance can hardly be determined by the use of money on very uncertain security on the one hand or the fair wages of a good draughtsman on the other. Such as we have each put in the hole, and both may draw out a good return or both may find we have sunk our investments. Suppose we get a patent all right after the further necessary expense, would not a sale that gives me only my money back with fair use and a little for time and trouble be still a fairly living deal for you? How confidently can we hope for much more? These are questions, among others, occurring to me and probably to you also.

And there the matter ended. So far as we know, Colman never mentioned the idea of charging for drafting work again and never attempted to revise the terms of the partnership agreement. On November 13, Barber sent him two checks to settle Morrison's legal bills and suggested that photographs be taken of the D.I.M. as a means of illustrating the machine's capabilities. At approximately the same time, it appears, Colman moved to Milwaukee to live with his parents, having no way to continue to support himself in Rockford. Henry Colman would refer briefly in his diary to this period of his son's life:

> In November, I think, Howard came home from Janesville and reported his drawing-in machine a failure. He then devised another plan for part of it, and Mr. Barber said: "Go ahead." Thursday he returned from Rockford with the unwelcome news that the new device had not succeeded. He is now home. What will turn up for him I do not know.

iii

By the end of the year, Colman's options as an inventor had become extremely limited. His parents' move to Milwaukee deprived him of a place to live that was close to his experiments, and Barber's denial of his request for additional drafting money made it inevitable that he would have to follow. While going to Milwaukee permanently was out of the question if he hoped to continue his investigations, he planned to live there temporarily and to commute back and forth to Rockford and Janesville.

Yet Colman's plans were complicated when the Janesville Cotton Mills unexpectedly shut its doors because of a lack of raw materials. Eventually, the owners of the company, who had been struggling to meet expenses even before the cotton shortages, decided to suspend their operations for good. Without a mill to test his ideas, and lacking the financial means to construct a better D.I.M. model, Colman had little choice but to look for ways to sell his design. He began compiling a list of companies, mainly in New England, who were engaged in textile manufacturing, and investigated the possibility of dismantling the D.I.M. and shipping it to the East Coast for exhibition to interested buyers.

Barber volunteered to review the commercial reports on any company that Colman considered a likely prospect. The "steady pressure of the times," he wrote (2/6/95), was forcing him "to slow up on all expenses and investments possible to curtail." He had found it necessary to "dispose of something that we have or hold onto it with less expense, at least until we know results from the patent office ..." He advised Colman to wind up the experiments and to put the D.I.M. in good enough shape so that he could "see and help pass upon" the device before it was shipped to New England.

Colman appears in the background of this photograph of the reconstructed D.I.M. and accompanying beam truck. The picture was part of a series showing the machine in successive stages of operation.

Colman rolls a warp beam and harness away from the side of the D.I.M. In cotton mills, finished beams were taken to a "weave room" prior to being fed into a loom.

It would help him get a better idea of its value, he wrote on March 26, if he watched it in operation, since he doubted that he could find anyone else to go to Rockford to give him an expert opinion.

On March 28 an article appeared in the *Rockford Morning Star* under the headline:

LABOR OF FIVE YEARS
Howard D. Coleman [sic], a Young Inventor,
Completes a Machine.

The piece described the visit of a *Morning Star* reporter to the Spengler Brothers' machine shop in the Water Power District. Accompanied by the inventor, the reporter had inspected a new device there for the threading of harness eyes in a power loom. The machine could do the work of six people, and it included a number of interesting features, such as a mechanism for stopping itself when it made a mistake. The reporter pointed out that this had occurred only "once or twice" in the course of the demonstration. The machine was able to pick up the individual warp threads and pass them "through the eye of the harness and reed with a rapidity and exactness that is astonishing." In October, it would be six years since the machine's inventor had begun studying the possibility of constructing a device to eliminate the hand-threading of harnesses. He had actually finished a working model of his invention more than a year earlier, and since then had been occupying himself with the kind of small improvements that were necessary in "an invention entirely new in its application:"

> In about a month, when he has it still further revised, he will take a trip to the east. For fifteen years, parties in Maine have been working on the same problem and have secured patents from time to time, but have not met with the success that Mr. Coleman [sic] has. He has applied for patents and now is sanguine, as he certainly should be, that his time and the considerable amount of money he has expended have not gone for nothing. Mr. Coleman's [sic] home is in Milwaukee, but he has been here off and on with his machine for two years …

Colman's willingness to operate his machine for a newspaper reporter and to promote his work in this way comes as a surprise to anyone familiar with his later aversion to personal publicity. It's hard to imagine him talking about his experimental successes or comparing himself favorably to Sherman and Ingersoll (the "parties in Maine"), as the *Morning Star* reporter notes, though Colman may well have been desperate enough at this stage of the D.I.M. project to conquer his scruples. He can hardly be described as "sanguine," however. While he was confident in his abilities as an inventor and determined to press forward with his plans to sell the design, he had no experience in negotiating and was temperamentally unsuited to the role of a salesman. Yet there was no one else to take his invention on the road and exhibit it to potential buyers. The D.I.M. project had been Colman's venture from the start, and he knew that it would ultimately succeed or fail because of his efforts.

Was the *Morning Star* article a result of Colman's efforts to create a third-party record of his investigative work and establish his credentials as a scientist? He was, after all, an unknown inventor with no employment history, no commercial connections, no ties to a guild or trade, no certificate of mechanical competency, and no one of consequence to vouch for his talents. The new D.I.M. might be expected to demonstrate its worth in actual tests, but it was hardly the most portable of devices, weighing hundreds of pounds and being bulky and fairly expensive to ship by rail. The machine also required a power source and a place to be assembled for exhibition; and its various arms and appendages needed to be carefully balanced and calibrated each time that the D.I.M. was installed in a new location. How did Colman expect to gain an entrée to the companies in New England who were possible purchasers of his machine? How would he introduce his invention? A newspaper article, even from a little-known journal such as the *Rockford Morning Star*, might be expected to give his efforts a certain measure of credibility and, at the very least, provide an interesting enclosure in a letter of inquiry.

Colman had photographs taken of the D.I.M. and stamped the back of each picture with the statement "For information, inquire of W.A. Barber, Warrens, Wisconsin" - acknowledging the uncertainty of his own future address. He continued enlarging his file of "variations" and "corrected designs," including in it prints of a "screw feed" and "automatic stop" that he had developed after the D.I.M. patent application was submitted. The cover sheet read simply: "Machine for drawing in warp threads. Howard D. Colman, Milwaukee, Wisconsin, May 17, 1895."

After this, he disassembled the D.I.M. and crated it up for shipment. His letters of inquiry to New England textile manufacturers had resulted in an offer from G.M. Cumnock, owner of the Social Mills in Woonsocket, Rhode Island, to conduct the warp drawing-in demonstrations there; and sometime before the end of May, more or less on the spur of the moment and without consulting Barber, Colman made arrangements to have the D.I.M. shipped by rail to the Woonsocket station. His choice of Rhode

Island was strategic geographically, since Woonsocket was located in an industrial area almost equally distant from Hartford, Connecticut, and the Merrimack Valley of northeastern Massachusetts, two major centers of textile activity. He intended to call on companies within a 100 mile radius, use the D.I.M. photographs and drawings to illustrate the machine's capabilities, and ultimately persuade the people he visited to return to the Social Mills for demonstrations.

Colman was becoming increasingly restless, weighed down by financial worries and what he considered to be a lack of productive work. On his way to Rhode Island, he stayed with his parents for a few days in Milwaukee, where he answered correspondence and made arrangements to visit several mills in the vicinity of Utica, New York, on his way to Woonsocket. He was subdued, even despondent, during his time at home, and his parents worried as much about his health as his future employment prospects: "We are quite anxious," Henry Colman wrote in his diary. "Wife is almost sick."

Howard arrived in Utica at the end of May and then traveled to Hopedale, Massachusetts, where he had a brief meeting with George Draper, the manufacturer of the famous Draper loom and owner of George Draper and Sons Company. The visit ended inconclusively. Colman left afterwards for Woonsocket, intending to await the arrival there of the D.I.M. and finalize plans for installation. In early June, he wrote Barber to explain his impromptu decision to ship the machine to Rhode Island and to apologize for any misunderstanding that his abruptness might have caused. Barber replied on June 14:

> Arrived home from a week's absence and found your letter waiting for me. Perhaps you are not feeling so blue by this time … I did think you were hasty when from an expression in [your] letter I inferred you had ordered the machine east with the conditions unknown to me. I had thought you would consult as carefully as heretofore but am not inclined to censure for two reasons: first, your evident conscientiousness in doing what you thought was best and, second, you see a mistake and take [an] opportunity to learn by it yourself. Mistakes are valuable factors in experiences; one who has never made any is but a baby, and one who has not profited by them is in a bad way. As it is, we will do the best we can. You better rest sufficiently anyway to get your spirits revived and your "head to working" all right.

It's likely that Barber's concern for Colman's emotional well-being outweighed any tendency to criticize him for his impulsiveness in shipping the D.I.M. east. He was accustomed by this time to dealing with Colman's darker moods and usually countered them with a kind of brisk paternalism. Here he reminded his friend of the remarkable progress that he had made to-date in the development of the invention. Colman should keep his spirits up, Barber said, and soldier on.

Colman wrote Barber a week later, concerned about George Draper's apparent lack of interest in the D.I.M. - nothing had been heard from him in more than three weeks - and wondering if they were "up the stump" as a result. Barber was philosophical in his reply. He told Colman not to waste his time on things that were out of his control. "If our talk, photographs, etc. will not interest a person sufficiently to induce him to want to go 100 miles to see it [D.I.M.], I would not think of his being the one we want." Colman should have enough faith in the value of his invention to await the decisions of "men of good judgment" (6/25/95).

Barber sent two more messages the following day. The first was in response to a telegram from Colman announcing an unexpected offer by Draper to test the D.I.M. at his factory in Hopedale (Barber wired immediately back: "I prefer Woonsocket. Avoid entanglement and obligations."). The second was a letter saying that he had decided to go to Rhode Island himself to offer assistance:

> If machine has arrived, write me and say how long you want to set up in if you agree to Woonsocket being the best place and are going to set up at once. If [it] has arrived and you [are] in doubt as to best course other than above, wire me to that effect. If not arrived, write all you can about opportunity at Woonsocket. I don't see why we need to get room and power in a cotton mill rather than some other factory. Our absolute independence is as important as anything and [we] need to maintain [it] at present. Don't be in too much of a hurry. Our goods are not of a very perishable character, nor are we trying to "catch suckers." If [you] need to hold mach[ine] boxed up until I arrive and cannot leave at station as cheaply as store safely somewhere, engage reasonable rate of board by the week and compose yourself until we meet.

In his telegram, Colman had favored going to Hopedale because of the uncertainty of knowing "what else to do." But this was exactly Barber's point: "You see, I am in favor of almost any other concern ... Possibly if I were there, I might see differently, but hope you will not get us tangled up at all and do not think you will" (6/26/95).

After the D.I.M. reached Rhode Island at the end of the month, Colman made the decision to bypass both Woonsocket and Hopedale as installation sites in favor of the Boott Mills in Lowell, Massachusetts, forty miles north of the Draper and Sons factory. The reasons for the choice are unclear, since neither he nor Barber had mentioned Lowell as an option in any of their previous correspondence. It may be that Barber himself pushed for the location as a way of avoiding "entanglements" with the Drapers or that the decision was made purely on the basis of demographics, since Lowell had the single greatest concentration of textile manufacturing of any New England city.

Whatever the reason, we know that Colman exhibited the D.I.M. there in early July to both the superintendent and overseer of the Merrimack Mills; to the officers of the Kitson Machine Company; to Thomas Entwistle, a local machine manufacturer; and sometime after the middle of the month, to Alonzo Rhoades, George Draper, and George Otis Draper of Draper and Sons Company. Colman's demonstration for the Draper officials lasted three and a half days and concluded satisfactorily, the occasional errors in drawing the warps - missing eyes, broken ends, doublers - falling within the limits of what was generally considered to be an acceptable standard for cotton production at the time.

On July 19 George Draper wrote Barber and Colman in care of the Milford, Massachusetts telegraph office with an offer to manufacture the D.I.M. on a profit-sharing basis. He suggested that Draper and Sons act as "manufacturers' selling agents and as managers of introduction," with responsibility for overseeing the business's patent applications in the U.S. and Europe. In return, they would receive a half-interest in the machine's patent rights. The Drapers also proposed hiring Colman for one year at a salary of $1,500 in the expectation that his real value to them would "furnish him further continuous employment at higher rates of remuneration." The Drapers thought that it would be reasonable to split the costs of making the first machines with Barber and Colman evenly and pledged that this figure would not exceed 20% of the machine's market price. They were plainly impressed by the demonstration of the D.I.M. in Lowell.

Barber had arrived in New England by this time and may well have been present during the exhibition for the Draper officials, since he refers to "your Mr. Rhoades" in a letter to George Draper of July 22 in which he speaks of the possibility of "going back [to the Midwest] and building a [new] machine from the drawings we have already prepared *before*

The D.I.M.'s warp carriage traveled on rollers along a stationary bar that ran the length of the machine, simulating the path of a lathe. The carriage, which advanced by rack and pinion, presented successive threads to a selector mechanism.

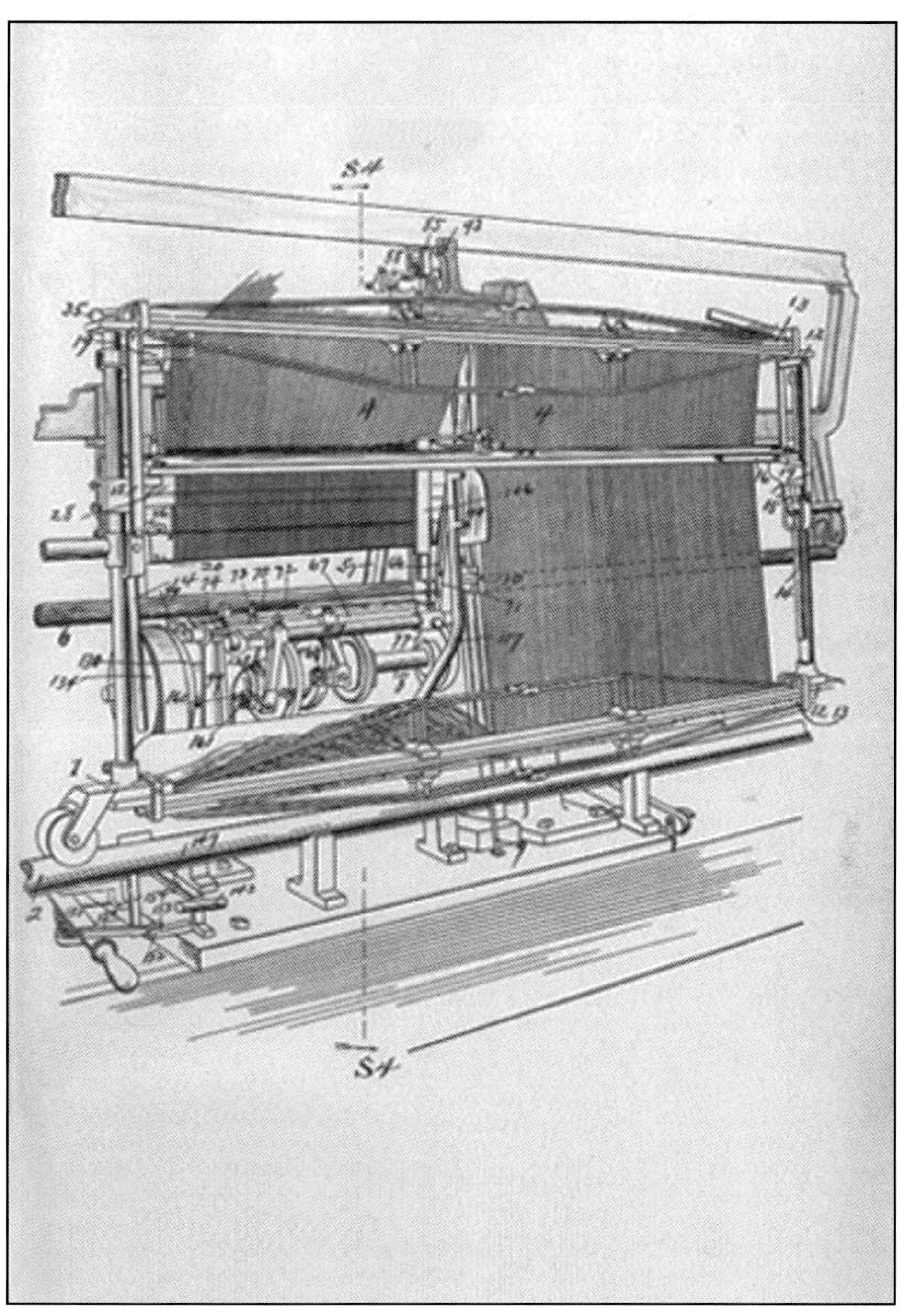

This "frontal view" of the D.I.M.'s principal working parts was completed by L.T. Mann from the photograph on the preceding page, as a close comparison of the illustrations indicates. The drawing was part of Colman's 1896 patent application and is reproduced here from a later blueprint.

proceeding further" (emphasis added). Although the Drapers' proposition was attractive in many ways - offering an end to the seemingly interminable D.I.M. experiments, providing a job for Colman, and holding out the possibility of significant future earnings for them both - Barber did not want to surrender a "valuable invention" without an equitable return. In particular, he felt, the offer made no allowance for recent improvements to the machine. "We can by accepting your proposition get nothing for them except as a factor of the general success in the profits of which we may share," he wrote Draper;

> ... while if we build independently, they put us a long way ahead, and also the men who worked on this mach[ine] have got some "hang of the thing." We can experiment if we wish to, much or little and no others directly interested. As to whether we can afford to experiment much further, perhaps you might care to consult "Duns" or Bradstreets concerning myself.

Overnight Barber's position hardened. The next day he wrote George Draper again to decline the offer and announce his plans "to go back and build another machine at once." Barber said that he had just received "a very favorable offer from the machinists who built the machine we have and believe it in our interests to act upon it." The only thing that would cause him to change his mind now was an immediate offer of "$20,000 net for our entire interest." He asked that all future correspondence be directed to him in care of his office in Warrens (8/23/95).

The "offer from the machinists" was clearly a bluff and meant to pressure Draper into improving his offer, but Barber and Colman had left New England by the time that Draper had a chance to reply. "I personally think well of your machine," he wrote on July 26, "and will make you a cash offer for your entire interests ..." As a pre-condition, however, Draper requested a copy of the application that Barber and Colman had submitted to the U.S. Patent Office. He wanted to be sure that they had a clear title to their warp-drawing design before entering into negotiations, and he would use the D.I.M. specifications to conduct a patent search. He also reiterated his interest in hiring the inventor. When the due diligence had been completed satisfactorily, Draper said,

> ... your Mr. Coleman [sic] shall carry out on his part the arrangement suggested with George Draper & Sons, namely, that he shall work for them for a year for $1,500.

He was dismayed that the negotiations had ended abruptly and wished that Barber and Colman had remained in Massachusetts to receive his proposal:

"I regret personally that you should have gone west before having an opportunity to take action on it."

Barber was driving a hard bargain. He sensed that the Drapers wanted to buy the D.I.M. and could be brought to terms with the proper inducements, but he also felt that catering to them was a mistake. As he earlier told Colman (6/25/95), he wanted to "get them looking after us instead of seeming anxious to win them." Although the Drapers were the only immediate prospect, he was willing to risk losing them as a buyer by maintaining an attitude of studied "indifference." He would focus on "alternatives as tho' they were really first in my estimation." His intention all along had been to identify a textile manufacturer with a serious interest in warp-drawing automation and to negotiate the sale of the D.I.M. to this business as rapidly as possible. He believed that his strategy would bring matters to a head, one way or the other.

In private, Barber remained optimistic about his talks with the Drapers and their readiness to enter into an agreement on favorable terms. While he was concerned about their request for copies of the patent application, he regarded it mainly as a negotiating ploy. "I think this is progressing all right," he told Colman on July 29. "They are merely 'taking another tack' and still showing a deep interest." His letter to Colman two days later indicated his willingness to "concede some from $20,000 if [it] seems necessary to sell," and thought that their immediate object ought to be to get Draper "committed to a sum conditioned on our [patent] papers being satisfactory."

Barber sent copies of the D.I.M. patent application to the Draper Company by American Express on August 5 and stated his readiness to "receive and consider any proposition that you may make in substantial accord with our letter of July 23." Draper acknowledged the receipt of the papers on August 30, promising to give them his immediate attention and to write further after "a few days."

But more than two weeks passed without a message from Draper. On September 4 Barber wrote him to complain that the "expected offer" had been "somewhat longer in coming" than anticipated and to announce that, as a consequence, he and Colman could no longer afford to delay the start of their work on the "new machine." While $20,000 was still their asking price, they would now be forced to add the expenses that they incurred in developing the new machine to this total, as well as a daily allowance of $7 for Colman's wages. "We will be ready to accept these figures for any reasonable length of time," he concluded, "but not after our new machine is completed." Barber asked Draper to send a "manifold or letter press copy of all communications" in the future to Colman in Milwaukee, thus assuring that he and his partner received information at the same time. Whether or not the request was prompted in any way by Colman's dissatisfaction with the pace of the bargaining, Barber had effectively assumed the role of chief negotiator in the process by continually increasing his demands.

Colman did many things well, but one of them was not to wait patiently on the sidelines for events to transpire elsewhere - events, especially, over which he had little or no control. Henry Colman, who believed that his son's difficulties in finding a buyer for the D.I.M. were somehow related to his lack of religious faith, worried anew in his diary about the effects of idleness on Howard's psyche:

> Howard is home now and may continue here for weeks. Waiting for the Drapers to determine what they will do - pay for his machine. These lawyers cannot get around to examine his specifications. O, that grace might reach his heart!

iv

On September 9, Draper wrote Barber and Colman with the promise of a final "report in full in two or three weeks," but then had to acknowledge on September 21 that the end of his research was not yet in sight, having recently dispatched a lawyer to Washington to study the British warp-drawing materials in the U.S. Patent Office. This, he estimated, would "take several weeks longer." On October 1 he wrote again, not so much to reassure Barber and Colman about the approaching end of his investigations as to prepare them for a further delay:

> There may seem to you to be [an] unreasonable delay on my part in regard to looking up the patents and claims in existence on drawing-in machines. This question of looking up different matters in this line takes weeks, and if the matter is important enough to consider a large outlay, it requires all this investigation.

Several more weeks passed without a response from the Drapers. After Colman himself wrote George Draper on October 24 to ask whether his lawyers had given him any real hope of "an early settlement of the matter between us," Draper reported that he planned to meet with his legal counsel "by the middle of next week to have a consultation," while adding the following disclaimer:

> From the tenor of his letter, I think it may take at least a couple of weeks more before he will satisfy himself definitely as to the situation, in view of various references which he is having to look up (10/26/95).

The Draper Company's delays seemed endless. Barber's threat to begin building a new machine and to withdraw his original offer when the model was finished had no effect on the negotiations. Nor did the Drapers react to Barber's plan to add Colman's daily wages to the purchase price of the machine. Barber wondered whether he and Colman should demand the return of their papers after a certain date as a way of forcing the issue. But would such a threat be any more effective than their story about the creation of a new D.I.M. model? Were the Drapers negotiating in good faith? Were the delays really being used as bargaining ploys to extract a lower price? There was renewed hope of an agreement on November 2 when George Draper reported that he planned to meet with his counsel at the end of the following week and possibly to "make you an offer, early week after next;" but seven days later Draper wrote again to say that when he arrived for his scheduled appointment with the attorney, he found that his man "was in either New York or Ohio attending an important patent case in the courts." Unfortunately, his lawyer was now expected to be "away from home for another week," and thus Draper would not be able to reply "definitively until the last of next or early the week following" (11/9/95).

In Warrens, Barber struggled to keep his own enterprise afloat. "The summer and fall are closing out with us all taxed to death to hold together the bulk of our business, just to reduce inevitable loss to a minimum," he wrote Colman on November 21. He had trouble paying routine expenses because of the debt service on "large sums of borrowed money" and apologized to Colman for the delays in meeting the outstanding financial obligations of the D.I.M. Colman declared that his patience had reached its limits, but Barber told him to try to hold on for at least a little longer:

> "Hope delayed" fits our side of the Draper Village surely, and I infer the realization "maketh the heart sick" as to one at least. However, the "Dreary wait" will end sometime, I trust, and [I] still hope Draper will reach it naturally ... If I did not have so many other things pressing, I, too, should be exceedingly impatient by this time (12/2/95).

The next day the Draper Company finally sent Barber and Colman its assessment of the D.I.M. patent application, but the news was negative and not at all what they had expected after a four-month delay:

> We have been through an expensive and exhaustive examination of patents pertaining to drawing-in mechanisms. Our counsel have examined the state of the art as regards United States, British, French, and German patents. As a result of this examination, our counsel advises us that patent No. 255038 of the United States, which is the foundation patent granted on the inventions contained in the so-called Moore drawing-in machine,* has claims which are infringed by your machine, and we agree with our counsel's view. The patent has some three years and a half to run, and we should be very fearful about taking up the manufacture and sale of your machine until the expiration of this patent, unless we can control it (12/3/95).

Although the Drapers believed that there was a "profitable field" for Colman's invention, they were unwilling to invest in it at the present because of the negative "patent situation."

Colman was stunned. He had been unaware that Moore's patent "stood in our way," he wrote Barber on December 7, but intended to "look into it more thoroughly." He left for Rockford later the same day to confer with L.I. Morrison about the Drapers' report and soon became convinced that he would be able to avoid the claims of the Moore patent by making a few alterations to the design of his machine, principally by changing the position of the reed from vertical to horizontal. Barber was more philosophical, preferring to believe that George Draper was actually "playing" them "a little," since the Moore patent was so close to expiration. If two minor infringements were all that a long and exhaustive legal investigation had turned up, then Colman should probably regard it as a favorable omen. "It may be we have [the] opportunity here to play the coquette with him to see if he will not run after all to secure our offer at $20,000," he told Colman. "I wish we had just now the right man to play against him" (12/14/95).

Colman agreed that Draper was conveying a mixed message. On the one hand, he recognized that the D.I.M. was likely to have infringed upon two claims of the Moore patent. On the other, he sensed that Draper wanted to keep the discussion going, and it was possible, even likely, that the whole infringement business was a bluff. Colman wondered why Draper had not asked him to look into ways to redesign the machine to avoid the claims in question. Wasn't this "the first thing" that a person who was used to working with patents would consider?

---

* An alternative name of the Ingersoll-Sherman patent (1882). George Moore, an apothecary, had underwritten the Maine inventors' drawing-in experiments.

> The more I think of it, the more it seems to me that the possibility of the changes I propose must have been evident to him from the first, but he hoped we would not think of them and would be correspondingly discouraged … Am devoting myself to the preparation of [a] drawing of proposed changes to send Draper if he should demand them and it should be desirable to comply … I am beginning to think it will be advisable to construct that way whether we infringe or not in our present construction (12/17/95).

Colman's point was reinforced by Barber's suspicion that the D.I.M. was probably "worth more than any sum that ever entered our heads to ask." Barber felt like telling Draper that they were really not that interested in selling at $20,000. He wondered if Draper would accept their proposal if they threatened to withdraw it. He was ready, in any case, to "make the time for further consideration at this price short" (12/20/95).

"I am heartily willing to say, 'Not a cent less than $20,000'," Colman told him the next day, "and stick to it so long as present conditions remain substantially unchanged." It seemed clear that the time had come to "meet his [Draper's] rather decided tone with a still more decided one." On January 2, 1896, Barber and Colman wrote him to demand that he "either accept or reject" their offer "with as little further delay as possible." If the reply was negative, he was asked to return their papers and drawings forthwith.

Draper's response on January 6 was succinct. Once again it appeared that Barber and Colman had misjudged their prospect:

> If we must decide immediately … on what we will do with you, we must take the negative position. If we were in your places, we ourselves would not attempt to push the machine; we would not invite litigation, and on the other hand should not fear the putting on the market of a successful machine by the present owners of the Moore patents. We ourselves should pursue, and suggest to you, a course of "masterly inactivity" for the present.

Barber received the news with equanimity, observing that the "tone and spirit" of Draper's letter was something that had impressed him from a "stand point of interest" (1/10/96). But Colman reacted badly. He realized that he would have to begin anew to market his device, and that his efforts during the past year had largely been for nothing. It had, in fact, been more than six and a half years since he conceived his original model of the D.I.M. in Beaver Dam, and he now seemed, in many ways, no nearer his goal of taking it to market than he did at Wayland Academy. Barber had invested thousands of dollars in the project since that time, and

Colman's own parents had contributed a considerable portion of their own modest earnings to support his investigations. But to what end? How much longer would it take him to find a buyer for the invention? And how was he going to support himself? For six and a half years, he had not drawn even a single day's wage, while suffering the frequent humiliation of being unable to pay his bills and having to badger Barber for the money that was due him. He had sacrificed opportunities to work in businesses that would have provided a substantial income so that he could devote himself to his scientific work. Each day he found himself "getting deeper in debt and accomplishing nothing," he wrote Barber (1/10/96), and he needed to resolve this feeling of inadequacy:

> ... It seems to me if we are going to submit to simply wait the pleasure of patent lawyers we will have the privilege of doing so forever. This does not mean that I am necessarily opposed to the adoption of Draper's suggestion as to "a course of 'masterly inactivity,' " but if that is to be our course, I want it decided so that I can write Draper, Merrimack, and Cumnock for a job, without danger of injuring our case thereby.

He was ready to give up:

> I think "emasculating" would describe my present inactivity more accurately than "masterly"... Of course, your interests and mine clash at this juncture in this: - that my investment goes on as heavily as ever, while yours stops altogether if we wait, and perhaps the shoe pinches me so hard that I am inclined to be unjust to you.

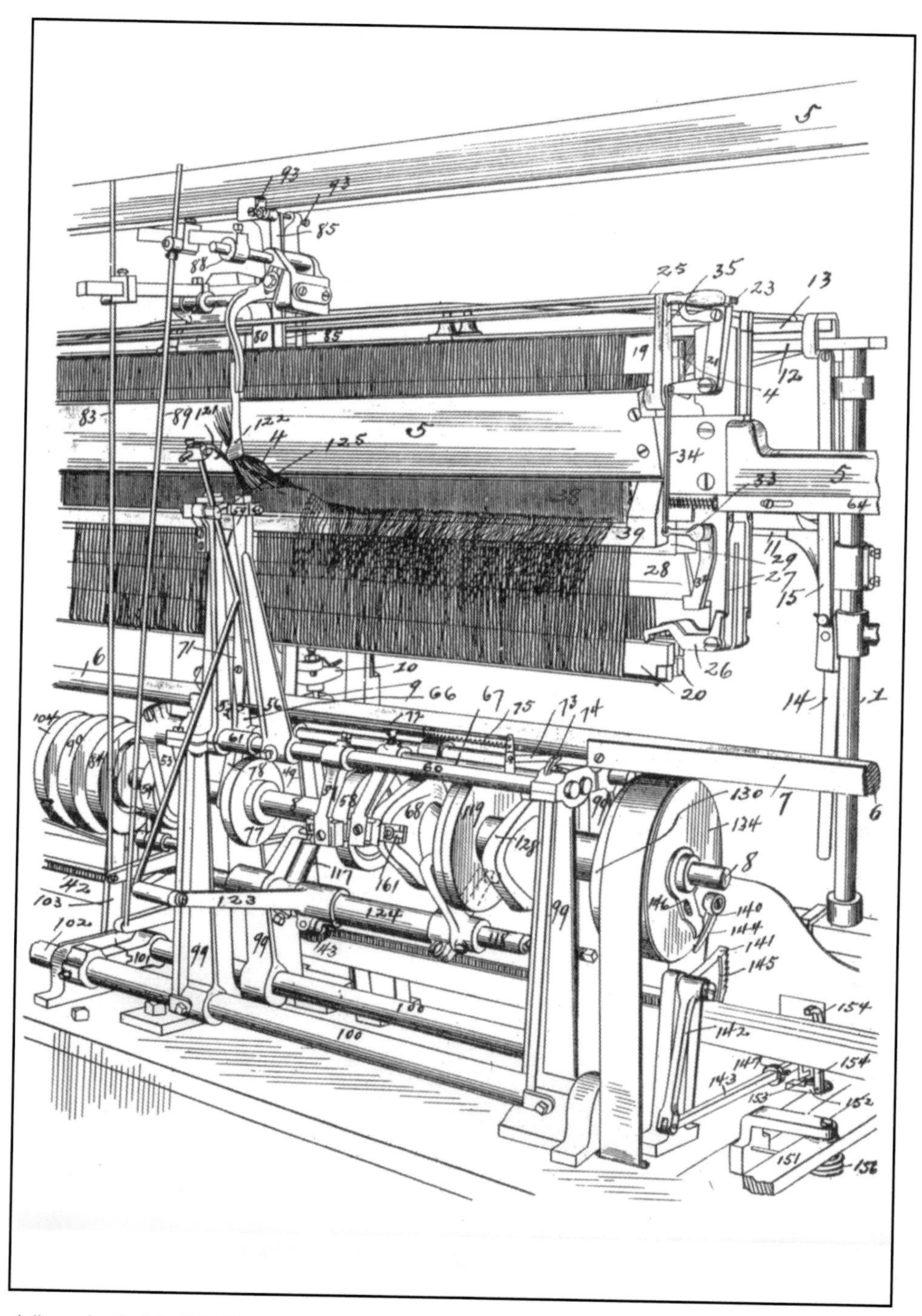

A "rear view" of the D.I.M.'s principal working parts shows the feeler arm, gear train, and pulley mechanism. In the drawing-in process, clamps on the harness bar held small sections of fiber tight while a tiny barbed needle drew individual threads through its eyes. The threads were then transferred to the "fingers" of a wheel. With each quarter turn, the selector mechanism advanced one notch to pick up a new strand and move the previous one out of the needle's way.

6

Breakthrough

McManners & others here think there is a big thing in the pump and counter attachment. Of course, they do not know the trials of inventors and investors of cash in visions of sheckels and glory as well as you and I do.

- Letter from William Barber to Howard Colman, January 18, 1896

i

It's doubtful that Howard Colman ever took much time as a young man to consider the odds against his improbable venture. Cotton manufacturing in the nineteenth century was a mature industry with elaborate networks of suppliers and distributors, and breaking into the market for textile machinery required a production capacity and level of capital investment far beyond that of an ordinary business start-up. In a sense, George Draper's initial offer to manufacture and sell the warp-drawing device for Barber and Colman on a profit-sharing basis offered a logical way out of this dilemma. Without the patent issues, in fact, they might well have been able to negotiate an agreement with Draper that was fair to both parties, for Draper appears to have been genuinely interested in purchasing the invention. In the end, however, there were few real choices. Barber's Wisconsin businesses had never fully recovered from the Financial Panic of 1893, and he was no longer in a position to be able to finance Colman's warp-drawing experiments indefinitely, much less to consider launching an independent enterprise for the manufacture of the device. Even tooling up Spengler's shop for the production of a few dozen machines would have exhausted his resources.

In a peculiar way, Barber's rejection of Draper's original offer, his stubborn refusal to agree to terms that he considered unworthy of the

Howard Colman at the time of his negotiations with George Draper and Sons Company.

invention, was as courageous as anything that Colman had ever done to keep the venture alive, since Barber risked losing his entire investment if a deal could not be struck. The partners had clearly reached an impasse. Draper was unwilling to proceed with negotiations so long as the Moore patent appeared to be infringed by Colman's invention; and Draper had little interest in trying to modify the design to get around this problem, as Colman repeatedly urged. The long and painstaking investigations that the company's legal staff had conducted into U.S. and European warp-drawing patents turned out to be more than negotiating ploys. It was evident that an existing design from 1882, which had never led to the development of a single successful product and which Draper himself admitted was unlikely to be exploited commercially by its owner, would now prevent Barber and Colman from making money on their invention. They had run out of ways to take the machine to market, and both men knew it.

After receiving Colman's gloomy letter of January 10, Barber's immediate challenge was to save the partnership. Colman's threat to go to work for another company, even Draper himself, needed to be taken seriously; and Barber had not helped his cause by attempting to view Draper's "tone and spirit" in a positive light. Was the bitterness of Colman's reply (1/10/96) precipitated to some extent by the lightheartedness of this remark? Barber may well have been trying simply to lessen the impact of Draper's rejection. Now faced with a deteriorating warp-drawing venture and a deeply dejected partner, Barber did the only thing he could. He changed the subject. "Dear Friend," he wrote Colman on January 11:

> I enclose a circular of [a] new adaptation of [the] nickel-in-the-slot principle, viz: to the weighing out of skim milk back to patrons of a butter factory. Something to accomplish this purpose is a real necessity, and I have thought of some fixture on a measuring pump such as is in common use for kerosene that will perfectly control the number of strokes that can be made while the fixture is in place. All the necessary conditions will readily occur to your mind, but unless an ample profit would be realized at a good deal less than $100.00 for selling price, I do not think it would be worth while. *Suppose you relieve the tedium of a little further possible wait on Draper and our further decision on our D.I.M. by studying a little the possibilities in this direction?* (emphasis added)

And that was all, a brief matter-of-fact note accompanying an advertising flyer for a device to weigh out skim milk, a far cry from the intricacies of textile machinery and automated cotton production that had been occupying Colman's thoughts for the previous six and a half years. Yet this would prove to be one of the most important letters that Barber ever sent him and a pivotal event in Colman's development as an inventor. While Barber had demonstrated his value as a partner many times before in his handling of Colman's moods and depressions, this was a situation requiring extraordinary care. How long Barber had owned the advertising flyer and whether or not he had thought of sending it to Colman before is unimportant. What matters is that Barber's wits had come to his rescue once again, and that the challenge of designing a pump for skim milk would provide a needed diversion for Colman.

According to Henry Colman, a design was developed practically overnight. He remembered that Howard and Barber met in the Colman parsonage to discuss the virtues of a "machine made in Lake Mills [Wisconsin]," presumably one of the measuring devices sold by F.B. Fargo and Company there, and traveled to Lake Mills the following day to "glance at the machine" and consider how they might improve it ("Peep"). Following Barber's suggestion, Colman decided to attach a counter mechanism to the spout cover of a standard pump. The mechanism, which would operate a plunger rod inside the barrel of the pump, was designed so that it could be activated by a series of tokens or "checks." Colman planned to put little notches in the rims of the tokens to represent different quantities of milk, typically increments of five and ten pounds, and to number the sides to identify the amounts.

The "nickel-in-the-slot principle" that Colman envisioned was fairly straightforward. When farmers delivered their milk to creameries, he proposed, the operators would be able to simplify their transactions by handing out tokens equal to the amount of skim milk that the farmers were due. No money would be involved. If separators extracted 15% of the total weight as butter fat, then the farmers would be given tokens equal to the 85% that was to be returned. One of the advantages of tokens was that they would allow farmers to dispense their own milk from pumps attached to the skim milk tank. After the transaction at the creamery was completed, a farmer could go to the pump, place a container under the spout, insert a token in a slot in the top of the counter box, and pull the pump handle down. Milk would pour out in a measured amount.

The chief difficulty in realizing this scheme lay in designing a counter mechanism that was both tamper-proof and consistent in measurement. Colman needed to find a way to align the edges of the tokens with the teeth

The Spengler Brothers' machine shop as it appeared in Rockford's Water Power District in the 1940s. Colman's experimental work was done on the second floor.

of a ratchet wheel inside the counter box - the wheel was to be his means of determining exact quantities and of activating the plunger rod - and to devise a friction sleeve and sliding collar within the pump itself that would not clog up with milk. "I think the tendency to coat surfaces and [to] stick [to the] working parts of any gravity automatic machine needs careful consideration," Barber wrote Colman on January 18, "and it will not do to depend on conditions absolutely that might be unquestionably reliable if [we] only had to measure water." Barber's experience in running a creamery in Warrens had taught him how easy it was for proprietors to be shortchanged by farmers, wittingly or unwittingly, in the dispensing of skim milk. Most creamery pumps leaked and worked haphazardly, and farmers always made sure that they received their full due. It was the proprietor who ended up bearing the costs of any "uncounted flow." Barber told Colman that at least three-quarters of the creameries in Wisconsin had this problem, and he felt that a check pump of the kind he had in mind would have a large market.

ii

The new project rejuvenated Colman. Barber urged him to "push" his work on the device "to the exclusion of [the] D.I.M. for the present" (1/18/96), and Colman applied himself with relish to the task of developing a prototype that could be tested at Barber's creamery. A standard pump was ordered from Hoffman and Billings for four dollars and George Spengler supplied with sketches of a counter mechanism - a small box with a hinged door and coin chute enclosing a pump rod, spring pawl, and ratchet wheel - and asked to fabricate it in metal. The first "P. & C." (pump and counter), as Colman called it, was shipped to Warrens, Wisconsin, in early February, scarcely two weeks after Barber had sent him the circular on the weighing out of skim milk. Colman made plans to go to Warrens to study the mechanism in operation at the creamery and to discover any obvious design problems before constructing a second model. "I spent yesterday mostly in cogitation," he wrote Barber on February 14 after returning to Rockford from Warrens, "with the result that I have concluded to adopt some slight additions to the mechanism which will make it impossible, I think, to have any trouble from checks catching, and also will prevent accidental discharge of [the] check before it has done full duty." Two weeks later he described himself as "weary but triumphant" after putting the pump's "automatic" valves to a thorough test. He had fashioned a little catch to hook into a notch in the valve stem at the top of the stroke, thus correcting a tendency of the valves to close prematurely. He said that he now felt confident enough in the feasibility of his model to begin constructing a new batch of pumps.

Colman was unsure if his design infringed on existing patents or not, but he was convinced, after conferring with L.I. Morrison, that he should "chance it and go right on to the market" (2/22/96), since the risks of doing this appeared to be minimal and help was readily available from Barber's associates in Warrens to peddle the device. Colman told Barber that they could always negotiate a settlement with the parties involved if they were sued for infringement; they could also make an effort to alter their design to avoid duplication or go out of business. In the worst possible case, they might be forced to surrender their profits from the sale of the pump, but this was a moot point for a partnership that had yet to earn its first penny. A much greater risk, it seemed to him, was not to promote the device and to delay any longer in starting the business. There would be ample opportunity in the future to apply for a patent, especially if pump sales warranted it and a search of the literature in the Patent Office turned out to be favorable. In the meantime, they ought to be as aggressive as possible in entering the market and learn what they could from creameries using the device.

Once Colman had freed himself from the constraints of his warp-drawing experiments - the patent worries, the costs and complexities of large-scale metal fabrication - he found it nearly impossible to shut off the flow of pump-related images in his head. "I am continually … [in] a fever of anxiety to try some new idea or to find one," he confessed to Barber on March 8, "so that I hate to take time for such things as reports, etc., and I am afraid that you are beginning to think me rather dilatory in that line." He had come up with "a brand new idea for [an] automatic valve," yet another variation of his original valve stop that promised to end "thru flow" difficulties for good, and he was anxious to test it. "Have a number of other ideas," he went on, "but maybe it is best to get our pumps on the market first and see what reception they meet and what demand there seems to be for an automatic before incurring the expense for considerable experimenting likely to be necessary to produce a thoroughly satisfactory automatic" (3/10/96).

What was "thoroughly satisfactory" to Colman, of course, was a moving target, with every improvement to the "automatic" resulting in a higher standard, and each new standard suggesting an even higher level of performance yet to be attained. He was someone who liked solving problems, but these problems had a way of generating their own momentum and taking on an independent life. Often he stopped working on a project because of a compelling interest in something new and returned to his original concept, if at all, through a future network of inquiry. His creative interests thus overlapped and recombined, producing the type of spin-offs (or "sideshows," in Barber's words) which sometimes caused his experiments to bog down in a mass of small details, but which also enriched his understanding and led to the creative breakthroughs that later made his name and fortune. Fine-tuning the pump's operation in this case forced him to consider a variety of specific problems such as the spout configuration, the proper casting of the counter mechanism, the effects of rust on the linings, the composition of the valves and float, sediment build-up, irregular spring action, handles that pulled too hard, deteriorating bolts, friction, and liquid flow. Each element spawned an independent web of speculation. After borrowing ideas from a kerosene counter mechanism and employing these in the development of a pump for skim milk, Colman reversed the process and applied the original features of the check pump theoretically to the measurement of kerosene. He wondered if his improvements to the counter would appeal to Standard Oil vendors. Was there a market?

Studying pump capacity in terms of pipe length and aperture size, and calculating the linear velocity of skim milk in feet per minute, Colman considered the power requirements of potential buyers. If his pipe was too long, the milk would continue to flow after the plunger stopped and produce a vacuum. If the valve in the counter was spring-loaded, it would perhaps be able to control the flow but then also need additional power to drive it. The atmospheric pressure in the outlet pipe, the amount of resistance provided by the counter-valve, and the overall pipe diameter would dictate the minimum power of the machine. A gravity feed might be sufficient for a small creamery, but larger concerns would almost certainly require other means of driving the liquid. Should he be thinking of using gas engines and driveline shafts? He considered the possibility of a motorized pump and, alternately, of marketing the automatic valve stop by itself, and each time that he studied these options there were new problems to solve and new circumstances to ponder.

One of his notions was to use a pipe coil to extract butter fat from milk. He speculated that the centrifugal force of the milk in the coil, under the right pressure, might be enough to separate the cream, an idea that seemed so astonishingly simple to him at the time that he wondered why no one else had thought of it. The idea was indeed *too simple*, and the experiment failed, though Colman would later incorporate conceptual elements from his spiral separator scheme into another device for raising rain water from cisterns through the use of a municipal water supply.

iii

In the spring of 1896 Colman's immediate practical concern was to find a way to manufacture his check pump without investing a great deal of money in tooling, fixtures, and materials. The logical solution was to job the work out to machine shops and other companies already supplying the dairy industry. There was no shortage of standard parts that could be purchased off the shelf - cylinders, plungers, valves, handles, hoses, fittings - and practically any pump manufacturer worth its salt could make parts-to-order if furnished with a pattern. Rockford had its own Ward Pump Company in the Water Power District. A big national concern such as Rumsey and Company of Seneca Falls, New York, offered more than 300 types of brass-lift and force pumps in its catalogue, as well as pipe boxes and hydraulic rams. In fact, it was well within George Spengler's ability, if not his usual practice, to fabricate the entire mechanism himself, though Colman eventually decided, in the interests of time, to ask Spengler to stick to the production of the counters and checks and simply to oversee the final assembly of the mechanisms. Not long after Colman's request, Spengler devised a flexible tool to punch out the metal checks, with their variable lugs and notches (the locations of these changed according to the checks' monetary values), in a single operation. He had much more difficulty building the counter boxes and aligning the plungers and check pins in the first batch of pumps, since the castings and other components that were purchased from suppliers contained serious irregularities.

With a growing optimism about the commercial prospects of the pump and a deepening concern about the possibilities of infringement, Barber and Colman dispatched Luther Miller, a new associate of L.I. Morrison's, to the U.S. Patent Office in mid-March to conduct a search of the existing literature. Miller spent nine days in Washington and concentrated his attention on the three categories of patents that seemed the most likely to have a bearing on Colman's invention: pumps, coin-controlled counter mechanisms, and valve stops. Miller's report was favorable. He had turned up only three patents, Colman wrote Barber (3/31/96), that might limit "the very broadest claim" they would be able to make, and this still left the way open to "an excellent patent." In only one of the cases did there appear to be "any danger of our infringing by manufacturing and selling," and this, in Miller's opinion, was "not great." Even more heartening was Miller's account of a conversation that he had had about the check pump with a patent examiner who "waxed enthusiastic" about Colman's concept:

> [He] declared it was new - he knew it was new - and his assistant said likewise. He told Miller to draw very broad claims!!!! Said he was glad to get something new in once in a while! ... Miller thinks it highly desirable to put in application just as soon as possible in order that the examiner may have it fresh in his mind and be of same opinion as when Miller talked to him.

The reports were also encouraging from L.T. Mann, who began making detailed drawings of the pump in preparation for the application. Mann, according to Colman, "worked up quite an admiration" for the device, wondering why it couldn't be sold to factories that needed "to mix large quantities of liquids in exact proportions, by making arrangements to drive [the pump] by power" (4/7/96). At creameries in Warrens and Roscoe, Illinois, where the pump was being tested, the users seemed equally impressed by the quality of the mechanism. Buoyed up by this and looking for some sort of marketing "puff" (4/27/96) to launch his enterprise, Colman persuaded the *Rockford Register Gazette* to feature the check pump in its business pages:

A NEW APPLIANCE

AUTOMATIC MEASURING DEVICE A GREAT SUCCESS

The invention of Howard D. Colman. A New Industry for Rockford - Its Simplicity and Certainty of Action. Its Method of Operation - A Large Field.

The 400-word article read more like an advertisement than a news story and included most of the standard elements of a business circular: an announcement of a "new pump for measuring back the return milk at creameries," an account of the needs in the dairy industry, a description of the pump's physical features, and various concluding testimonials:

> The first of three pumps completed was sent to Warrens, Wis. The manager of the creamery was so pleased with its workings that he made immediate arrangements to put a man in his place and go on the road for the milk-measuring pump. A second one has been on trial for a week at the Roscoe creamery. Mr. Alex McColl, the manager, was somewhat skeptical at the outset, but has found its practical use very satisfactory. The third has just been shipped to Wisconsin on a hurry order (4/23/96).

What the article failed to mention, what may well have been implicit in Colman's conversation with the *Register Gazette*, was the fact that the manager of the Warrens creamery worked for William Barber, and that the decision to "go on the road" had less to do with the manager's satisfaction with the "workings" of the device than it did with Barber's interest in drumming up customers. In any event, the story served its purpose. Colman was furnished with an "objective" third-party evaluation of the check pump that could be distributed to potential buyers. He made 100 copies of the article, presumably by typing them, and sent 35 of these to Barber. Henry Colman was given some of the others with instructions to mail them to any regional newspaper that would be likely to take notice, as well as to *Hoard's Dairyman,* a leading national trade publication, with whose namesake the elder Colman had formed a personal relationship.

When Mann's drawings were finished, the check pump application was mailed to the U.S. Patent Office (5/8/96). Colman's signature appeared on the document as "Inventor," but not Barber's, Howard having persuaded him to leave his name out of the "Specification" ("Be it known that I, HOWARD COLMAN, a citizen of the United States ... have invented certain new and useful Improvements ..."). It was a delicate situation for both men. At Morrison's suggestion, Colman had written Barber to advise him against signing, pointing out that Barber had not really functioned in a creative capacity in the design of the device; his contribution had been merely to suggest controlling "the operation of a pump by means of a check thru' the means of some (undescribed) mechanism." It was just as misleading, Colman argued, "to put in some one as joint inventor whom the technicalities of the law do not admit to be such, as it is to omit one who really was joint inventor." Barber did not dispute the point.

As interest in the pump increased and orders began arriving, Colman found himself involved in the operation of a de facto mail-order business. Surprisingly, he seems to have been unprepared for this, lacking a budget, bank account, and bookkeeping system. He tried to manage the pump shipments from his lodgings in Rockford, a rooming house on North (later Park) Street, but soon realized that he needed to find a work area closer to the Water Power District, where the pumps were being assembled, and persuaded Spengler to let him take over a corner of the factory temporarily. For a business start-up, it was less than ideal. Although he brought in a drawing board and acquired a rolltop desk and two revolving chairs to create the semblance of an office space, Colman lacked any printed materials (i.e. letterhead, envelopes, shipping tags) with which to conduct his affairs.

He had no typewriter of his own, no safe or storage area, no heating stove for colder weather. He sat in Spengler's shop in the din of the cutting metals and whirling overhead belts and attended, as best he could, to the shipments and assembly problems, wondering how he would deal with the many things demanding his attention. He knew nothing at the time of product warranties, sales bonds, sales commissions, sales contracts, sales territories, and distribution rights. What may have been worse for someone attempting to launch a dairy-related business, he did not even own a map of Wisconsin.

All these matters would be resolved eventually. Colman dealt with problems as they arose, doing what he could within the limits of his resources. Not owning a horse and buggy and finding the railroads of little use in reaching many of the rural creameries in the region, he resorted to traveling, as he called it, "a la bicycle," pedaling to Roscoe with Miller and Spengler to study the performance of the check pump installed there, and setting out occasionally to visit customers as far away from Rockford as Fort Atkinson, Wisconsin, using dirt roads that were rutted and full of stones, but also, by mid-summer, baked hard in the sun. At creameries he installed pumps, made repairs and adjustments, and talked to farmers about their impressions of the device. In responding to complaints of "defective" machines, he discovered some interesting cases of owner neglect:

> The check slot [was] so full of dirt [that] the checks would hardly drop, the oyster too weak to be certain, the levers so rusted that their weak springs hesitatingly pulled thru' the bolt ..., the rod nearly worn thru' and stones enough under the leather valve to build a small wall (5/6/96).

After several such incidents, Colman wrote up instructions for the installation, operation, and care of the pump and prevailed on Fred Barber to take photographs of the device; these pictures were then labeled, duplicated, and given out to new pump customers along with the typescript. The same concerns about product liability that caused him to write the pump instructions led him also to consider issues of dealer warranties and the kinds of precautions that a manufacturer might take to protect himself from unjustified refund claims.

iv

Colman shouldered the entire burden of the check pump operation because there was no one else to do it. Barber's support was financial and advisory and his place of business more than a hundred miles away, and Colman understood from the very beginning of his pump experiments that the day-to-day problems of any commercial venture would be his alone to solve. Selling to the dairy industry, of course, was something that Barber had long been accustomed to doing through George Warren and Company, and he was able to offer the services of one of his creamery agents, a man named McManners, to help promote the pump. The assignment fell within the normal scope of McManner's job responsibilities. It cost the company nothing. At the same time, Barber was reluctant to add anyone to the payroll until the new business had generated enough revenue to cover this expense. Colman was on the horns of a dilemma: he could not, by himself, take care of the paperwork, direct the pump production and assemblies, and get the shipments out. To complicate matters, his customers were slow in paying for the pumps, so that Colman was forced to add receivables to his growing list of concerns. Strapped for cash, he hesitated to push for payment for fear of jeopardizing these business relationships.

It's unlikely that any other phase of Colman's early career generated as much letter-writing as the first year of his check pump venture (1896), when he not only corresponded with Barber several times a week but also conducted a large number of commercial transactions. Lacking a typist, Colman wrote out every one of his letters by hand, making copies of the business correspondence that he considered to be important and filing these in his desk. For a new enterprise, there was little that did not seem important. Colman grumbled to Barber about the inefficiency of hand-copying - he felt that life was "too short to do much of that" (4/28/96) - and how this work detracted from his other job duties. After struggling with the problem for several months, he made the acquaintance of a young woman studying stenography in Rockford and managed to convince her that his paperwork offered a great opportunity to improve her typing skills. Each day, in exchange for streetcar fare, she went to his office and took dictation, returned to her home and typed the dictation up, and then brought the finished papers back to him for mailing and filing. She was just beginning her clerical studies and lacked any practical experience, but the simple fact of having someone to delegate paperwork to lifted Colman's spirits. When Barber eventually agreed to allow Colman to hire a handyman named James Charles Allen to take over the shipment of the pumps and to help with office tasks, Colman began to think of ways to expand the business.

For a fledgling manufacturer of skim milk pumps in the late 19th Century, the best way to attract attention was to advertise in trade publications

The interior of the Spengler Brothers' machine shop in the 1940s. The space was essentially unchanged from the time that Howard Colman used a corner of it for an office a half century earlier.

and to set up shop at county fairs. Barber and Colman, with the assistance of Henry Colman, had previously mailed copies of the *Register Gazette* article to Midwestern papers and the editor of *Hoard's Dairyman*, but they now recognized the advantages of a more systematic approach to advertising in journals such as *Hoard's, Chicago Produce, Elgin Dairy Report,* and *New York Produce Review,* especially in conjunction with scheduled demonstrations of the pump at major dairy events. They printed 30,000 pump circulars and stamped "Barber and Colman" on hundreds of metal checks for hand distribution. Colman, Allen, and McManners agreed to take turns exhibiting the pump at fairs and conventions in Iowa, Wisconsin, Illinois, and Minnesota, the main focus of their advertising.

The exhibitions enabled Colman to gain first-hand knowledge of competing products and to consider the relative strengths and weaknesses of his own invention. Ordinarily the pumps, which were also known in the trade as "weighers," were grouped close enough together at fairs for the agents to witness each other's demonstrations. Advertising circulars and business cards were available on tables for visitors to collect, and the agents themselves frequently mingled before and after the exhibition periods to compare notes and exchange claims and counterclaims. This was part of an elaborate ritual, with polite inquiries and offhand remarks being tailored to elicit product and sales information from competitors, but also, in the case of smaller businesses such as Colman's, to introduce the pumps to manufacturers and suppliers who might wish to add them to their existing product catalogues. It was a fine line to walk. Competitors one day might be collaborators the next. Overtures from a company might be a ruse or a first step towards a more serious negotiation over an exclusive agency for the product. Barber and Colman were manufacturers by necessity, testing their machine in as many creameries and cheese factories as possible in order to explore the market. They recognized the advantages of selling their design to an established dairy supplier or of concluding some type of royalty arrangement. They were, after all, in the business of invention, and Colman's fondest wish was to return to the trials of his drawing-in machine, which had been put into storage in a warehouse adjacent to the Spengler Brothers' machine shop.

With the check pump's commercial success, it was inevitable that other companies would come calling, causing Barber and Colman to balance the offers of one supplier against another and to worry about these companies' own competing pump lines and hidden product loyalties. "We understand you are manufacturing a pump for delivering skim milk,"

Cornish, Curtis & Greene (C.C.& G.) of Fort Atkinson, Wisconsin, wrote on May 9, "… and we should like to have you send us circulars and quote us prices on the pump which you manufacture. Could we not make some arrangement with you to handle these pumps exclusively?" C.C.& G. was one of the largest and best-known dealers in the country, and Colman had encountered its standard weigher on many of his visits to Wisconsin creameries. He considered it to be a "fine machine," particularly for businesses needing to process thousands of pounds of milk per hour. It was "well-made and practical in every respect," he wrote Barber, and their own device, without significant modifications, could only hope to compete with it on price:

> At present hasty writing, [I] think we would better make large machine and keep price of it near $50 and cut as much as we can on smaller machines ... Don't think we could build them for $50, and if they can work so much cheaper, perhaps we would better let them manufacture and pay us royalty (8/7/96).

Colman was approached by a dairy agent from Walworth, Wisconsin, named C.T. Ray, who claimed to have "talked up … [the] pump to about 20 creameries" in the region and who felt that he could sell quite a few (8/8/96); but when Luther Miller, at Colman's request, drew up a sales contract, Ray refused to sign. W.S. Goodhue, the creamery manager of the A.H. Barber Company of Chicago, told James Allen that he had had a "number of inquiries" about the pump and thought that there might be a "big demand if [the] pump worked all right" (8/12/96). This was followed by a letter from A.H. Barber himself, requesting Colman's "very lowest price." Colman admitted that he was

> quite strongly inclined to think it well to sell to him and perhaps to give him exclusive agency if satisfactory arrangements can be made. The fact that he is in the dairy supply business and a competitor of C.C.& G. and Fargo but has no machine to meet theirs makes it seem likely to me that he would push the thing and take a real interest in it (letter to William Barber, 8/18/96).

Six days later Colman received a new letter from A.H. Barber "expressing a desire to take hold and push'" (8/24/96), but after meeting him in person to discuss arrangements, Colman allowed that he was not very favorably impressed. He hesitated to give him any kind of "exclusivity" and worried about the risks to other relationships: "If he [A.H.

This photograph of the Barber check pump was distributed to all purchasers. An accompanying typescript outlined the procedures for cleaning and oiling the device twice a week.

Barber] does anything, I suppose C.C.& G. will know of it directly and perhaps we have spoiled our chance to do anything with them if we should want to" (9/4/96). At the Iowa Dairy Fair in Des Moines, Colman met yet another agent who said he was interested in selling the check pump for him. "Wish you would look up the rating of J.G. Cherry of Cedar Rapids, Iowa," he wrote William Barber, "and perhaps inquire of your friends about him. He is a dealer in creamery supplies and wishes to handle our pump. Says he has never seen a weigher he would handle" (9/14/96).

By the third week of October Colman seemed ready to choose C.C.& G. as a primary agent, only to hear some disturbing news from Allen after he returned from visiting prospects in Walworth County, Wisconsin. Allen told Colman that he had been canvassing a few of the creameries that showed an "special interest" in the check pump at the recent Walworth County Fair and discovered that each had experienced a sudden change of heart. "… Cornish of C.C.& G. had been all thru' there just after the fair and talked us down as much as possible," Colman informed Barber. "He [Allen] thinks that they are very much afraid of us" (9/21/96).

> I think there is force in Cherry's argument against handling thru' dealers promiscuously, and it seems to me that we have not given the subject the careful consideration it should have before we decide on a definite and permanent policy. I wish I knew more about what the experience of others has been on this point. It certainly seems quite clear that no dealer would put much expense into advertising and working up a demand unless assured of exclusive territory for a considerable time, and if we proceed on our present policy, we will have to carry all that expense (of advertising and printing) ourselves, which would lead to the conclusion that we might better - having borne all the expense ourselves - make the sales and gain the profits ourselves. On the other hand, it seems very risky to [assign] exclusive territory unless the agent pays a lump sum for it or guarantees a certain amount of business, and I don't see how anybody can do that. As the inquiries are now beginning to come from the reliable houses, we must decide soon what we are going to do, and I must confess it beyond me to see what is best. In the case of Cherry - I should hate to lose him for I judge him to be a good man, and he seems to take the most interest in it of anyone, but at the same time Iowa is our best state, and I should want to see very distinctly what we are getting for it before we give it away (letter to William Barber, 11/16/96).

J.G. Cherry now emerged, almost by default, as Barber and Colman's leading candidate to represent them in the creamery supply business, though Colman admitted to being in a quandary about which way to turn. He was still learning on the run, trying to figure out the intentions of the people he met, and regretting his lack of experience with agents and salesmen.

Colman not only struggled with dealer relationships and problems of distribution during the first year of his pump business but spent many hours exploring ways to add value to his invention. A cash cabinet, lock, and anti-siphoning device became standard features of the pump as a result of his conversations with creamery owners, and he eventually saw fit, after extensive testing, to replace the leather valve in the anti-siphoning device with a much more durable metal one. He improved the design of the pump spout so that milk would discharge more quickly and evenly. He also tinkered with a counter attachment, sometimes called a "percentage wheel" in his letters, as a means of accurately measuring the volume of liquid. An internal rotary was aligned and calibrated with the external "wheel," whose revolutions served as "counters" of the amount of milk being processed. This little mechanism was indispensable to Colman in his efforts to increase the check pump's capacity, since he needed a way to measure his output accurately and to demonstrate to customers the efficiency of his machine. Before long Colman was speaking excitedly of the possibilities of a new "double-capacity power pump" and making plans to modify the design of his patterns, enlarge the aperture of the discharge pipe, and add a spring to the counter-valve (1/12/97).

Reluctant to give any dealer an exclusive agency for the pump, Colman decided to allow several dairy suppliers to carry it temporarily on consignment, including C.C.& G., Cherry, Creamery Packaging of Chicago, and F.B. Fargo and Company of Lake Mills. He agreed to furnish them with whatever quantities of stock they requested, provided that they paid promptly for the machines. Otherwise he continued to operate his mail-order business as before, waiting to see which companies, if any, would be distinguished by sales and a commitment to the product. His letters to Barber show that he expected this to be J.G. Cherry, based on a positive impression of the man's character and the agent's stated enthusiasm for the pump's design.

V

In a field as crowded and competitive as the dairy supply business, rumors continually circulated of new inventions and product lines with the potential to revolutionize the industry. Part of this was the result of the

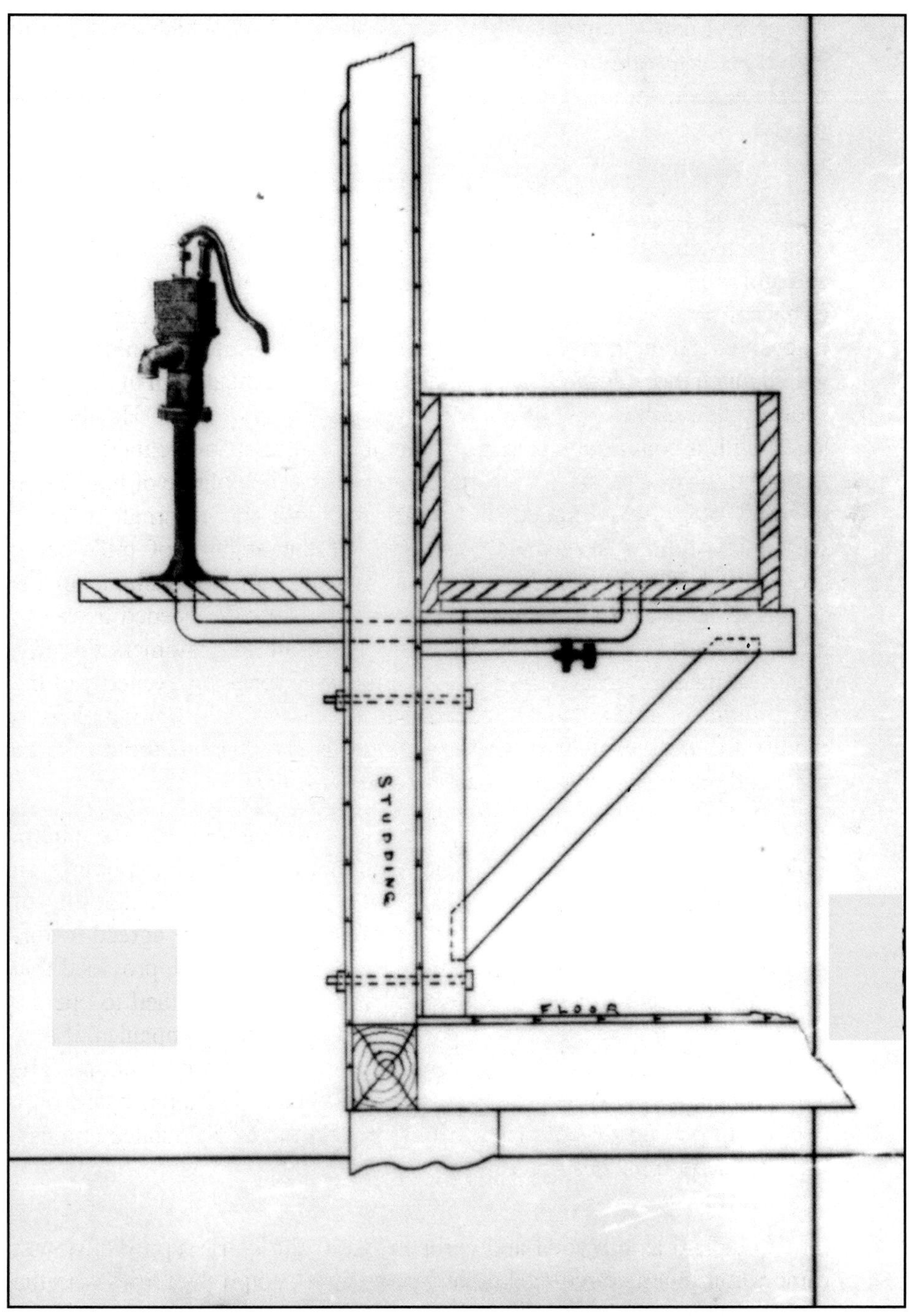

A diagram showing the proper method of installing the Barber check pump.

companies' own exaggerated sales claims - there were no laws at the time governing product standards and truth in advertising - and part of it was the result of actual advances such as Colman's check pump. James Allen was undoubtedly correct when he suggested that C.C.& G. was "very much afraid" of Colman, despite C.C.& G.'s relative advantages of size and reputation; but after Colman's pump achieved its early commercial successes and gained a reputation among Midwestern creamery managers as a reliable device, Colman himself began to hear stories of new products in development that rivaled his weigher.

In early February the editor of *Chicago Produce* wrote Colman with information that would be appearing in an advertisement in the next issue of the magazine:

> Already you have a competitor on the ground in the shape of J.G. Cherry of Cedar Rapids, Iowa, who is making a power pump which runs just by putting the checks in the slot and a ratchet is thrown in motion and out automatically.

At almost the same time another letter arrived from Rumsey and Company, Colman's supplier of standard pump parts, indicating that Cherry was intent on copying the design of the check pump's base:

> We have a letter from J.G. Cherry of Cedar Rapids, Iowa, stating that he wants pump bases the same as we are making for you and wants us to quote him prices on them. We have written him that we could not do this without your consent. Please let us know your wishes in regard to this matter.

The news was upsetting, though Colman maintained his equanimity in reporting it to Barber:

> So it seems that there is really something to this. I don't believe the chances are very great that he [Cherry] will make a success of it, but still it seems to emphasize the desirability of having our patent issue soon ... I have thought of writing to Cherry and warning him that we have a cinch on check pumps and that he will be only throwing his time and money away by experimenting in that line. Really, it would be an act of kindness to him to do so, but probably he would not look on it in that light (2/5/97).

Barber and Colman conferred extensively on the best way to respond to this threat. With the check pump scheduled to be exhibited at a forthcoming dairy convention in Owatonna, Minnesota, Colman told Barber that they should draft some kind of policy statement concerning Cherry's device, since customers were likely to ask them about the differences between the two machines. Colman doubted that Cherry's weigher was far enough along to be ready for an actual exhibition at Owatonna unless he had "taken at least as much as a counter out of one of our machines," and if he did this, "it would be a good talking point against him." Colman proposed informing customers of Cherry's deceit and warning them that they would be opening themselves up to possible legal action by owning a weigher after the Barber and Colman patent issued (2/12/97).

On February 13 Colman received more disturbing news. Allen, who returned to Rockford from a sales trip, showed Colman a handbill for a new "F.B. Fargo weigher" that was being circulated among creamery owners. "They [Fargo and Company] seem to have copied our checks ...," Colman wrote Barber, "and probably have something like our counter and very likely infringe several of our claims." Colman wondered if he should go to Owatonna and examine the Fargo machine himself, while re-emphasizing to Barber the importance of a check pump patent (2/13/97).

Colman wrote Barber again, on February 14, calling his attention to an advertisement for the J.G. Cherry weigher in the new issue of *Chicago Produce,* the same advertisement that the editor of the *Produce* had earlier written to warn him about. Colman had been anticipating the issue for more than a week, wondering what Cherry's weigher would look like with its replica base, but he was astounded to see, when he studied an illustration in the advertisement, that Cherry appeared to have stolen the rest of the pump design as well:

> What do you think of the "ad" of Cherry's on [the] inside back cover of Chicago Produce this week? He has got a lot of gall to insert our own pump with his top. I think he is making a jackass of himself, as it can't be possible that he has made tools and is ready to manufacture and sell so soon. I don't believe he has given his device any really practical test, and I doubt very much if it is any good. I had pretty well matured plans in my head long before I ever heard of Cherry for accomplishing all that he advertises but abandoned them for the time, considering that inherent difficulties made it a very doubtful scheme ... Probably for the present the best thing is to keep quiet and see if he won't make still more [of a] jackass of himself. Already he has given evidence by publishing a cut which shows that he has simply swiped our pump, which would make it awkward

> for him to try to prove priority. If he is at Owatonna and you think best, Spengler or, better yet, Miller would go out and, without appearing to be in any way connected with us, he could poke around and examine [Cherry's weigher] at his leisure ... I don't think McManners would be sufficiently intelligent patent-wise and mechanically to do the business.

Colman wrote Barber, revealingly, on stationary from the "Law Offices of L.I. Morrison" and said that he had been busy reviewing some legal options in regards to Cherry's device. He asked Barber to approve an expenditure for additional work by Luther Miller so that they could resolve a check-pump issue still pending in the U.S. Patent Office. They needed to speed up the patent process, Colman said, and "stop Cherry and others as soon as possible" (2/14/97).

When Miller mailed the original Barber and Colman pump application to Washington in the spring of 1896, he had expected the patent to issue quickly and to be granted some fairly broad claims for checks and counter mechanisms. In the months that followed he had submitted a few routine letters of clarification in response to inquiries from the patent examiner and made several additional claims as a result of Colman's improvements to the mechanism; and because of this, the review process had taken longer than initially anticipated. By February 1897 Colman told Barber that it no longer made sense to submit new claims and thus delay the decision on their application, even when these claims were in response to other companies' infringements. He was satisfied with the scope of the application. "I think we have covered all that we are entitled to pretty thoroughly" he wrote, "and that we are going to get a very good patent" (2/12/97). On March 17 he asked Barber to "send in" the "final [patent] fee" of $20 so that the case could "pass to issue as soon as allowed."

If Colman's warp-drawing investigations had taught him anything, it was that important events seldom occurred in the way one expected. The more eagerly he anticipated an outcome, it must sometimes have seemed, the more likely he was to be faced with new obstacles; and while he was far too rational an individual to be superstitious, Colman had learned from his warp-drawing work to hold something back emotionally, to prepare himself for possible disappointment. Miller thought that a check pump patent was a foregone conclusion, a matter of routine, but Colman knew first-hand the uncertainties of the approval process.

"I telegraph you 'Unfavorable action rec'd'," Colman wrote Barber on March 26. "If coming down [to Rockford], come as soon as possible."

Despite Miller's assurances to the contrary and the patent examiner's own often-stated enthusiasm for the invention, the pump application had been denied. Colman now had two competitors in the field and no means of stopping them from copying his design, and the only good news was that the Patent Office had left open the possibility of appeal:

> The examiner didn't do what we expected at all, and he seems to be clearly and exasperatingly wrong, but he doesn't finally reject [the application] so we cannot appeal. It places things in worse shape than we thought them a month ago, for now we cannot get patent under two months, unless we send Miller down there, and then there is only a slim chance of it. Probably we are in for interference suits and all kinds of delay. The C.C.& G. people appear to be pushing their pump at $30 and $35, and I think we should have a conference at once, and here if possible.

At a hastily-arranged meeting in Rockford, Miller volunteered to go to Washington to speak to the patent examiner personally and to oversee an immediate appeal. He was confident enough in the outcome, he said, that he would be willing to charge only $5 a day for his time if he failed to get the case allowed. If he were successful, on the other hand, if he were able to convince the examiner to include the check pump in the next batch of patents, he would expect to bill $20 a day for his time. Barber and Colman were quickly persuaded, and Miller left for Washington.

Colman had little time to dwell on the news from the Patent Office. The rejection notice from Washington coincided with a surge in check pump orders, and worries about infringers, temporarily at least, gave way to the need to address a rapidly dwindling supply of pumps. McManners reported an increase in business among his Wisconsin customers. Messages arrived from salesmen and distributors throughout the region asking for pumps on consignment and testifying to a growing demand for the Barber and Colman model. Most of the appeals were tied to special requests for discounts, incentives, and commissions, requests that Colman referred to as "the hair-splitting variety" and refused to consider. Trying to conserve his limited cash reserves, he now resorted to building pumps strictly "on time," assembling each device from his stock of standard parts and specially-fabricated valve stops and counter mechanisms according to the number of orders received. Yet he struggled to keep up. With an expanding business, he found himself once again on an exhausting operational treadmill. April 11 marked a new single day record for check pump orders. At the current pace, he believed, the company would eventually surpass $15,000 in annual sales, a prospect made all the more bittersweet by the lack of a valid patent.

Nine days later word reached Colman that Luther Miller had worked his magic in Washington. The check pump patent had been approved. As Miller predicted, the patent examiner had responded positively to the Barber and Colman application after its language was modified to get around the original objections. Miller's point-by-point review of the changes had led to a favorable judgment. "At last our patent has actually issued," an ecstatic Colman wrote Barber, "and we can get after infringers to our heart's content" (4/20/97). In his mind, Fargo, Cherry, and C.C.& G. headed the list of companies pirating his designs, though the check pump market in general had become so crowded with counterfeiters and imitators - "demoralized," as he liked to put it - that he hardly knew where to begin. He considered placing advertisements in dairy journals to announce the receipt of the patent and to threaten legal action against anyone who purchased a counterfeit pump, but concluded that a direct approach was probably his wisest course of action. He could at least write to the infringers he had identified.

Inevitably, the replies to his letters varied. C.C.& G. offered to withdraw its "stop pumps" from the market in the face of Colman's charges. Fargo denied that it infringed on the new patent at all, since it manufactured something called a "measuring device" rather than a weigher and "disks" instead of checks, differences that Colman attributed entirely to semantics. However, Fargo left the door open to further negotiations by referring the matter to its lawyers and asking Colman to keep it in mind if he ever decided to license the pump for manufacture. A third company, Hanna and Swanson, was openly defiant. A spokesman would not deny that its products duplicated features of Colman's pump but believed that Hanna and Swanson could break his patent in the courts. Many years earlier, Colman was told, the company had invented a machine for another purpose that anticipated the check pump's key features and thereby invalidated the present claims.

Colman would not tolerate the evasions. "I think they should be dealt with rather sharply," he wrote Barber of the infringers, "and that we ought to proceed to sue them without much delay if they do not come to time … We've got the club, and we might just as well swing it a little" (5/10/97).

vi

In June Colman's plans were complicated by a slump in check pump sales, a downturn apparently connected in some way to a fall in the price of butter. Now that he had addressed his supply problem, reduced his assembly time, and discovered ways to manage his periods of peak activity, his business was starting to contract. "Something seems to be wrong here," he wrote Barber on June 4. "Only 1 order in a week." His complaint was much the same on June 12: "Orders are slow, in fact practically nothing." By June 17 he had hit rock bottom:

> Must say that the check pump business is decidedly dead. Absolutely no orders, and some few pumps coming back, so that our stock on hand is actually increasing ... Don't know what to make of it. Low price of butter doesn't seem sufficient reason to account for such a very bad state of affairs.

In just three months Colman had gone from a booming check pump business without a patent and imitators at every turn to an extremely depressed check pump business with a valid patent in hand and the same number of imitators. To "swing his club a little," to make examples of Fargo and Hanna and Swanson by suing them in the courts, would be expensive, and Colman found that his interest in litigation was lessening as his worries about new orders increased. Miller charged $20 a day, ten times what Colman's per diem living allowance from Barber had been only a few years earlier and roughly equivalent to the profits on the sale of two check pumps. Colman was in a quandary. To push his claims now would be to spend his cash reserves on legal fees at a time when liquidity was critical to his business. To allow infringers to go unchallenged, on the other hand, would be to surrender the advantages that his patent conferred and effectively to concede the market.

A way out of this dilemma was suggested by the manager of C.C.& G. who wrote Colman in mid-June to reaffirm that his company had never knowingly copied any of the check pump's features; C.C.& G.'s lawyers were taking the possibility of infringement very seriously, he said, and preparing a definitive response. The manager wondered in passing why the two companies had never thought before about entering into a strategic alliance, since it seemed to him that they could control the market for automatic pumps and weighers between them. He also suggested that C.C.& G. was in a position to manufacture and distribute the check pump along with its own machine, thus offering both companies some monetary advantages. If they could come to an agreement in principle, he said, they would be "in a fair way to get the most of the trade in this line."

How receptive Colman would have been to such an idea three months earlier, when his sales were stronger, is open to question, but it's clear that he was growing tired of the check pump business by the summer of 1897 and resenting the time that it stole from his other experimental work. While he was pleased with his own earnings from the pump - he had been able to pay all his living expenses for the first time in his life and to settle a number of debts - he had nevertheless been brought down to earth by the realities of running a small, cash-strapped business in a cyclical commodity market. The only way to grow the company and to free himself from its operational headaches, he realized, was to take advantage of a licensing option from someone like C.C.& G. Colman knew that a licensee would have a vested interest in helping him get rid of infringers after he reached an agreement on royalties.

With Barber's encouragement, Colman made immediate plans to visit the C.C.& G. office in Fort Atkinson to discuss a manufacturing contract. The pump business was "rather going to the dogs," he told his friend, and would need "some pretty strong medicine before long" (7/7/97). Just how quickly his negotiations proceeded is evidenced by the announcement on July 22 that he had reached a tentative agreement with C.C.& G. on the terms of a two-year contract. It was proposed that Barber and Colman receive 15% of C.C.& G.'s annual check pump sales in exchange for an exclusive license to manufacture the device. Colman was now working on terms for the sale of his spare-parts inventory and rental of his special tooling. No provision was made in the agreement for a minimum guarantee of royalty payments, however, and this turned into a bone of contention.

Colman resumed his negotiations on July 25:

> After some preliminaries, I asked Curtis [one of the namesakes of Cornish, Curtis, and Greene] what he would consider a fair amount of business under this contract. He didn't want to answer, but I pressed him, and he said, "Well, two or three a day." I asked him then, if that was fair business, wouldn't they guarantee half that? He said he didn't think they would, but he didn't say it very positively. Assured me that they intended to push it [the check pump] for all it's worth and asked me if I hadn't confidence in their ability to sell a good deal more than 300 machines a year. I assured him that I thought they could and ought to sell a thousand a year, but said that if they didn't feel dead-sure themselves that they could sell 300, why then I couldn't see how we could bank on them at all. Well, he said, they never had done such a thing in royalty contracts and had always given the holder of the patents satisfaction and expected to in this case.

Eventually both parties agreed to a clause in the contract guaranteeing sales of 300 pumps a year. Colman, who was becoming concerned about the continuing market slump, was reluctant to prolong the discussions any longer. On August 8 a formal licensing agreement was "signed, sealed, and delivered," the Barber and Colman inventory of pumps, hoses, and checks dispatched to Fort Atkinson, and the special tools readied for shipment. Colman had escaped from his operational treadmill, finally, and was ready to resume his experiments. He felt confident that he could support himself now, pay himself a regular wage, while indulging his interests in the concepts and designs that would recommend themselves to his fancy in the weeks ahead.

7
The Process of Invention

Have met with many minor vexations and delays in completing the two-inch ball machine, so that it is only today that I have been able to test it to any purpose. I find that with two streams, one at something over twice as fast as the other, it is inaccurate to the extent of about 5%. This is not as good as I expected, but I am inclined to think it is good enough for all practical purposes.

- Letter from Howard Colman to William Barber, 1899

i

At the end of the summer of 1897, Colman found himself in the agreeable but entirely unfamiliar position of an inventor with the time and resources necessary for sustained experimental work. His royalty arrangement with C.C.& G. assured him of an income for 24 months, perhaps as much as four thousand dollars a year if pump sales were strong, even though there was nothing on the experimental horizon that immediately commanded his attention, no important unfinished project besides the D.I.M. Colman's first inclination was to tinker with a few elements of the check pump's design, such as the counter mechanism and automatic valve, and to look into the possibility of applying for individual patents on these, since he believed that they were unique devices with wider commercial applications.

As in the case of the Lake Mills weigher a year and a half earlier, Barber tried to direct Colman's attention to other opportunities. A U.S. Post Office circular soliciting bids for the manufacture of a stamp-canceling machine had crossed his desk in Warrens, and he wondered if Colman would be able to design a mechanism that met the requirements of this contract. Colman read the circular carefully and undertook a cursory examination of the state of the art by visiting the Rockford postal office.

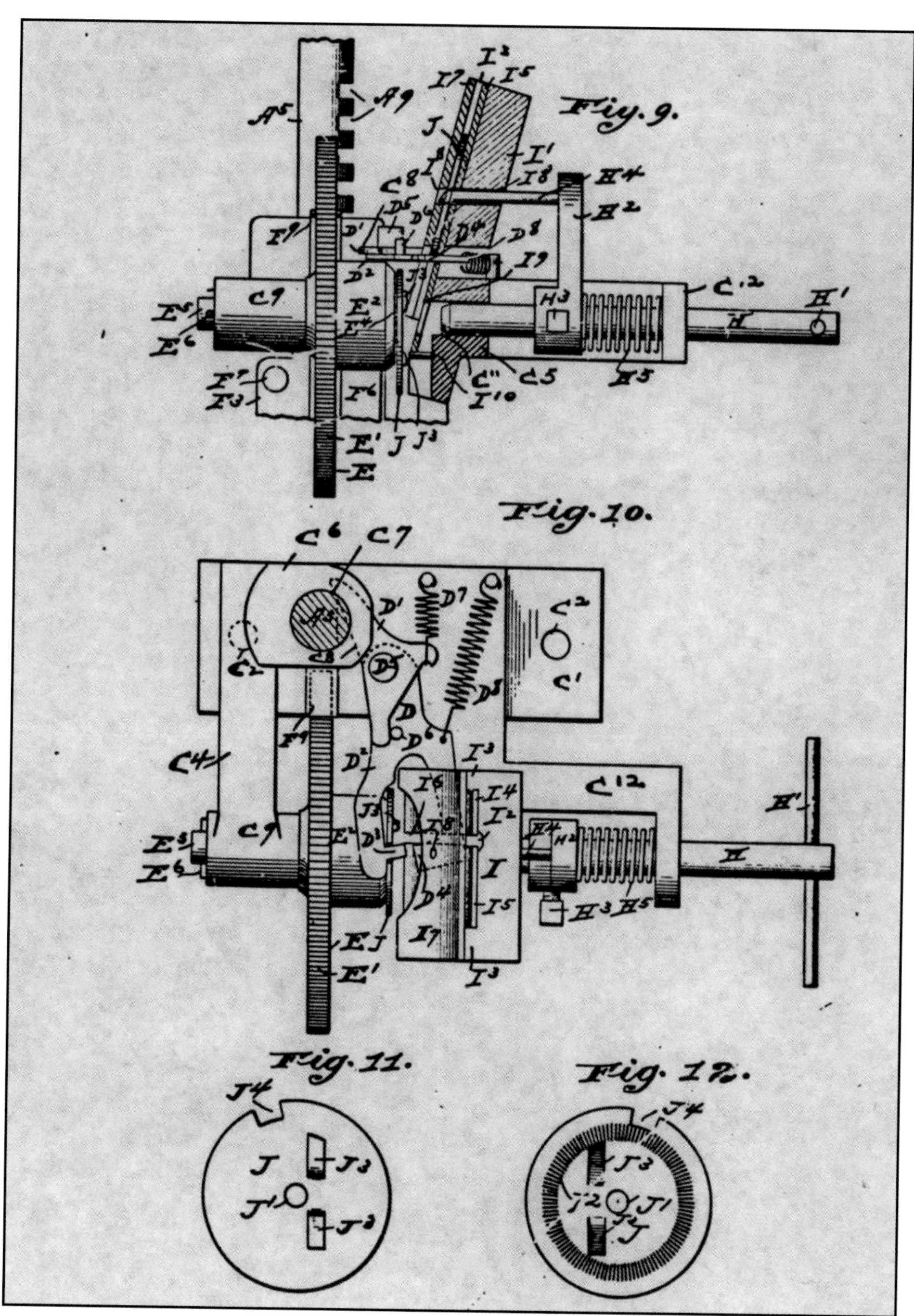

Colman's counter mechanism, shown here in the original patent drawing, was one of the devices that he briefly experimented with after his sale of the check pump in 1897. Figures 9 (elevation) and 10 (top view) show a check (J) in the mechanism with the pusher rod (H) withdrawn. Figures 11 and 12 show top and bottom views of a check, the latter revealing the radial depressions that engaged the teeth of a ratchet wheel (E).

He discovered a stamp-canceling machine there, manufactured in Iowa, that could process 800 letters a minute, and he was told that 40 similar machines were being used in the Chicago office. Further research revealed that at least 80 patents had been issued on stamp-canceling devices. This was a well-worked field, he concluded, and to be competitive as an inventor, he would have to devote himself to months of study just to differentiate his claims to originality, an effort that seemed unlikely to repay itself in the short term. "Should like to have something in mind which may lead to something else of value if this is our cue," he told Barber (12/10/97).

If it was hard to discover cues in other people's inventions, Colman could possibly find them in his own. With pumps still a major interest, he spent time in the autumn browsing through sales catalogues, visualizing the various products in operation and allowing himself to free-associate. Sometimes ideas came from memories of past experiments. In January he wrote Barber about his notion of a cam pump and described the sequence of events that inspired it:

> Last summer when experimenting with that spiral separator of ours, which proved such a complete and unmitigated failure, I had a bright idea for a pump to furnish the requisite pressure, which I expected would be great. After the separator failed, I forgot all about the pump until the other day, when it happened to come to mind again (1/26/98).

Colman's memory of the long-forgotten pump was prompted by his study of a Gould Company catalogue and, in particular, its triplex power pump, a single-cylinder mechanism with a "double-acting piston" that was purported to generate a more or less continuous liquid flow. Colman's "bright idea" a year earlier had been to replace the crankshaft in a similar device with cams, thereby eliminating the intermittent pump action. The concluding line in the catalogue description of the triplex pump had made him think of this:

> While it is impractical to build a pump that will produce perfectly uniform action upon the water, the work wasted in this particular by the triplex is only about one-third of that wasted in the best-designed duplex or four-plunger pumps.

Colman took the Gould reference to "best-designed" pumps to heart. He told Barber that he thought he could "accomplish perfectly and absolutely what they aim to accomplish but succeed in doing only imperfectly by their own statement." His goal was the creation of a constant-action machine for the transmission of hydraulic power.

What he wanted to do was purchase a triplex pump (discretely, perhaps, using Barber's name), fit it with the cams, hoses, and iron pipes that were needed for a constant-motion configuration, and begin experimenting. He proposed actuating the pump valves by cams "in the same manner in which the fluid is supposed to actuate them" and applying this pressure to the suction pipe, thereby turning the pump into a "motor." The "constant stream of water flowing through it," he believed, "would produce a constant movement of the shaft."

> By using a pump at one point and such a motor at another connected by two lines of pipe, one for the water flowing in each direction, we would have a method of transmitting power which I think might prove advantageous for distances too great for belts and not great enough to make electricity economical, say from 200 to 2000 feet.

Previous attempts "to transmit power hydraulically" had been unsuccessful because of the "inefficiency of the apparatus." Piston-activated devices wasted energy because they started and stopped the liquid flow. Water-wheel mechanisms generated power, but they failed to use this power to maintain their own momentum. "Then, too, some of the head is always lost in making room for the tailings." The device that he envisioned would circulate water through the system at a constant rate of speed and harness its energy for useful work. Its practical value could be determined by the amount of water it raised to a particular height, for example, or by its rate of work, as measured in horse power (1/28/98).

Colman went over his idea with George Spengler, who believed that a cam pump would be cheaper to build than a triplex. They both thought that such a device could be designed to be lighter and more portable than the Gould machine, and to run faster, on less energy, because of the constant motion. Luther Miller investigated the relevant patent literature and felt that there was room for a good claim if Colman could prove his concept. If this happened, Colman realized, he would want to exhibit the pump at regional and national expositions during the summer. And to do this, he would have to move quickly.

The cam-pump project, however, turned out to be "as flat and complete a failure" as the spiral-separator concept that inspired it. Colman had not reckoned on the valves malfunctioning, and as perfectly conceived as his configuration might have been, it was reduced to the level of an ordinary pump by the weakest link in its chain of mechanisms. Yet Colman was surprisingly nonchalant in making this admission, revealing that he had been hard at work on the development of an alternative scheme since the cam pump experiments had failed (letter to Barber, 3/22/98).

He was now thinking of putting his constant-action idea to a very simple and practical test: "elevating rain water to attic tanks by the use of city water pressure." Instead of transmitting hydraulic power over long distances, he would develop a new low-cost mechanism to pump cisterns dry. If successful, he believed, the device would have a great deal of consumer appeal since the majority of American homeowners still used hand pumps to elevate their soft water. In fact, he had become so enamored with the possibility of a water lift powered by constant pressure from city mains that he had gone ahead and built a prototype device without waiting to contact Barber. "I have so often known your lenience that I do not feel all the trepidation which my own culpability would, perhaps, justify."

The change in focus was characteristic. When Colman was intrigued by a idea, as he clearly was by the possibility of constant action, he was usually reluctant to give it up without considering different applications. During his cam-pump experiments, he had systematically investigated a number of related topics in hydraulics as a means of challenging himself conceptually; and he acknowledged to Barber that he had borrowed an idea from an article on fluid power for his reformulated constant-action scheme. He had discovered that certain mine pumps, which used hydraulic pressure, operated according to principles that were remarkably similar to those of manual water lifts, given the difference in physical force. His idea was to replace the manual apparatus with a hydraulic system generated by municipal water power, and to ensure that the pressure within the new system was constant by discharging the drive water and suction water into the same pipe.

ii

To the extent that a complex mechanism can be simply described, Colman's water lift worked in the following way. One end of a pipe (the "intake") was placed several feet below the surface of rain water in a cistern, while the other end (the "delivery") was placed 15-20 feet above it inside a house's attic tank. This pipe, in turn, was connected to a smaller pipe coil, with a superstructure of air and vacuum chambers, that attached directly to the municipal water supply (see illustration on page 150). An operator activated the water lift by opening up the mains. He then used a hand lever to compress a pulse valve long enough for a portion of the delivery pipe to fill with water. The rush of liquid into the pipe snapped the pulse valve shut. A rising column inside the cylinder carried a floating piston upwards, causing a check valve to close by its own weight and trap the incoming water after the momentum was exhausted. The rising and falling columns of water created partial vacuums in the system. After the pump was primed, the intake pipe drew rain water up the channel, while also opening a waste-water valve and discharging the hard water. The key to the device was a special arrangement of pulse and check valves that allowed the operator to bleed air out of the system. When the pressure in the air chamber became greater than that of the municipal water supply, the necessary suction was produced to raise the soft water.

Rising and falling columns of water, which were balanced by the interaction of air and vacuum chambers, kept the liquid in constant motion. It was a specialized application of a fundamental hydraulic concept. "My new water elevating apparatus is clicking away with great cheerfulness ...," Colman wrote Barber on March 26. "It seems so unquestion[able] that this lead is worth following that I am not waiting for your approval, tho' I wish I had it."

Blueprints and specifications for a new "water elevator" (referred to variously as an "aqua elevator," "aqualevator," and "water lift" in Colman's letters and other writings) were soon dispatched to Barber, and a second prototype, with a vacuum gauge attached to the suction pipe, readied for testing in George Spengler's home in early April. Improvements in certain "minor schemes" were also carried out in preparation for a possible patent application, as Luther Miller had reported on a recent trip to Washington that there was little on the books in the U.S. Patent Office that seemed to limit Colman's concept.

The initial "rough tests" of the two prototypes were promising. Colman found that his machine could raise 19 ¼ pounds of soft water to a height of 17' 8" by using 20 pounds of city water, an efficiency level of nearly 50%; and that by sacrificing a few feet of lift, he could increase this efficiency to 65%. If he held down the valve of the intake pipe, on the other hand, he could create a suction depth of 26 feet. He told Barber that he would probably have to spend a considerable amount of time experimenting with "different heads and ... different city [water] pressures" in order to make the adjustments to the "weight of the lower valve" that would give the water lift the greatest commercial appeal. In the future, he said, he hoped to be able to print a table that correlated valve settings with heads and pressures in order to help plumbers install the device (4/18/98).

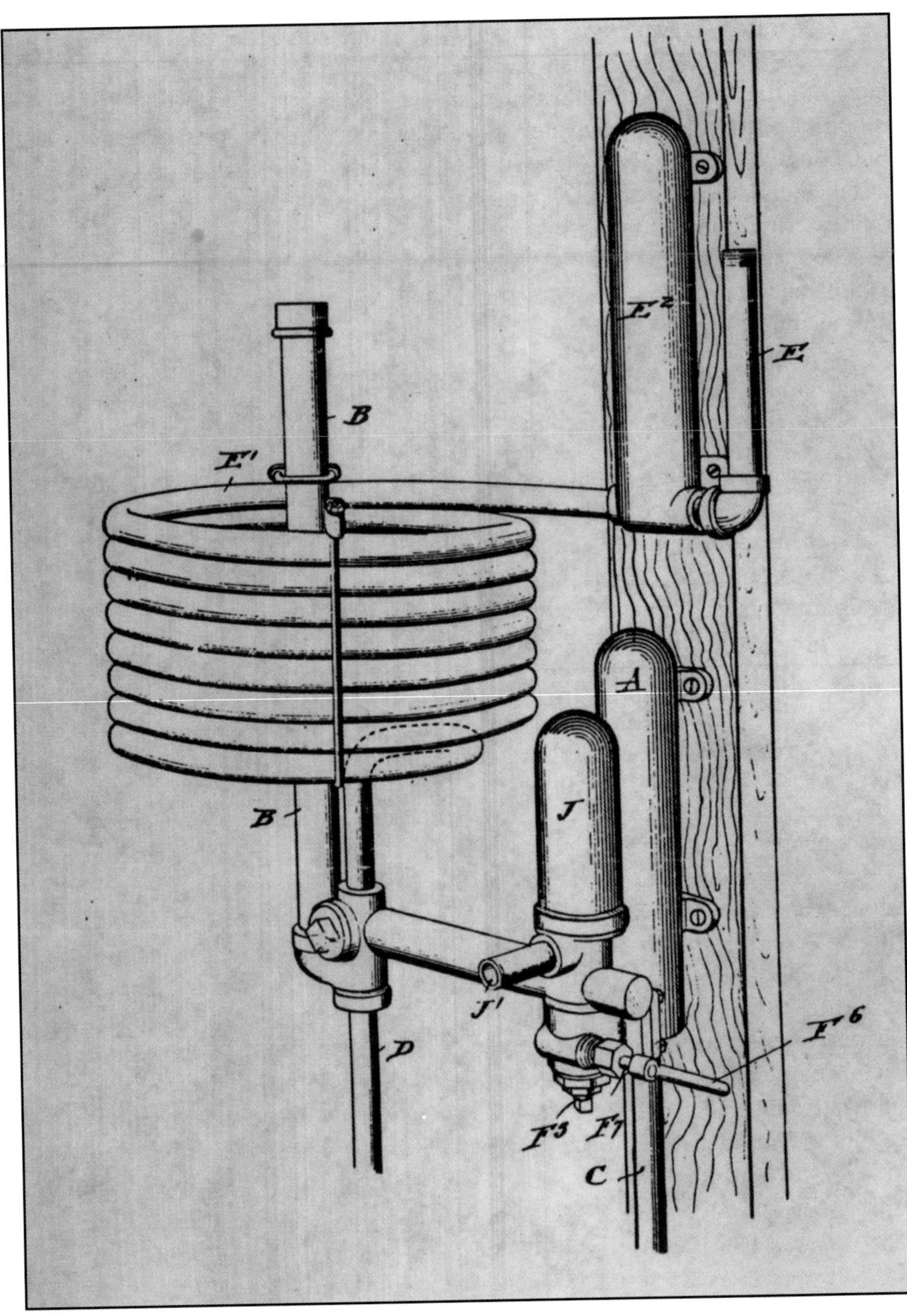

L.T. Mann's drawing of the water-lift accompanied Howard Colman's patent application of November 2, 1898. The illustration showed the air chamber (A), vacuum chamber (B), municipal water-supply pipe (C), intake pipe (D) leading to the cistern, and delivery pipe (E) leading to the attic tank. A secondary air chamber (J) was also represented.

Experiments of this type apparently continued during the spring and summer of 1898, with Colman intent on determining the specific adjustments to the lift's valves and air chambers that would be necessary to accommodate municipal water pressures between 20-100 pounds. Because of the "deafening" clatter that his machine made when it was first installed in Spengler's house, Colman had to replace the metal valves with rubber ones and study ways to quiet all the working mechanisms (4/23/98). As was his habit, he also cast about for new opportunities to exploit the water-lift technology, designing a special "cess-pool machine" or slurry pump at Barber's urging and later modifying the design when it failed to start automatically. "The machine is defective in some particulars," he wrote Barber, "and I think I will make you another and keep this one here for further experiment and exhibition to a possible customer" (6/11/98).

Colman's free-ranging investigations in 1898 were intended to demonstrate his water lift's versatility and to establish a scientific basis for detailed patent claims. We know that he asked for Barber's permission to "go ahead with [the] patent application" as early as April, but that for some reason - there is a four-month gap in their existing correspondence after June - a letter was not sent to Washington until early November.*

iii

After completing the water-lift patent application, Colman worked for several months on a gasoline-powered skim milk weigher and conducted tests of a configuration that he had cobbled together from off-the-shelf components. As in the case of the cam pump, however, the theoretical possibilities of the weigher were eventually eclipsed by a long list of operational headaches ("practical difficulties in minor details" was his usual way of describing this); and by the summer of 1899 he had made up his mind to abandon the project altogether in favor of a return to more familiar territory. Drawing on lessons from his check-pump days, Colman now set out to design a "skimming device" (skim-milk pump) that would extend the capabilities of his original manual apparatus by: 1) running automatically; 2) dispensing milk at the high rate of speed; and 3) providing precise liquid measurements. He explained it to Barber this way:

> I have had a new idea for a liquid measuring device which seems to offer material points of superiority over any possible weigher. It measures "a flowing stream" and is very simple indeed. I have already tried it roughly with some success - as much as could be expected from the apparatus, and I think, with some further development, it can be made accurate (11/10/99).

* The patent was granted on May 22, 1900.

Colman constructed his machine with air and vacuum chambers, a two-inch race, and a spherically-shaped valve or "ball" that formed a tight seal against the sharp-edged seat of the pump, the valve opening and closing with each stroke of the piston. The ball machine's pulse was controlled by an adjustable percentage wheel, so that the flow increased as the dial was advanced.

One marvels at the range of Colman's activities during this period and the ease with which he moved back and forth between different fields of interest. It was Barber's belief that his young friend could make himself the master of virtually any subject that he chose to explore, given the time and financial resources necessary to undertake a thorough study; and Colman, with his facile intelligence and eagerness to tackle new challenges, did little to dispel this notion. Besides the check pump, stamp-cancelling machine, spiral separator, cam pump, water elevator, and gas-powered weigher, his letters of the late 1890s allude to unspecified trials with rotary pumps, a "combined churn," a typewriter-like device for receiving skim milk orders, and an automated milk-bottling apparatus undertaken at the express invitation of the Creamery Packaging Company. It was enough to ask. Colman's inventiveness was becoming widely recognized by dairy-industry professionals in the Midwest, and both Barber and Colman understood the leverage that this gave them in their dealings with other companies.

The opposite side of the coin, of course, was Colman's tendency to skip from subject to subject rather than concentrate at length on a single topic or single experimental field, a tendency that sometimes troubled Barber, who urged his friend to "stick to the knitting" when projects were delayed, and which worried Colman in spite of himself. To a certain extent, this habit was indicative of the way that Colman's mind worked. Creative thinkers are, by their natures, associative; they tend to visualize relationships where there are none and make up things out of disparate elements, and it behooves them to incorporate as many ideas and as many dimensions of meaning as possible into their schemes. Associative thinking is also an instinctive human strategy for dealing with obstacles: creative people find ways to get around problems rather than ponder them indefinitely, and fruitlessly, from a single point of view. They adopt new perspectives on things, turn them upside down, mix and match the parts.

The ball machine project reflected both sides of Colman's nature, his facility for invention and his endless questioning of his own assumptions. It appears that he quickly put together a set of technical drawings for a prototype and then went to work assembling his measurer from off-the-shelf components. He was encouraged in his efforts by an associate of Luther Miller's in Washington, who thought that the "ball device" was "patentable," even though "balls and ball races in measuring devices" were "not new" (11/25/99). Colman experienced some "minor vexations and delays" in the completion of a working model, not entirely unexpected in a complicated assembly operation of this kind, but he was able to begin testing the ball meter on December 5 and decided to install it in Barber's creamery a week later. "I find that it is not advisable to put it in the creamery here," he wrote from Rockford somewhat cryptically (2/13/00), perhaps alluding to the fact, revealed elsewhere, that he was actually developing the machine to supplant a popular liquid measurer from the Creamery Packaging Company. The choice of a remote testing station in Wisconsin would thus have made good sense, given the worry of premature exposure. Colman sent Barber's butter-maker specific instructions for the installation of a pump, vat, piping, and hoses, and promised to furnish the "balls" when the assembly was completed (2/17/00).

Colman soon began to have misgivings about the feasibility of his design, however, wondering if a disk meter would not be preferable to a ball configuration in terms of precision measurement. As a result, he proposed delaying his visit to Warrens for the final ball-machine assembly so that he could address these concerns. By the time that he reported to Barber at the beginning of March, he had reformulated his liquid-measuring concept and embarked on a new course:

> I have been investigating water meters and fear I made a hardly excusable mistake in not doing so [long] ago. The reason I didn't was because those whom I suppose knew told me they were merely "stream measurers" and therefore inaccurate. I find, however, that such is not at all the case, and it now seems to me probable that some adaptation of the ordinary "gyrating disk" water meter will prove better than the ball machine in every respect except care of cleaning and possibly accuracy to some slight extent, altho' I think the chances rather favor the "gyrating disk" in that particular also (3/9/00).

Colman decided to abandon the ball machine temporarily and try out a "disk scheme" as soon as it was feasible; and he proposed cannibalizing the former for its percentage wheel, screws, and pawl dog in order to shorten the development time. He also alerted Miller to the possibility of a future patent application, provided that the way was open for a good disk-meter claim.

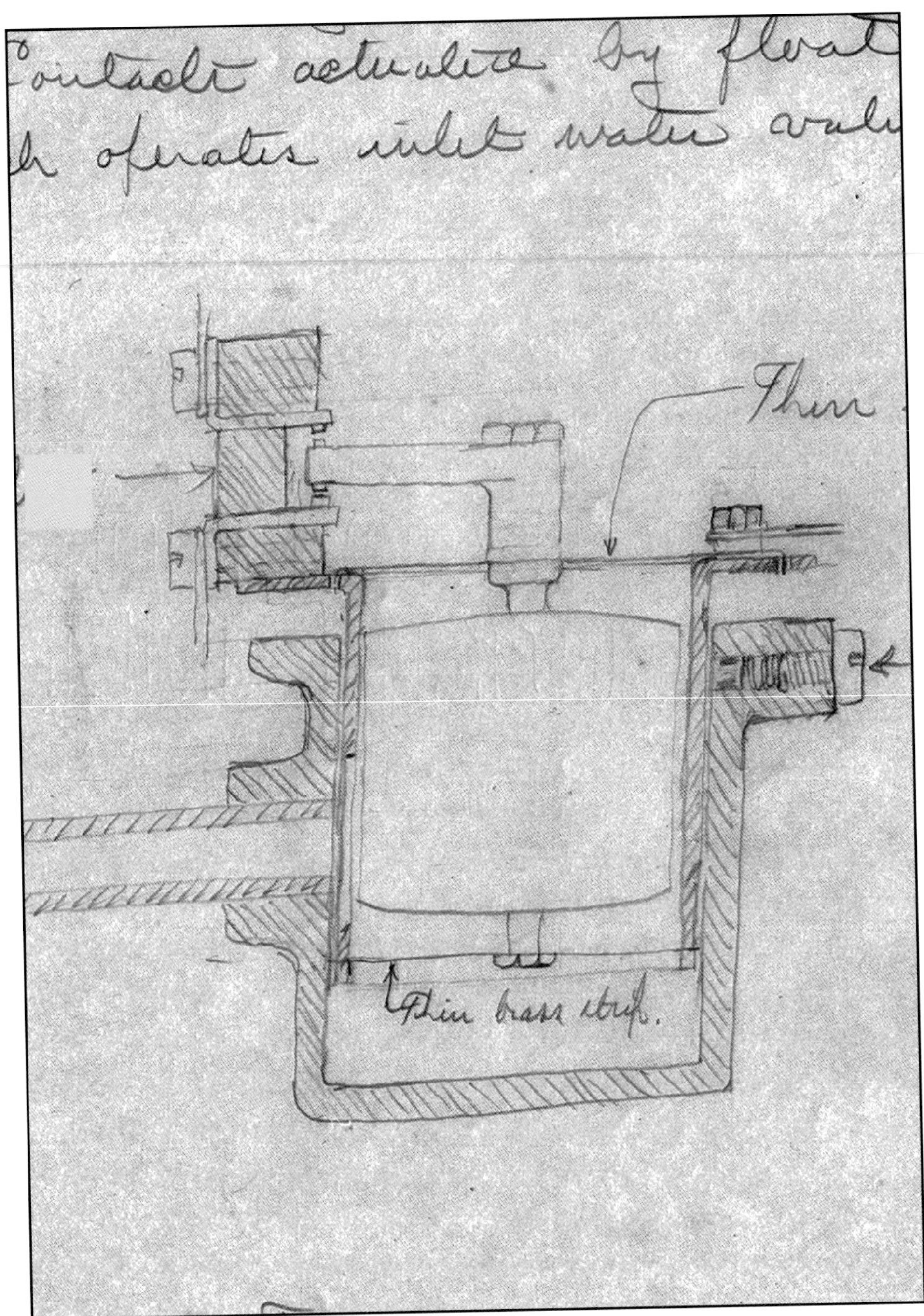

Colman's drawing of a float-valve mechanism.

Yet "practical difficulties" in testing the disk meter caused him to rethink his options once again, and scarcely two months later he was touting the advantages of his original device. "As ball machine seems the most promising now," he wrote Barber, "it strikes me as highly desirable to get it running ... I blame myself very much for being so overconfident in the disk meter that I neglected having the ball meter repaired ..." (5/18/00).

And so it went. Colman continued testing both devices for several months, while readily admitting to Barber that he was becoming "very doubtful, after all, as to which is better" (n.d.). The upshot of his liquid-measuring experiments was that both projects were finally abandoned, and no application was ever submitted for either to the U.S. Patent Office. There is nothing more about the disk meter in Colman's letters, and one assumes that it went into storage and was salvaged for its parts. The ball machine, ironically, was acquired by the Creamery Packaging Company, the same organization whose liquid measurer Colman had originally targeted in the development of the invention. How and why this occurred is part of the story of the expiration of the royalty arrangement with C.C.& G. and the final months of Colman's venture into fluid power.

The licensing contract that Barber and Colman signed with C.C.& G. in 1897 proved to be generally satisfactory for both parties - despite occasional slumps, the check pump sold steadily over the 24-month term of the agreement - but this is not to say that the relationship between the sides was always harmonious and without its periods of frustration. Chief among the Barber and Colman concerns was the chronic tardiness of C.C.& G.'s royalty payments; the letters between the two men during this period are full of cash-flow worries and accounts of the manufacturer's many broken promises in regards to its remittances. Colman was forced to make repeated calls on the C.C.& G. factory to plead his case and even, in a few instances, to threaten legal action, but after July the situation changed dramatically because C.C.& G. was purchased by the Creamery Packaging Company of Chicago as part of an effort to consolidate the American pump and weigher markets.

Barber and Colman were now faced with the challenge of dealing with an entirely new party in the renewal of the check-pump license, which expired at more or less the same time that Creamery completed its acquisition of C.C.& G. Creamery continued "on a verbal understanding" to honor the royalty arrangement as before (letter to Barber 7/24/00), while

Colman negotiated with its management over a new agreement that would permanently transfer the check-pump tools and patent to Creamery for $7,500. He sweetened his offer by throwing in both the ball meter and a working model of a milk-bottling machine, which he had designed at the request of Creamery's managers, and which he now offered to them for an additional $2,500 if they agreed to purchase the check-pump patent.

In September 1900, a sale of the Barber and Colman dairy-market assets was concluded with the Creamery Packaging Company for $10,000.

iv

Howard Colman wrote more than two hundred letters in the 1890s that have come down to us, and many of these refer at length to the progress of his experiments, his work habits and ways of visualizing, or conceptualizing, ideas. He's unusually candid in the letters about his instincts as an inventor (i.e. "I am continually in a fever of anxiety to try some new idea or find one …"), and he shows a willingness to discuss, or at least disclose, his reasons for pursuing particular lines of inquiry and for choosing one kind of a project to investigate over another (he typically refers to his projects as "schemes," as in "I have been considering a new scheme …," "Another one of my schemes …," "My scheme, which is so doubtful in some ways and promising in others …," and so on). Colman also writes a good deal in the letters about the process of invention itself. He refers to his habit of devising mental puzzles to get his "thinker working" and of routinely "studying up" on the state of the art in patent literature as a preliminary to more focused and systematic experimental work. He reveals that he sometimes uses commercial catalogues to stimulate his thoughts, critiquing the designs and specifications of the products that are shown on the pages of these catalogues in terms of the claims to performance; and he sometimes loses himself in the manipulation of his own prototypes by dwelling on the mechanisms, mentally altering and realigning the components, and imagining them in other contexts.

Colman tends to lump all these habits together in his letters under the term "brain cudgeling," a tongue-in-cheek reference to his thought processes that reflects the involuntary nature of his creativity. Despite his extraordinary visual-spatial powers, he could no more will himself to dream up a scheme than he could act to stop his thinker, during an experiment, from veering off track into the contemplation of an (apparently) unrelated subject. "An idea came to me," he tells William Barber matter-of-factly in the way that he might have talked about the discovery of a twenty dollar bill. The idea simply happened, he could not say why. "It occurred to me ...," he writes Barber in another letter, explaining a sudden turn of events in his experiments. Or he speaks elsewhere about a brainstorm ("I had a bright idea ...") that helps him resolve a technical impasse, as surprised by his insight as he is by his previous difficulties in coming to terms with the problem. Colman knew that the process of invention depended on his ability - on *his thinker's ability* - to hatch new schemes: find hidden meanings, make unexpected connections, formulate possibilities, even as he recognized his inability to start this process intellectually. His thinker was notoriously fickle - he refers to it in the third person because he considered it to be out of his control - and it had to be stimulated, enticed, appealed to indirectly (i.e. by browsing through commercial catalogues) in order to elicit its creativity.

Invention, for Colman, began with a feeling, a hunch, an insight, a sixth sense. It then "evolved" or "matured" in his head (the words are used interchangeably in his letters) into some kind of quantifiable commercial proposition. That is to say, his original notion translated itself into the design of a device or apparatus that could be given a "severe test" for performance and reliability before being taken to market. Relatively few of his notions matured to this stage. Prototyping involved a serious expenditure of time and money, and Colman had to be convinced that there was "really something in it" (a favorite expression) before committing his limited resources to the actual development of a mechanism. Instead, his notions were likely to keep turning in his head, evolving into other interests and other lines of inquiry, and coming to mind when his queries brought up related concerns.

What usually convinced Colman to build a prototype was not so much the apparent sophistication of his concept in terms of the technical state of the art as it was his assessment of the market opportunities. His schemes often started with the recognition of some kind of unsatisfied consumer demand (the check pump is a case in point) and matured into the design of a product to address it. On a few occasions this happened rapidly, virtually overnight, his speculations proceeding with a sure sense of the prototype to be built, but usually it happened more slowly, his original notion failing to take definitive shape in his head and only coming into focus after many hours of brain-cudgeling.

Colman prepared for his work as an inventor by spending considerable amounts of time "in cogitation." After familiarizing himself with his subject - studying up on the state of the art, feeding his brain with related readings - he liked to meditate on what he had learned, sometimes while sitting alone at his desk or drawing board; although if there were too many interruptions in his office, he isolated himself in his living quarters and lay on his back to think. Solitary walks were also a favorite way of incubating information, "getting it in mind," as he liked to say, before conceptualizing his schemes. Motion had a salutary effect on his imagination, the changing landscape apparently relaxing his concentration just enough for his thinker to go to work. According to the accounts of contemporaries, Colman could be easily absorbed by his thoughts and oblivious to the world around him, a potentially amusing sight on one of his early-morning walks but a matter of some consequence when he later got behind the wheel of an automobile.

To make sense of Colman's routines, it's important to remember his fickle imagination and the priority he gave to arranging his workday so that he could pursue his experimental interests without distraction. In one form or another, everything he did was intended to spur his creativity, open himself up to ideas, and provide the wherewithal, financial and otherwise, to take his most promising schemes through to the stage of prototyping. Fortune favors the prepared mind; and Colman's success as an inventor, at least in part, was due to his ability to absorb large amounts of technical detail and later to recall this information, with precision, in the development of new concepts. He seems to have remembered all the mechanisms he ever manipulated in an immediate, almost palpable way. We all draw upon mental images and associations in interpreting experience, but it was the depth of these impressions that set Colman apart. A Barber-Colman associate likened the gift many years afterwards to having "an open file at his fingertips," and most of Colman's contemporaries simply took for granted the richness of his visual memory.

Yet it was not only his recall that distinguished him from others, but the particular way in which he approached his schemes conceptually. Each of his projects involved a mechanical configuration of some sort that transmitted power through its system, either manually or as the result of an ancillary apparatus like a gasoline engine. Colman had a knack of envisioning these devices as wholes, as single dynamic entities, in which the parts worked, in unison, in time and space. When his friends said that he thought like a machine, this is probably what they meant. Instead of focusing on the elements of a causal sequence, one part at a time, as most of us would do, he had the ability to visualize the entire sequence at once, sensing

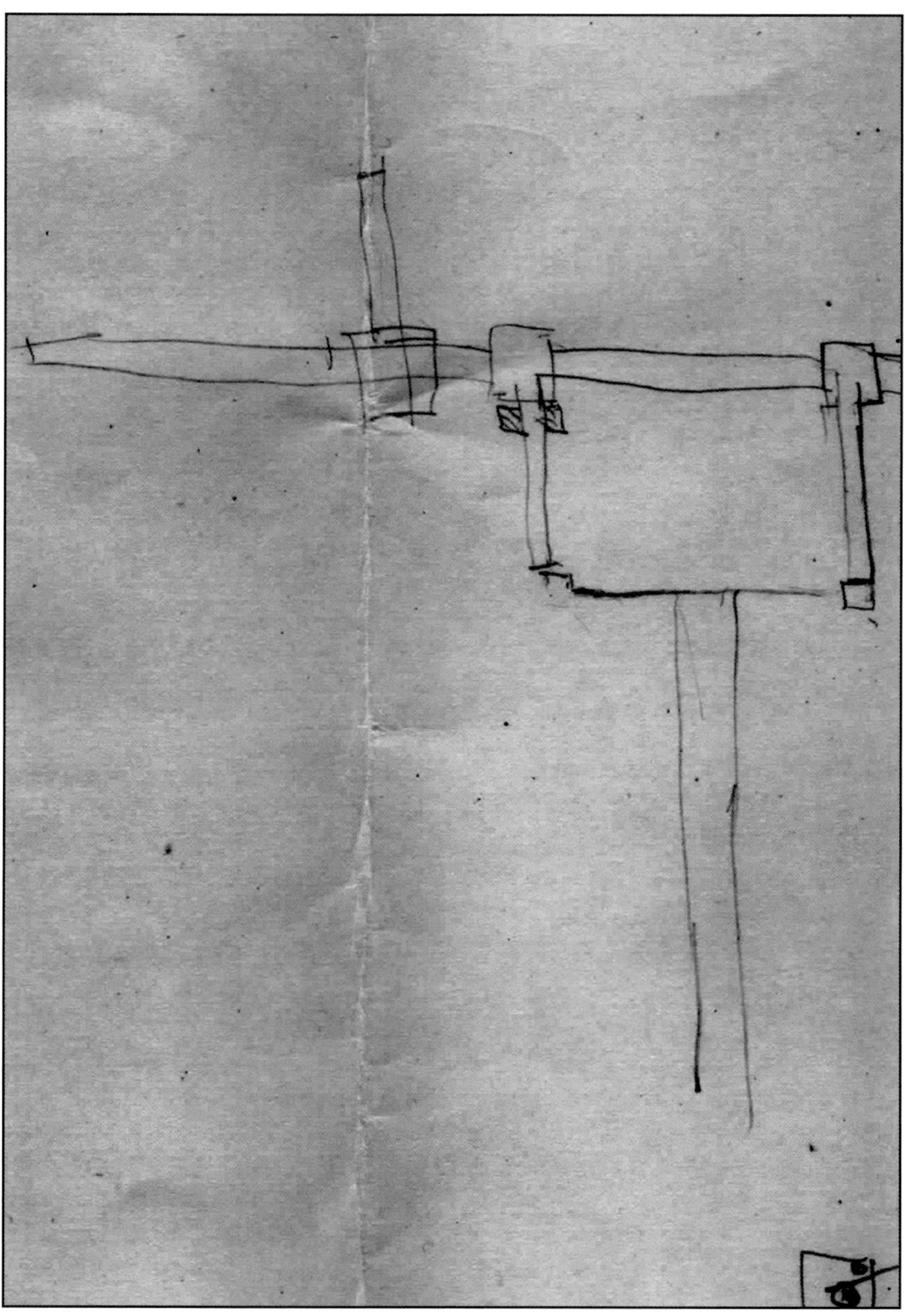

One of Howard Colman's freehand sketches of a mechanical device. Such doodles were rare, as the inventor usually worked out ideas in his head before reducing them to engineering drawings.

the linkages that conducted the mechanical power. His challenge was always to refine this understanding, give his intuitions a more definitive shape by turning them into numbers and deducing an operating formula (his usual term for this step was "going into it mathematically"). In the end he had to be able to grasp the dynamics of a working machine and know what its approximate specifications would be. "I have looked into the requirements and difficulties and am inclined to think I might be able to do something" was his way of putting it. His scheme had been "completed to the experimenting point," in other words, and he was ready to build a prototype.

Colman used few, if any, written notes to record the progress of his speculations. "I hate to take the time for such things as reports, etc.," he had told Barber in the early days of the check-pump project; and the truth is that Colman's mind worked best when he was free to pursue his brainstorms, wherever they led him, without the need to be immediately accountable. One guesses that note-taking would have impeded this process and turned out to be fairly useless to him in the early development of his inventions, since he relied so much on memory as his primary source of evidence. "I have pretty well matured plans in my head ...," he would say in announcing a concept, or "I have done a great deal of that sort of exercise" in recalling the conceptual problems that he had wrestled with in formulating a new scheme.

It's true that Colman, on the advice of his lawyers, later recorded some of his most important "idea trains" in preparation for patent lawsuits and applications; though in these instances he completed the reports retrospectively and relied on his colleagues for much of the relevant documentation. One of the chief responsibilities of his personal assistant, Davis Sprague, was to minimize Colman's record-keeping distractions, routinely preparing typed memoranda of discussions and experiments for Colman's signature at the end of the day (i.e. "On December 28, I witnessed the operation of the machine shown in Negative X ...;" "On December 28, I discussed and disclosed to X the possibility of ..."). Sprague eaves-dropped on Colman's shop-floor conversations and regularly discussed the company's ongoing projects with the members of the Experimental Department. Everything possible was exhibited, witnessed, dated. Sprague coaxed Colman into dictating brief "position papers" on hypothetical future experiments ("I have for many years intended eventually to consider the possibility ...") and into listing the advantages and disadvantages of specific fields of investigation (these were filed under the heading "Arguments Affecting Decisions"). But even these pedantic exercises in record-keeping could not obscure Colman's ingrained habit of self-reflection, as repeatedly evidenced in his accounts of his own mental processes: "Last night *I worked out in my own mind* a quite definite arrangement ..." (emphasis added)

Colman's controlled demeanor, which is apparent in the reserved tone of his letters to William Barber, masked the nervous energy of his investigations. His self-confessed "fever of anxiety to try some new idea or find one" extended to most of his speculative work and resulted in the critical questioning of the fields he explored, a readiness to pick things apart and make them up anew. While most people are content to know, in general, how a machine works (or not to know it at all), Colman indulged in fundamental conjectures about his inventions, looking for root causes and asking "questions behind the questions." He also scrutinized the devices of his competitors, reverse-engineered their mechanisms, so that he could learn their secrets and figure out how to supplant them. Always impartial in the affairs of science, he saved his harshest criticism for himself, putting his own prototypes through severe tests in order to expose their weaknesses.

Everything in Colman's mind contained its opposite, and no process was ever final, complete, or what it appeared to be at first. His investigations proceeded by a kind of inverse reasoning that concentrated on a scheme's *otherness:* a fundamental form of a complex mechanism, say, or the increased functionality of a basic tool. He would try to simplify a device by reducing the number of parts and streamlining its operation or, conversely, add to its capacity by incorporating it into a larger mechanical configuration and attaching a new power source. If he made concrete things more abstract by deducing an operating formula, he was just as likely to turn around and extract the kernel of an idea for a new invention from his calculations. Sometimes he assumed multiple perspectives on the same device by putting it to different uses in his imagination. At other times he visualized it working backwards or upside down, as in the case of the gravity-fed "liquid deliverer" (check pump) for skim milk that turned into a device for overcoming the effects of gravity and raising rain water to attic tanks. Pumping up and down is akin to pumping continuously, and in the dialectical progression of Colman's ideas, it was a short step from this to the creation of a mechanism that used fluid power to transmit fluid power. His skim milk concept thus had a further incarnation as a constant-action machine.

Simplification was one of Colman's favorite creative strategies, though, as his spiral separator project proved, it could also on occasion be something of a red herring. Had he stumbled on an easy way of separating butter fats from milk through the use of a pipe coil under pressure? Did his concept embody a hydraulic principle the others had overlooked? No, as it turned out; but the lessons learned were important to him and went into a memory bank that contributed to other projects and other visionary plans. Or so one assumes. The trouble with Colman's schemes was that they were "wagers against time and chance," shots in the dark at best; and he could never tell if they would "prove out" or flame out in the end. Accidents happened to him on purpose, and little gems turned up unexpectedly. He had to know what he was looking for, and be ready to discover what he wasn't.

V

An interest in invention had held Colman in thrall since childhood and was the driving force in his life. It satisfied his need to be original, produced his happiest moments, and gave purpose and meaning to his work. For nearly four years, from the time that he devised his original wood-framed D.I.M. and committed himself to serious scientific investigations, balancing his Wayland studies with the much more intriguing challenges of warp replenishment, to the early days of his check-pump experiments in 1896, he labored in obscurity, trying to keep his head above water financially and doing everything he could to maintain a belief in the value of a creative life. The three-and-a-half years that followed, the so-called "fluid-power phase" of his young career, provided the capstone of a long apprenticeship, consolidating the experiences of his warp-drawing labors.

What had Colman accomplished? He had earned his first money in the market-place from experimental work, no small achievement after the many frustrations of the D.I.M. and the months of wrangling with the Drapers, and no small boost to his spirits. He had also obtained a patent on the check pump, his first successful patent application, and had had his mechanism validated by a governmental authority as a "new and useful invention." It had become his legal property, his exclusive right to manufacture, and no one else could even offer it for sale without his written permission. Check pump revenues, moreover, had offered him a measure of financial independence, an important issue for a young man in his twenties who had been relying on an older friend's generosity for most of his living expenses. Because of the sale of the check pump patent to the Creamery Packaging Company, he could now feel reasonably confident about the near-term stability of the Barber and Colman partnership and his own continued employment.

The daily challenges that Colman faced in overseeing his fledgling enterprise had given him a crash course in small-business management that would stand him in good stead for the remainder of his career. Out of necessity he had learned budgeting and bookkeeping; written sales literature; answered customer inquiries; supervised employees; filled orders; overseen the fabrication and assembly of his inventions; and found a way to distribute and install these products, even when this sometimes meant pedaling his own bicycle to remote creameries in the region to provide technical assistance. On more than a few occasions he had butted heads with customers and suppliers over credit and payment terms, and he had successfully fended off competitors' attempts to steal his ideas. When it became expedient for Barber and Colman either to sell off the check pump patent or license the use of the designs to another manufacturer, he had taken the lead in royalty negotiations and reached an equitable agreement. And after the licensing contract expired, he had found a way to liquidate his dairy-market assets through the sale of the patent, providing himself with the experimental resources necessary to take his career in another direction.

8
Launching the Company

> Hope you are again manipulating the D.I.M. or at least getting it in shape for [the] Drapers' observation once more. I shall be disappointed if they are not more enthusiastic than before. Shall look for interesting letters from you before long and hope you will not feel as blue again as when I arrived in Lowell four years ago and met you.
>
> - *Letter from William Barber to Howard Colman, 1899*

i

By the end of the 19th Century, American cotton manufacturing had become a highly automated mechanical process, with power-driven equipment encompassing almost all its spinning and weaving operations. Larger, faster, and more complex machines were being steadily introduced into the mills of New England and the South, reducing the need for manual labor and lowering the costs of cloth production. Only in two of the preparatory stages of weaving did bottlenecks occur and prove resistant to automation. One was during the spooling phase, where workers were still required to tie the threads of the old and new bobbins together by hand before winding them onto a beam. The other was after the warp on the beam had run out during the weaving operation itself. Here an attendant needed to use her fingers to pull the thread ends of the new warp through tiny openings in the reed and harnesses and tie them to trailing ends of the old.*

Howard Colman had attempted to address the second problem with his invention of the warp drawing-in machine (D.I.M.) in 1890, a device that he slowly perfected, with design changes and more precisely-machined components, over the following years. When he put the D.I.M.

---

* This overview of American cotton manufacturing at the turn of the century is based on the "historical record" in a "Brief on Behalf of Howard D. Colman," submitted to the U.S. Patent Office (1915).

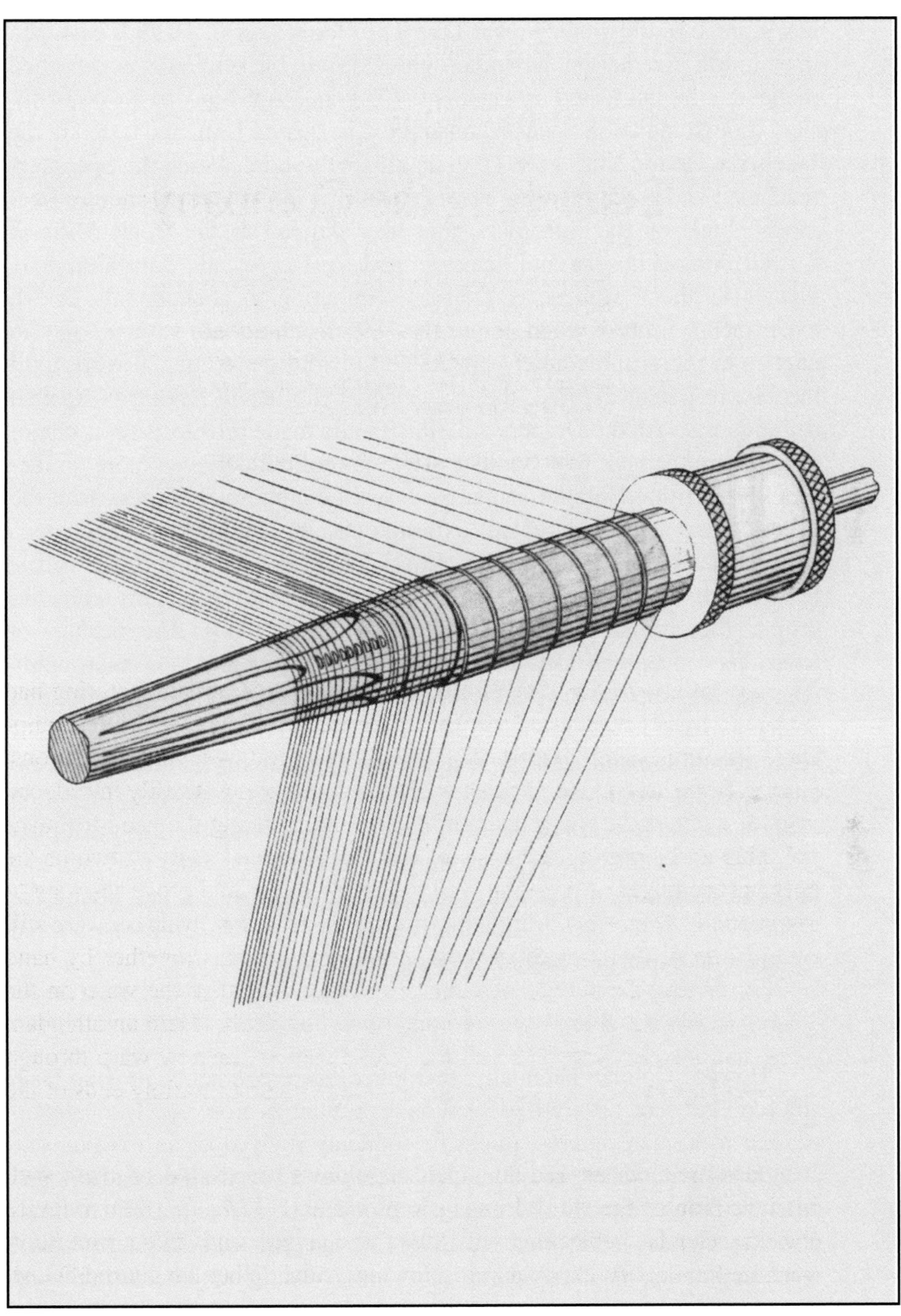

Among Colman's many D.I.M. improvements was a tapered screw mechanism for separating and positioning the warp threads.

into storage in the Water Power District in the winter of 1896, it was then in its fourth incarnation, having progressed from the original wood-framed model that he fabricated as a student at Wayland Academy to a wood-and-steel framed model that was reconstructed in Beaver Dam and tested in the Janesville Cotton Mills (1891); to an all-steel model, which the Spenglers machined and assembled for him in Rockford (1893); to yet another steel model, built by the Spenglers, that was shipped to the Boott Mills in Lowell, Massachusetts and demonstrated for Draper and Sons Company there (1895). It was never Colman's intention to abandon his D.I.M. experiments entirely when he put the 1895 machine into storage, only to engage in more immediately-profitable kinds of experimental work until the Moore patent expired, the existence of the patent having postponed negotiations with the Drapers indefinitely and made prospects for a sale or royalty arrangement with another machine-tool builder even more unlikely. The fact that Colman had some limited commercial success with the check pump and conducted experiments in fluid-power mechanics between 1896-99 should not obscure the fundamental importance of the D.I.M. to his creative development. It was, in many ways, his signature project, the proving ground for all his later textile work. The mechanism tested his conceptual skills and determination longer and more thoroughly than anything else he ever devised, and in a strange way, the obstacles that he encountered in taking the D.I.M. to market led him to explore the other areas of cotton manufacturing that eventually made his name as an inventor. Colman would revolutionize the world-wide production of cotton cloth in the early years of the 20th Century by solving the last great puzzle of warp replenishment, succeeding where countless other mill men had failed in designing a practical thread-uniting mechanism, and laying the groundwork in the process for the Barber and Colman Company's rapid commercial expansion before the First World War.

ii

Howard Colman habitually intermixed his experiments, moving back and forth between different projects as opportunities arose and fancy dictated, and a dormant interest might be suddenly revived or an existing one abandoned without explanation. His creativity obeyed an eccentric logic. After the failure of the D.I.M. and his subsequent entry into the field of fluid-power mechanics in the winter of 1896, Colman pursued both interests, as it were, in parallel, his check-pump activities crowding out his warp-drawing concerns, pushing them temporarily into the background, out of his thoughts, though never entirely out of his mind. There were scattered references to the D.I.M. in letters here and there, the notice of a new warp-drawing invention by a man named Millard Field, comments on the Drapers' success in selling its power loom, a request to Luther Miller to analyze an "infringement opinion" issued by the Drapers' lawyers, and remarks on plans to complete his personal library of American and British warp-drawing patents by ordering missing copies.

Resigned to waiting for the Moore patent to expire before selling his rights to the D.I.M., Colman nevertheless decided, in February, to construct another prototype, a fifth incarnation of the machine, to include the use of steel harnesses, an automatic stop, and a change in the reed's position from vertical to horizontal. The "revised construction" was seen primarily as a way of evading the claims of the Moore patent, though Colman felt that his new reed position worked better in any event from a mechanical point of view (letter to William Barber, 2/23/96). He decided to keep the 1895 model in the building adjoining the Spengler Brothers' shop, and asked George Spengler to oversee the reconstruction as time allowed, adapting or cannibalizing the majority of the parts for the new model from the existing machine. One assumes that, true to past experience, the 1895 model was disassembled to its steel frame and a new mechanism built on this platform.

Because of the Spengler Brothers' labor shortages and Colman's own fluid-power priorities, the reconstruction of the D.I.M. languished during the next two years. In March 1898, Colman complained to Barber that he had "all along endeavored to hasten [the] D.I.M. as much as possible," while doing his best to hold down expenses. And yet:

> I am afraid I don't know how to change my course to attain these desiderata in any greater degree. Spengler's best man left him New Years and, since then, the work has progressed very slowly. He hopes to have another good man soon, but that won't help much except as it may relieve him of other work and enable him to devote more time to ours. Of course the cam pump and now aquelevator … have delayed the D.I.M. (3/30/98).

Colman showed renewed interest in the D.I.M. during the spring and summer of 1898, reporting to Barber in August that the new model had been "completed to the experimenting point" and was "performing as well as could be expected" under the circumstances (8/1/98). He had been spending most of his time on routine tests of the device prior to proving it up in a mill. Barber's own "cramped" finances and a painful sense of the resources expended on the D.I.M.'s development so far - it had been seven years since his first meeting with Colman at Wayland Academy to study the invention - increased his desire for a resolution. "It does look to me," he wrote a few months later, "as if your time should principally be given to the D.I.M. until it is either a chicken or a rotten egg" (12/5/98).

Yet the new D.I.M., in Colman's mind, was close to being a success:

> Since my last writing have devoted myself almost entirely to D.I.M. and have been (and am) astonished at the old girl's good behavior. Had been having troubles innumerable before - as soon as one trouble was fixed, another more serious appeared. But during the past few days every touch has seemed to help matters - until today, I drew in a perfect warp - the first I ever did.

A "perfect warp" meant that every thread was exactly in place, not a single one broken, no threads missing from the eyes, and no doublers: an amazing performance in an industry where an average of five errors per warp was considered the commercial standard for *hand-drawn* fabric. Here the D.I.M. had manipulated 64 threads to an inch, 90 threads per minute in rapid succession, its tiny steel needle pulling fibers with nearly the fineness of human hairs through rows of quarter-inch vertical loops. Colman was understandably elated and noted the possible larger significance of the event: "By the way, it seems very likely today is the first time in the history of the world that a perfect warp has been drawn by machinery" (12/7/98). After his often-stalled D.I.M. investigations and the heartache of the Drapers' rejection, he felt much of his earlier enthusiasm returning.

In March there was more good news, though from an unexpected source. A letter arrived from Draper and Sons Company, noting the recent expiration of the Moore patent and inquiring into the possibility of re-opening discussions over the sale of the D.I.M. Colman did not know whether to be more pleased by the timing of the letter, after his recent success in running the machine, or by the fact that the Drapers themselves had initiated the contact. "Several years ago you called to our attention a drawing in machine," George Draper had started the letter.

> We made more or less exhaustive tests of this machine, and investigated as carefully as we could the state of the art. At that time we felt you had a perfected, or substantially perfected, machine, but we were advised by our counsel that there were other patents which controlled your machine, that is to say, which would be infringed by its use… Now I believe the patents above referred to have expired, and I write you calling the matter up. Are you still in a position where you desire to do anything with your machine? (3/28/99)

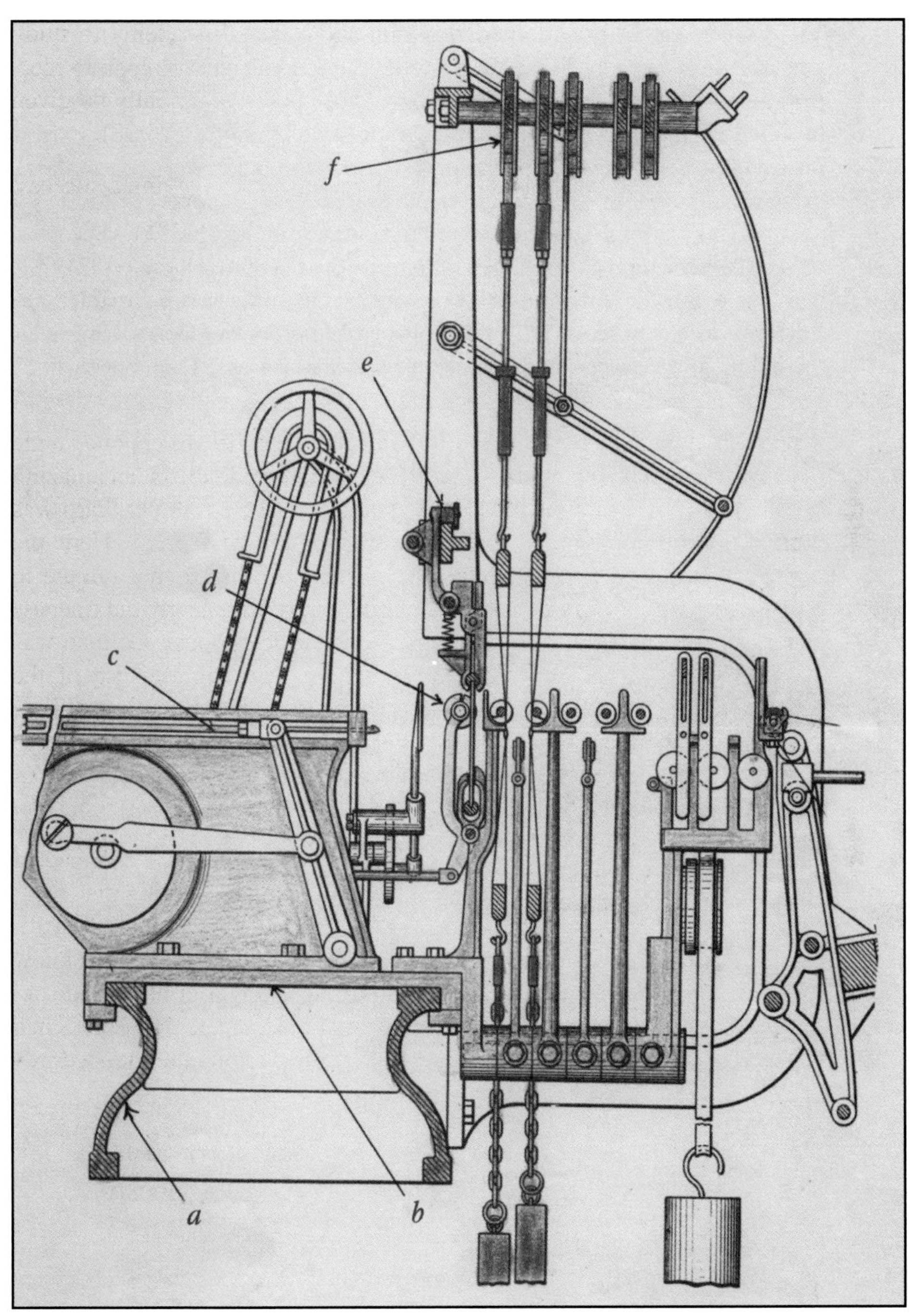

An end elevation of the D.I.M. shows the machine frame (a), carriage (b), needle (c), reed opener (d), reed support (e), and harness support (f).

Barber and Colman talked at length about the best way to respond, whether it made more sense to invite the Drapers to visit Rockford or to ship the D.I.M. to a cotton mill in Massachusetts for exhibition. The former had the advantage of practicality - most of the costs of a Rockford visit would be borne by the Drapers, whereas the latter seemed to offer a more promising long-term solution, since it involved a demonstration in a commercial facility, a necessary step in determining the D.I.M.'s final value. As welcome as the Drapers' inquiry had been, Colman realized, it was also somewhat premature. "I consider it desirable to run the machine, for some weeks at least, in a mill doing actual work before showing it to them," he told Barber, "and because I think that [in the] East there would be some possibility of at least making a bluff at interesting other capital before showing it to them." He suggested that they tell George Draper about a "new machine" that they intended to "take east shortly," while promising to make contact in due course to discuss "an arrangement profitable to both parties" (4/3/99).

Colman immediately began keeping a detailed record of the warps drawn in by the D.I.M., the operating speed, the specific pressure of the pick-up spring, the weather and temperature, the number of errors - things that he could point to in his negotiations with the Drapers and build upon in mill experiments. He also tried to make up for lost time by extending his workday and running extra tests. "Drawing-in machine is doing very well," he wrote Barber on April 17. "I expect soon to send you some copies from my record, which I think are quite satisfactory."

But Colman had not reckoned on the effect on his nerves of this kind of sustained, exacting manipulative work. While the D.I.M. continued to make "good progress" and would likely be ready for shipment to the East "in about three weeks," he had changed his mind "about the desirability of a long, continued run with the machine either here or in the mill." Recent experience made him doubt that he "could stand the nervous strain … and still be in good shape for exhibiting to possible purchasers" (5/3/99). By May 12 he was nearing his emotional limits:

> My health has been bad for the past few weeks. Indigestion, resulting in sleeplessness and consequent dullness when awake, has interfered quite materially with my work. Nevertheless, D.I.M. is in a fairly satisfactory condition, and I think we can hold our final conference to advantage any time you may choose ...

When the D.I.M. was shipped by rail to Massachusetts on June 8, the break in routine came as a welcome relief. Colman left Rockford soon after this to visit friends in Maine, and then traveled to Lowell to await the arrival of his machine.

For reasons that are never explained in the letters, Barber and Colman chose the Merrimack Mills (Merrimack Manufacturing Company), not the Boott Mills, as the site of their D.I.M. test. The machine, which did not arrive in Lowell until June 29, was up and running by July 6, with Colman reporting "fairly satisfactory results as to the quality of work done," but expressing frustration with the amount of work actually produced. The latter had been mainly due to a "greater variation" in the Mills' harnesses than he had anticipated, a condition caused by "rough handling ... in carrying them about." Bent strands and missing eyes had stopped the D.I.M. so often that Colman needed to spend most of his time simply trying to keep it running. An additional problem was the Mills' use of "drop-wires" and "double-knotted harnesses," which had become standard features on the new Draper-Northrup loom, but which the D.I.M. was not then equipped to process.

On July 14 Colman acknowledged that the D.I.M. was "getting down to business a little better," though he thought that it was now "going to be impossible to make any record such as we would expect to do in practice." Regrettably, the whole reason for taking the D.I.M. to Lowell in the first place was open to serious second-guessing: "Have had a little doubt as to whether it would not be profitable in the end to take the machine back to Rockford and revise somewhat in light of what I have learned before exhibiting to the Drapers." The main question was whether they should consider adapting the D.I.M. to handle the drop-wires at their own expense or ask the Drapers to pay for these changes.

Colman wrote Barber again five days later to suggest that they schedule a meeting in Chicago with Luther Miller to weigh their options going forward. Did it make sense to proceed with the D.I.M. exhibitions in Lowell and assume that the Drapers would be willing to "make allowances for the inchoateness of the thing?" Should they take the time to apply for a new patent or allow the existing D.I.M. application to pass to issue? Should they attempt to pursue foreign patents and, if so, in what countries? Colman thought that he could easily leave the D.I.M. behind in Massachusetts for a week or more after disassembling the "readily removable parts" and locking them in a trunk. He could also place an oilcloth over the rest of the machine, though he did not think that prying eyes would be able to make much sense out of the parts that were left.

To Barber, patents were an absolute priority:

> Am somewhat at a loss to understand the advantage of showing up the D.I.M. even to the Drapers before putting our claims in shape for all the protection we can have from the U.S. Patent Office. I fully supposed that we had done so and hardly understood your apparent hesitation to confer with Drapers at once when the mechanism should be ready to show up there ... Was it not a mistake to send [the] Mach[ine] east at this time? (7/16/99)

In reply, Colman said that he had gone east with the D.I.M. when he did because he assumed that the Drapers would want to submit their own patent application after purchasing the device. "No doubt it would have been better for you, I, and Miller to have thoroughly canvassed it [the patent situation] before I left," he wrote. "I did not suggest doing so because there did not seem to be anything that could be done to better it without expense, which I knew you were reluctant to incur." He foresaw a hard legal road ahead in any case, with the possibility of infringement claims, and wondered if it would not be "years before any one manufactures under the patent and whatever life it runs before that is lost" (7/19/99). The practical difficulties that had so long been dogging the D.I.M. were rearing their heads again.

It's unclear whether Colman actually disassembled the machine in Lowell or shipped it back to Illinois as a single unit, for the Chicago meeting with Barber and Miller did not take place until the fall - in early October, to judge from the correspondence - and by that time both the inventor and the D.I.M. were back in Rockford. His only other reference to the Lowell exhibition is a short note, in December, to Eben Draper, who apparently had inquired about the status of the project:

> Yours of the 12th inst. duly received. I regret to note that the prospect of any deal with you seems remote. If, however, you think it worthwhile, I shall be glad to call upon you when next I am east (12/15/99).

It's apparent that the Draper Company had declined to pay for retrofitting the machine with drop-wires, and that Barber and Colman had also demurred. On January 18, 1900, we know, Colman removed the D.I.M. from the Merrimack Mills and shipped it to Illinois, in spite of the fact that he had received orders for drawing-in machines from both the Merrimack and Pacific Mills a few weeks earlier. But Barber and Colman lacked the means to manufacture the devices, and the latest roadblock in the interminable D.I.M. project seems to have shaken Colman's confidence in the technology. We also know that he found a new experimental interest in the fall of 1899, something more appealing than the D.I.M., and turned his attention to this project. He often dealt with his frustrations as an inventor by finding things to explore outside the scope of his existing investigations. In one letter he was worrying about the D.I.M.'s prospects and requesting a special meeting in Chicago to consider the alternatives; and in another letter he was recapitulating this meeting in the context of an entirely different subject:

> I have been working on the knotter scheme which I mentioned to you and Miller in Chicago, and have found the preliminary difficulties very much less than I anticipated. I already have an apparatus which will tie the knot and cut off the ends satisfactorily ... The device is so far much simpler than I had any idea it could be made (10/17/99).

The knotter scheme had come to him out of the blue, he said, an idea that seemed so inevitable, so right for his purpose that it was impossible to fathom. Before the excitement of his discovery had worn off, he'd begun refining the apparatus, reducing its size, making it more precise. "Have experimented only a little with the knotter," he wrote Barber on Thanksgiving, "but have made some changes which I think improve it. Have at last got the small gear cutter and expect to go to work next week on [a] smaller machine." There seemed to be little to deter him. On January 10 he was practicing with his device on an "extempore spooler" and attaining what he considered a remarkable speed. On January 25 he was studying a report from Luther Miller that showed little in the way of attaining a good patent on the design. A knotter prototype was finished in the spring, and Colman pronounced himself well-satisfied with the results: "Everything has turned out rather astonishingly according to [the] program so far ..." (4/5/00).

iii

To appreciate Colman's invention, it's important to understand the state of the art in cotton manufacturing at the turn of the century, particularly the problems existing in the earliest stage of the weaving process, where yarn was wound from bobbins onto spools prior to being fed into the looms. The mills' mechanical spoolers were attended by operators whose job it was to keep the machines running as fast as possible, with a minimum of interruption. Each woman was required to maintain 30-50 rapidly-turning spindles, to replace the bobbins when they ran out of thread and the spools when they filled up with thread, and to tie the old and new thread-ends together to form continuous strands of fiber. Knots had to be small and tied as tightly as possible to prevent the threads from pulling out. Loose ends had to be cut close to the knot.

The attendant, in essence, fed the machine, removing empty bobbins and placing new ones in the holders. She would stop a spool opposite her from spinning, pick up a loose thread from this spool and tie it to the end from a new bobbin, place the tied thread in a metal guide, and take her hand off the spool so that it started spinning again. In the course of a ten-hour day, an attendant tied an average of 1,500-1,700 knots.

Knot-tying was frustrating, nerve-wracking, and often unsuccessful because of the fineness of the threads and the inability of fumble-fingered operators to form knots with precision. Too much handling weakened the fiber, resulting in blemishes in the finished cloth. Large knots and long ends also ensnared adjacent threads and got caught in the drop-wires when they passed through the loom, activating automatic stop-detectors and shutting down the machine. The result was second-quality cloth ("seconds") or a loss of production time, or both.

Not surprisingly, mill owners regarded spooling as their single biggest headache. No less an authority than George Draper estimated that 75% of the warp breakages in the loom were due to bad knots at the spooler stage. The Drapers had attempted to develop and patent their own mechanical knotter and sold some two dozen other models on a royalty basis during the previous decade in an effort to solve this problem; but mills generally found the devices to be too large and unwieldy to maneuver in close quarters and of little real value in increasing the pace of production. Some mills simply went back to hand-tying, while others attempted to do their best with a makeshift assortment of commercial knotters and cutting tools.

We have no way of knowing whether the "winders" or spooling attendants at the Merrimack Mills used mechanical knotters when Colman spent time there in 1899, but if they did, their devices probably included a McVeigh knotter, which was then considered to be the best available model from the standpoint of efficiency. The McVeigh knotter resembled an over-sized pliers or pruning shears and was attached to the spooler frame along a sliding iron bar, which saved attendants the trouble of picking it up and putting it down between their other tasks. The sliding bar allowed a worker to move the device into position opposite the spools, but the weight of the device required two hands to slide it, and the number of spools that each person managed inevitably meant wasted time in setting up the tool. When it was properly positioned, the attendant placed the threads in the slots of an upright bar and engaged a knotting mechanism and pivot knife by pushing a sliding shelf. The resulting knots varied according to the amount of pressure. If an attendant pushed too hard, she risked breaking the knot, and if she pushed too lightly, she left an oversized knot.

It's instructive to compare the McVeigh knotter with Colman's creation, which was much lighter and smaller, and attached to the back of the attendant's left hand by a leather strap, leaving the thumb and fingers free for work. The Barber knotter, as it came to be called, employed a spring-activated, rotating tying-bill similar to that of a traditional grainbinder. It tied tight tiny knots and left ends that were less than 3/16th of an inch, something that was very hard to do without a mechanical device.

The Barber knotter worked this way. A spooler attendant selected threads from the new bobbin and spool, and laid them on a side arm of the device. The threads were thus aligned to pass over the top of the tying bill, which rotated when the thumb-lever was depressed. The rotation picked up the threads, wound them around the bill (forming a loop), sheared off the ends, and drew the severed ends back through the loop, forming a knot: all in a continuous motion. The initial slack in the threads, which was used for the loop, played out in the bill's rotation. The bill had a clamping jaw on one side and a cutting jaw on the other; and the rotation activated each of these in turn; a final half-revolution pulled the threads in the knot tight as it slipped off the end of the bill. When the attendant released the thumb-lever, a spring was activated, and the side arm popped back into its original position. The entire operation was instantaneous, no more than a snap of the thumb, and nearly impossible for an observer to follow.

iv

As revolutionary as the Barber knotter seemed to be in 1900, it was still untested, and Colman's strategy was to make a number of prototypes and give them to the Merrimack Mills to use. The initial reception to the device by spooler attendants there was lukewarm, with the main difficulty being the women's reluctance to change their ways of working. Colman was more hopeful on July 5 after a short visit to Lowell, informing Barber that the attendants, while "at first opposed to the use of the knotter," tended "to like it first rate after a while." Upon his return to Rockford, however, he learned that the attendants had "objected" to the device and done "all in their power to avoid using it, short of open rebellion." Colman hired his own worker in the Beaver Dam Mills to get around this problem, but the person was pressured into quitting by the other women, who feared

The Barber knotter was attached to the back of the operator's left hand by a leather strap (top). The operator used her right hand to drawn yarn over the top of the device (bottom).

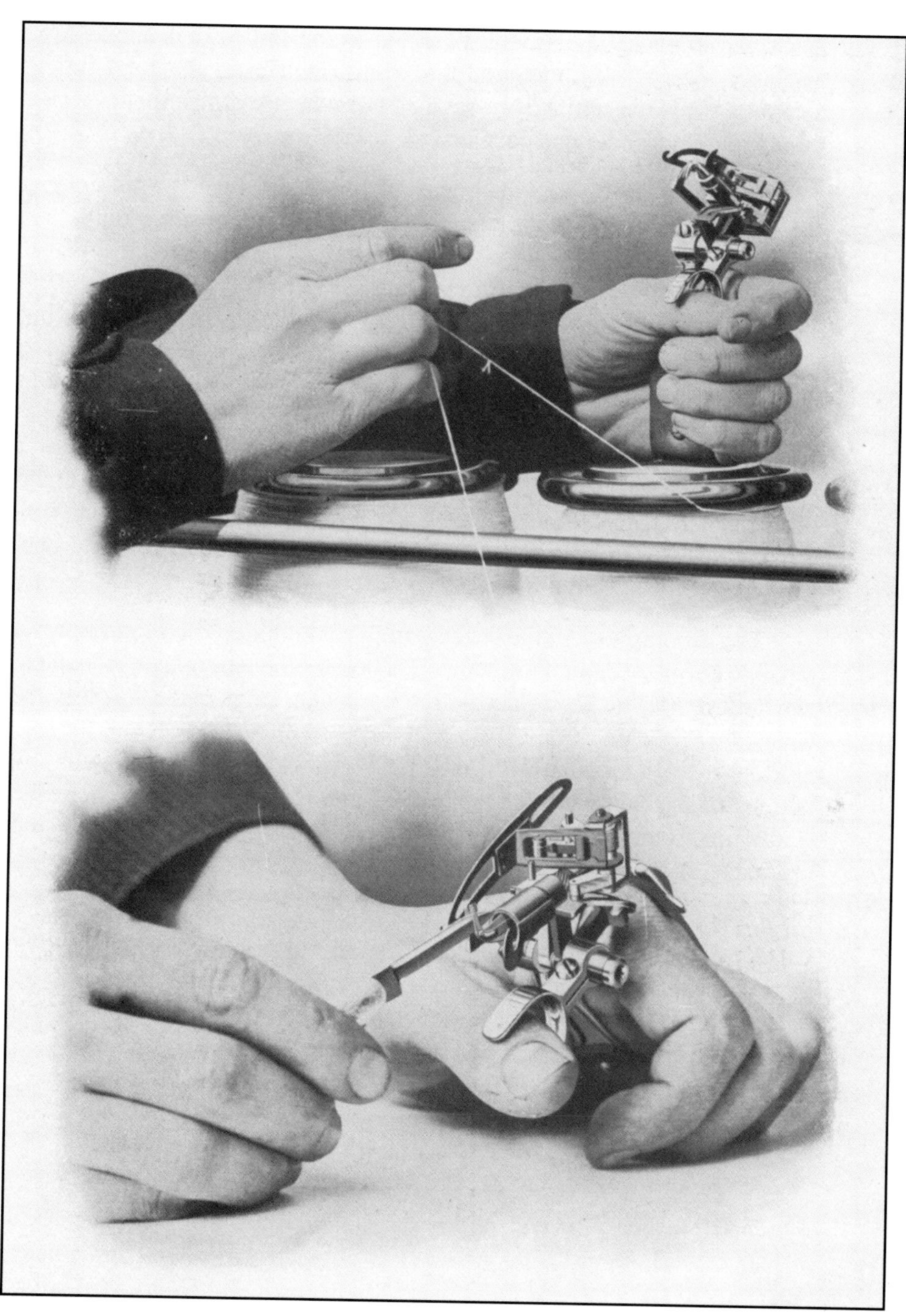

By depressing the thumb-lever, the operator tied a knot and trimmed the ends of the yarn in a single motion (top). The working parts of the Barber knotter were designed to be easily replaced. Here an operator is shown removing a bill spring from the mechanism (bottom).

that some of their jobs would disappear if the mill owner adopted the machine (7/13/00). Colman told Barber that their main challenge was to determine what the actual labor-savings from the use of the knotter would be and to demonstrate this conclusively to mill owners.

Prospects for the knotter improved seven days later, with Colman reporting to Barber that four attendants in Lowell had begun using it voluntarily as the result of a piece-rated incentive plan introduced by company management. In a huge factory like the Merrimack Mills, with 3,700 looms and more than 156,000 spindles, this was a drop in the bucket; but the good news was that the attendants appeared to growing accustomed to it and increasing their production in relation to other workers. Colman felt confident that the knotter would prove itself in the end if given a fair test. To seize the moment, he hired a friend from Milwaukee named Robert Webster to go east and begin drumming up business. Colman warned Barber that he might be called on to make a substantial investment in knotter tooling in the following months if Webster succeeded in getting orders from the New England mills.

The pending sale of the check pump patent during the summer was a possible source of capital for increased knotter production, though Colman was unsure of whether to accept the lump-sum offer of $5,000 that the Creamery Packaging Company was then proposing or to hold out for royalties over a longer period of time. "All this, you see, is in line with my notion that the palmy days of the check pump business are over," he wrote Barber on August 18, "and it behooves B & C to find something more profitable, if possible… "

> The reports from Lowell have continued favorable, and nothing has occurred to lessen my confidence in it [i.e. the "knotter scheme"] since I saw you, but of course we know there are many uncertainties about it. If I knew that it would succeed and that $5,000 would be sufficient … until it begins to pay, I think I should prefer to take that sum from Sherwin [agent of the Creamery Packaging Company] rather than draw on you for it, even tho' I knew it to be possible to obtain thrice that in driblets on a royalty basis. But on the other hand, if the knotter fails, I will wish I had the driblets. To make any great sacrifice of our check pump interests merely to float [the] knotter is perhaps placing rather more confidence in the success of the latter than the situation justifies.

This was another of Colman's "hair-splitting" analyses: out of fairness, he always did his best to make a case for the point of view opposed to his own interests. But only in the most pessimistic sense could the situation be termed unpromising. Colman himself calculated that there was a potential market for as many as 13,000 knotters in the U.S., based on an average of one device for every 2,000 spindles in the existing factories. If Barber and Colman only sold 9,000 machines in the future at $40 each, they would reap a huge reward. And this said nothing of the market outside the U.S., in Canada, Britain, Europe, Russia, and parts of Asia, where the combined textile industry dwarfed its American counterpart.

The Spenglers began manufacturing Barber knotters under a special contract in August, while Colman devoted much of his time to designing and fabricating the tools necessary for expanded production. The device itself continued to make slow but steady headway in the spooling departments of the Merrimack and Beaver Dam Mills, where a total of 29 devices were in daily use by late September. The simultaneous sale of the check pump and other dairy-market assets to the Creamery Packaging Company for $10,000 provided Barber and Colman with ample resources to start their new business.

In October the company recorded its "first official knotter sale" and submitted a formal application for the device to the U.S. Patent Office; thereafter every machine manufactured in Rockford would bear the words "patent pending." Luther Miller looked into the possibility of foreign applications in Canada, England, Russia, Germany, France, Belgium, and Austria-Hungary. With an average cost of only $100 per patent and an ample Barber and Colman financial reserve, it was hard to justify not going ahead. Colman predicted that new tooling would enable the company to make knotters at a cost of only $4/device, so the asking price was reduced to $25 in an effort to jump-start sales. By early November knotter orders were coming in at an average of 6-8 per day. "Webster continues to send favorable reports," Colman wrote Barber, "and if we can only maintain a monopoly by our patent, there seems to be little doubt of success" (11/12/00).

The Spenglers installed Colman's new tooling in November and saw their output increase to 10 knotters per day, but orders soon surpassed this. In a typical transaction, Colman sent 31 machines to Webster and received 25 orders by return mail. On December 5 Miller wired from Washington with the news that the patent examiner had made a favorable preliminary ruling on the knotter's "hand-held feature," significantly increasing the chances of the application passing to issue in the near future. Colman's biggest existing concern was the machine's ability to withstand the "hard knocks" of practical use. He worried, in particular, about the durability of the little spring that activated the side arm:

> The longest test of actual use [in the Merrimack Mills] has been under conditions more favorable to the machine than average practical conditions will be … I believe we have met every difficulty as it has arisen, and have no special reason to fear that we cannot meet any which will arise …; my doubts are only what may come from the ... limbs of the unexpected.

The limbs of the unexpected, in this case, were stretching in promising directions. Colman thought that a turning point in the project might have occurred when people began putting down "their hard cash;" this was the only test that really mattered in the end. He placed an emergency order for 500 knotters with Spengler on December 14, hoping to increase the supply of available stock. Two weeks later, when a mill agent from Massachusetts asked to buy 12 machines, Colman received a ringing endorsement of the knotter's capabilities: "Said the knotter is the most ingenious device he ever saw, and that it was a necessity for every mill to use it."

Over the course of the next two years, the Barber knotter swept the world of American cotton manufacturing. By most accounts the device allowed spooler attendants to reduce the time that it took to produce a standard section beam by 30-60 minutes and to eliminate 95% of the errors in the weave room. Overall, the increase in cotton production was estimated to be 10-12%. The Draper Company considered the invention to be a "revolution in the art" and decided to take its own knotting products off the market. "We have attempted to introduce various knot-tying devices …," its catalogue explained:

> but have withdrawn from the field, as an outside firm is introducing a more satisfactory device. We are so glad to recognize any improvement that assists the operation of weaving that we view our own immediate defeat undisturbed.

George Draper would later say that the Barber knotter "went into use more rapidly than any other improvement in cotton machinery of which I have recollection. Its reception was surprisingly unanimous."

If the road ahead for business looked more promising than ever in 1901, Colman worried anew about his ability to keep up with knotter orders. Two things were becoming clear to him. He needed to find more production space, and he needed to find professional help. In an effort to address the first problem, he discussed with the Spenglers the possibility of constructing his own factory and of moving their men, machines, and knotter tooling into this space when the building was completed. As a means of solving the second, he contacted a family friend from Milwaukee, Harry Severson, who was then a senior in civil engineering at the University of Wisconsin in Madison. Colman hoped to recruit a mechanical engineer from the university to oversee the knotter production, and he asked Severson to introduce him to the dean of the engineering college.

As Henry Colman recalled the event, Severson took Howard to the dean's office and left him there to present his case (Diary).

> Howard told him his errand, and the dean replied at once, "Take Severson."
>
> "But he is a civil engineer."
>
> The dean repeated, "Take Severson!"
>
> When Harry met the dean, he asked: "Did Mr. Colman find a man?"
>
> "Yes."
>
> "Who is going?"
>
> "You."
>
> "But he wants a mechanical engineer, and I am civil."
>
> "If I am a judge of men, he [Colman] is the man you want to be with."

Colman wrote Barber on March 25 that he had just offered a job to a "young man named Severson" whom he "had known for years and ... was highly recommended by the dean of engineering" (commemorative booklet "Honoring Harry A. Severson"). On April 2 Severson accepted the offer, and after graduation, moved to Rockford to begin his duties on the knotter production line. He impressed Colman almost immediately with his work ethic, patience, and sense of humor. "Harry is a long way ahead of the shop, and I am quite a way ahead of him," Colman told Barber. "I have been telling him so many things to do 'someday when he hasn't anything else to do' that he thinks he will die of overload if that day ever comes" (7/23/01).

V

Little has been written in this book so far about Howard Colman's private life because there has been remarkably little to say. His letters contain few personal references besides the discussions of his experimental work and occasional commentaries on his health. We know that he lived by himself in his twenties, in various rooming houses in Rockford and elsewhere - we can trace the address changes in city directories - and spent

The first permanent building of the Barber and Colman partnership was constructed in 1902 at the corner of River and Loomis Streets in Rockford. Later known as "Section No. 1" in the enlarged factory complex, its first two floors were devoted to manufacturing, while a third floor was reserved for offices, drafting, and experimental work.

most of his conscious hours absorbed in his investigations. He walked, bicycled, or rode the trolley between his rooms and the Spengler Brothers' shop in the Water Power District in Rockford; he traveled by train to Milwaukee, Beaver Dam, Elgin, Chicago, and places as far away as Saco, Maine, and Lowell, Massachusetts, and occasionally lived for extended periods of time in hotels in the most distant locations. His best friends seem also to have been his closest working associates: William Barber, above all; Luther Miller, his lawyer, who divided his time between Rockford and Chicago; George Spengler; and L.T. Mann, his Chicago draftsman. There may have been other persons of importance, but they are not mentioned in his letters. On a regular basis, we know, he visited and corresponded with his parents and sisters in Wisconsin, but the letters have disappeared, and we can only guess now at the nature and timing of these contacts. So strong was his interest in invention that he devoted the majority of his waking hours to experiments, a habit that continued throughout his adult life. He did not make an effort, apparently, to attend the wedding of his friend and Wayland classmate, Fred Barber, or to convey his regards afterwards. "Hope the wedding passed off pleasantly," he wrote William Barber (9/2/99). "Sorry that I forgot to send congratulations." "I have no engagement for Thanksgiving and no desire to take it for a holiday," he wrote Barber two months later (11/25/99), without the slightest hint of rancor or regret, preferring, we assume, to spend the day on his investigations. He judged most things in life by their value to his scientific work and thus had difficulty putting himself into other people's shoes:

> Webster is to be married [on] the 27th ... Am sorry that this is so, but he has given me some explanation so that I do not feel quite so much disappointed in his good news (9/10/00).

But Colman was not nearly as much of a curmudgeon as he sometimes portrayed himself. At the time of his early knotter experiments (1899-1900), we know, he attended a number of dancing parties and progressive dinners in Rockford, whose broader social purpose seems to have been to serve as meeting places for members of the city's moneyed families. Our knowledge of this phase of Colman's life rests almost entirely on the accounts of his two daughters. Ruth maintained that her father "always liked to dance, to waltz and fox-trot," and that he became "part of a special social group ... at the turn of the century - possibly as a result of his friendship with Luther Miller, who had grown up in Rockford." Dorothy described "an old Edison" blaring out the Skater's Waltz and Blue Danube, and "Father and his crowd waltzing, waltzing,

Luther Miller as he appeared in his thirties (c. 1902).

and waltzing." But these were reconstructed impressions, after the fact, from bits and pieces of others' conversations; and both daughters admitted that their father never referred directly to the dancing parties when they were growing up and was characteristically tight-lipped about his social activities as a young man.

According to Colman family lore, Howard had at least two romantic relationships, or interests, before 1899. One was with Pearl Peterson, whom he briefly pursued in Beloit after his return from Northwestern University in 1891, accompanying her to Baptist church functions until her mother intervened to break up the relationship. A second was with an unnamed Rockford woman whom Colman "greatly admired," according to his daughter Ruth, although this person "eventually married someone else" and was later "killed by a runaway horse." Such are the meager details of the inventor's early social life.

In late 1899 or early 1900, it's assumed, Colman made the acquaintance at a party in Rockford of an attractive blue-eyed, brown-haired young woman named Bertha Maguire, who was a member of one of the city's most socially-prominent families. Her parents were George H. Maguire, the president of both the Woodruff and Maguire Lumber Company and the Hess and Hopkins leather goods business in Rockford, and Adella Woodruff Maguire; and the family residence at 623 North Main Street was one of the locations of the dancing parties that Colman attended with his group of friends. He was very much taken with her, in any event, and the relationship grew closer over the course of the following 12-18 months. We still have 41 of the letters that he wrote her between October 1900 - September 1903, as well as a short diary that she kept in the summer and fall of 1892; and these help us to fill in some of the gaps in our knowledge of Colman's activities during the early years of the 20th Century and give us a sense of the guarded and highly-mannered persona that he sometimes adopted in his courtship of the woman that he would eventually marry.

The letters to Bertha Maguire do not contain much of interest in terms of Colman's inventions, and are full of fairly standard accounts of the weather and scenery on his trips, readings and meals, passengers on the train, hotel accommodations, and projected itineraries. He likes to estimate the time that it will take to write and post his letters in his opening remarks and then to apologize, at the end, for the hastiness of the message, the "disjointed jumble," "mistakes," and "awful handwriting." "This is horribly written," he tells Bertha in May 1901, "and worse expressed. Please be indulgent." There's also a good deal in the letters about his health, more perhaps than Bertha would have wished to know, reminding us of the headaches, indigestion, and nervous tension that plagued him throughout his life, and suggesting that he may well have felt freer to discuss these things with her than he did with William Barber. If they seem slightly out of place in love letters, they are yet indicative of Colman's growing confidence in her and the intimacy of their relationship:

> I went to a doctor Saturday and told him I needed to be braced up as soon as possible, and told him my symptoms. Guess he was on his job for he seemed to think he could relieve me of the headache I had been having, but he said I must spend as much time as possible on my back, and ever since I have been the laziest man you ever saw but not in any pain. Whether the laziness is the result of his advice and my natural indolence or whether it is partly due to his medicine, I don't know; but anyway, I was never so diligent in taking medicine before in my life (11/1/00).
>
> *   *   *
>
> The Dr. and his assistant put me through a regular examination such as I have never had before, made me strip, … and kneaded me all over, listened to my heart and lungs with a stethoscope, looked into my eyes … etc., etc., besides no end of questions. Finally, when I was again clothed and in my right mind, the Dr. told me that I was absolutely sound and that my whole trouble is nervous, due to overwork and worry. He doesn't think it all serious and went on to tell me how to avoid it and gave me some stuff to take temporarily - during my present trip anyway. I understand it is merely to quiet my nerves (5/13/01).

These are serious letters for the most part, with none of the punning and tongue-in-cheek jesting, say, of his later correspondence with his daughter Dorothy (cf. "In Colman's Own Words," pp. 329-32). Reading them now, more than a century after the fact, we find the humor they evoke is largely unwitting:

> If you could know how much and how often I think of you in the midst of this swirl of things, I'm sure you couldn't doubt that I love you. They are very pleasant thoughts and don't hinder my attention to business a bit (5/15/01).

Colman's letter of June 11, 1901 is a model of Edwardian politeness, notable for its elaborate contingency planning and applications of logic to the affairs of the heart. His reason for writing was to invite Bertha to meet him in Chicago for lunch, either on Friday or Saturday of the following week, and to ensure that his invitation did not create a sense of obligation. It may also have been his way of testing her, of determining whether she thought a trip to Chicago was really worth the time and expense:

> Now, first of all, please don't let me interfere with your plans or inconvenience you in the slightest degree, will you? But if it is convenient and if you would really enjoy it enough to pay for the effort, I would like very much to have you come into lunch with me and spend as much of the afternoon as you can.

He felt that Friday might recommend itself to her because she was likely to be in Chicago anyway, shopping for a wedding gift. And she probably already had plans for Saturday afternoon. It made no difference to him. If she chose Friday, he would plan to go into Chicago that morning, spend part of Saturday in Milwaukee, and return to Rockford on Monday. If she chose Saturday, he would leave Rockford on Friday evening, and go to Milwaukee on Monday morning, returning to Rockford at night. "So you see it is a 'stand-off' for me." He had no preference himself. At the same time, he wondered if Friday would not be better in the end, given the reasons already mentioned, and "because if we get at that little lake trip, the boat will be less crowded Friday." He assured her, again, that he had no personal preference. If Bertha wanted to take in a matinee instead of a boat trip, she ought to make it Saturday.

Colman's habit as a scientist was to visualize the outcomes of his experiments and to prepare himself for any contingency. It's unreasonable to think that he would have acted otherwise in his personal life:

> If you are not far from a telephone station, why not call me up to-morrow morning? It will take less of you[r] time than to write, and it will be worth the price to me to know that much sooner what to plan on. But if that isn't convenient, just drop me a line telling me what you think about it. If you think you can do it and then, at the last moment, you find something else that you want to do, that will be all right too, for I will take that possibility into my calculation.

Colman told Bertha that he already talked to her mother to see if she knew "of any plans of yours which would prevent your doing as I have suggested," but had drawn a blank. So a decision had to be made. If it turned out to be a "perplexity" to her, he said, she should drop the entire matter. But if she decided to go ahead, he hoped that she would not forget "to name the time and place where we will meet."

Bertha wrote to accept his invitation several days later, choosing Saturday afternoon, and asking permission to bring along a friend, Bess Emerson. Colman had not anticipated this, but he graciously extended an invitation to Emerson to join them for lunch and pledged to wait at "the place you mention" from 1:00 - 1:30:

> If you simply don't appear, that will be all right too, for I will know that you have good reason for it, and I will not count on your being there so confidently as to be badly disappointed if you are not. I would a great deal rather you would not come than to force things in order to do it. If I don't see you, it will be just as I expected before you left anyway. If I do, I'll be that much ahead. Please do just what is best for you and your friends.

And then (of course): "This is a deuce of a hasty scrawl, but it covers a lot of loves and good wishes" (6/19/01).

In the summer of 1901 Colman was busy filling knotter orders and working with his field agent in Boston, Robert Webster, to expand the company's sales efforts in the East. After his knotter patent passed to issue in April, he hired a second agent, R.H. McCullagh, and sent him to England to lay the groundwork for a sales effort there; and he seems to have felt that there was less of importance for him to do in Rockford now than in the places where potential customers were located. He was regularly on the road, in Chicago, Boston, New York, and Buffalo, and these trips required him to conduct a long-distance courtship, a situation that was complicated somewhat by Bertha Maguire's habit of spending her summers in Three Lakes (now Woodruff), Wisconsin. Colman's challenge, on returning to Rockford in August, was to persuade her to come home but to do this in a way that was free from special pleading:

> I hardly know what to say about the need of your returning. Certainly there is nothing to call for me to telegraph you, but I think you would wish me to write you not to delay unnecessarily. Your mother says "you can stay as long as you want to," but she would be mighty glad if you were home, I am sure. I don't think she is any more disappointed than you knew she would be, so perhaps I ought not to have said as much as this. There is nothing that need worry you or cut short your pleasure, but if you want an excuse to come home, I think you can quite truthfully say that you know your mother wants you. There is someone else who won't be sorry to see you, but I have tried to give you the facts without prejudice from my own desires (8/17/01).

By the fall Colman was on his way to Europe to consult with McCullagh and to investigate the overseas "knotter situation" for himself. He sailed from New York on the U.S.M.S. St. Paul in mid-October, carrying a special present in his luggage from Bertha: a steamer letter with separate envelopes that were to be opened each day of the trip (they were labeled "Tuesday," "Wednesday," etc.). He apparently read and re-read the messages throughout his cruise, savoring the expressions of affection and occasionally detecting larger meanings in some of the more casual remarks. "Do you know, Bertha dear," he wrote,

> I hardly can believe what you seem to say, that you hope that you will sometime take an ocean cruise with me. Perhaps I am assuming too much to read it that way, but I do so wish and hope for it! You say plainly enough that you would like to be here now, and it is a pleasure to me to think that we wish alike about that (English postmark of 10/26/01).

Colman's European letters provide an interesting turn-of-the-century travelogue. He writes about starting each day on the St. Paul with a cold salt-water plunge in the swimming pool and promenading for "miles and miles" with the other passengers before retiring to a steamer chair on deck, where he's wrapped in blankets against the cold Atlantic spray. He reads a manual on gas engines to pass the time, while hiding the title from the other passengers so as not to " 'flash' a technical book." (He eventually selects *Old Virginia and Her Neighbors* as a more socially-acceptable option.) Whales and porpoises follow the ship, and when a dense fog appears off the banks of Newfoundland, the engines are stopped to avoid colliding with another vessel. Colman seems to worry about seasickness constantly, but he also complains about the lack of time between the meals and teas to work up a regular appetite. He enjoys the companionship at his dining table of a patent lawyer from Albany named Cameron and two college boys named Eli and Brewer, who ply him with "fruit, confectionary, and cigars" (he accepts the tobacco out of politeness and then presumably manages to lose it overboard). He also confesses to having to do "a little dodging" now and then to maintain his privacy. He sees a "fly" young woman on deck smoking a cigarette, and though she later sings a beautiful solo in a shipboard concert, he finds her voice the "only thing about her that is not repulsive." Why? "The only explanation of her seems to be that she is an actress."

Once ashore in England, Colman goes immediately to Manchester to meet with McCullagh and discuss business opportunities for the knotter. He visits the cotton mills where the device is being tested but finds that the "conditions" there are "different from those existing in the U.S." and is unsure of "what the outcome" of the trials "will be." Next he travels to Paris to explore obtaining a French patent, staying overnight in

London on the way and experiencing one of the city's infamous "pea-souper" fogs:

> . . . A London fog of the real genuine kind settled down so thick that [my] "cabby" had to get down and walk by the horse's head. He wanted to march me out and let me find my way home, but I ran a big bluff on him and made him think I was somebody, and he concluded that the fog wasn't as bad as it might be. I never saw a fog like that before. The street was brightly lighted and full of vehicles, and I could hear drivers shouting on every side, but I couldn't see them at all (10/27/01).

As a non-speaker of French, he feels "deaf and dumb" in Paris and envious for the first time in his life of people who can read a simple advertisement ("I never knew what it was to want to before.") Returning to England he meets his "Waterloo" on the Channel, becoming "horribly sick" as a result of the rough seas, even though it seems to him that the conditions are no worse than those on the St. Paul. In London he buys a macintosh to keep dry in the rainy weather and spends much of the time with McCullagh "driving around town and getting a general idea of things and in talking business." He, McCullagh, and Cameron, his friend from the St. Paul, also manage to take in some of the city's sights, including the Tower of London. "Most every old fellow that amounted to anything got his head chopped off there," he tells Bertha, "and, besides, that is where you see the crown jewels."

In Manchester again, preparing to sail for the U.S., he's alarmed by reports of an outbreak of Bubonic Plague in Liverpool and considers leaving from the port of Southampton instead. He's unsure of the knotter's "prospects" in England and doubts the value of his visit, but decides to wait for McCullagh to open a Barber and Colman office and avoid rushing to conclusions. His concerns are becoming more personal and physical at this stage of his trip, since his stomach "fights back" every time that he eats:

> Eating is such a nuisance when you have to do it at hotels and restaurants . . . What you get here, even at the best places, is frightful, and they hardly know what you mean by ice water. They charged me a shilling (25 cents) for some at the [Hotel] Cecil. If you get up before 9 in the morning, you can't get any breakfast (no date but received 11/12/01).

Fortunately, his return passage to the U.S. is enjoyable, no less for the "pleasure of coming across the Atlantic the fastest that anybody has ever come." He claims that his vessel has set a "world's record" for speed; and when he arrives in Rockford at the end of November, he's ready to stay put for a while and press his case with Bertha Maguire.

By all accounts, Bertha was a reluctant quarry, and even though we lack a single letter of hers today, we can sometimes read her words "between the lines" of Colman's messages. In January, after his return from Europe, she apparently consented to marry him but hesitated to set an actual wedding date. In response he pushed hard for a wedding during the summer of 1902, holding out the promise of an Alaskan honeymoon to entice her. The "Alaska trip" thus became a kind of code for the proposed summer wedding in his letters, where indirection was still a preferred mode of expression:

> I have thought a lot about what you said over the 'phone yesterday morning, and I do hope you will see your way to taking that Alaska trip this summer. I could give you lots of practical reasons why it would be better this year, but they all seem so paltry, and the real reason I want it this year is just because I love you and don't want to wait longer than is necessary. Guess I am mighty selfish about it, and I ought not to urge you so much (1/24/02).

Bertha eventually agreed, if not in January, then soon afterwards, to a wedding date of June 15; and the event proved to be one of the highlights of the Rockford social calendar. All three Rockford newspapers, the *Rockford Republic*, *Morning Star*, and *Daily Register*, featured the wedding in long articles, a tribute both to the prominence of the Maguire family and Colman's growing reputation as a businessman. Already a new three-story Barber and Colman brick building, with an attached one-story power-house, was rising at the corner of River and Loomis Streets in Rockford, a few blocks south of the Spengler Brothers' shop, and plans were underway to transfer all the knotter production machines to this facility as soon as it was finished. With knotter sales continuing to increase, there was widespread talk in Rockford of Colman's important new invention.

The wedding ceremony occurred on the south lawn of the Maguire residence at dusk, under a large elm tree, with arc lights, American flags, and a floral carpet of yarrow and red roses identifying the place where the vows were to be exchanged. At the center of the carpet, the monogram "MC" was spelled out in pink and white carnations. Promptly at 8:00 pm, to the strains of the wedding march played by a full-piece orchestra, the bridal party emerged from the front entrance of the house, led by Harry Severson and Beach Maguire, the ushers. They were followed by Colman and his best man, Luther Miller; the matron of honor; two flower children, who were twins, carrying baskets of pink sweet peas; the maid of honor in an elaborate gown of white crepe de chine over taffeta; and finally the veiled bride herself in an elegant white Argentine satin gown trimmed with duchesse and rose point lace. She carried a traditional shower bouquet of lilies of the valley.

The party walked along the porch to the south steps, where the bride's father, George Maguire, was waiting to escort her. Ahead of them the ushers unrolled white ribbons. A brief ring ceremony was then conducted by the Rev. Peter Snyder of the Second Congregational Church, with the assistance of Henry Colman. After accepting the congratulations of the wedding party, Howard and Bertha adjourned to the house to await the arrival of guests. Members of both families stood in a receiving line by the front door. The library and adjacent sitting room, where wedding gifts were on display, had been decorated with nasturtiums and yellow daisies. The dining room had a table centerpiece of red roses. Refreshments were served on the lawn throughout the evening, as the orchestra played in a tent pavilion and guests strolled about the house and grounds. "None of the numerous weddings of the season had attracted more interest than this," the *Daily Register* observed the next day.

> Prominent in the social life of the city, each having a wide circle of acquaintances and friends in enviable number, the union of the young couple was a notable event. The bride is a member of one of the sterling families of the city, one of which the city is proud, and herself a young lady of fine personality, a favorite in every circle in which she moves. Mr. Colman's strength of character and genial ways have made him generally admired, and he is an important factor in the business life of Rockford, and widely known through his numerous successful inventions. The union of these excellent young people is to their friends an especially happy one.

Bertha Maguire Colman.

9

Tying Machines

The machine must be seen to be thoroughly understood. It is almost intelligent. For instance, should there be an empty heald in the old warp, which if passed over would cause a conspicuous defect in the cloth, the fact is noted, and after four repeated attempts to proceed with a single thread, and without the pair of threads, the machine will stop. The simplicity of this beautiful arrangement is delightful.

- Manchester Guardian (U.K.) on the "try-again mechanism" in Colman's warp-tying machine, September 9, 1906

i

With the commercialization of the Barber knotter, Howard Colman hit his stride as an inventor, earning the respect of cotton manufacturers and machine tool builders nationwide and assuring himself of a steady stream of working capital with which to build his business. For more than a decade he would enjoy a virtual monopoly of the North American hand-knotter market without a single serious competitor. So strong was his intellectual property position, in fact, that few companies attempted to introduce alternative products while his patents were in force. (One that did, the Byrd Manufacturing Company of Durham, North Carolina, found itself almost immediately embroiled in infringement litigation initiated by Luther Miller.) Colman obtained four separate patents on knot-tying devices, and between them, they controlled the use of a wide range of mechanical "instrumentalities" related to warp replenishment, including a rotating tying bill, cam barrel, clamping and stripping arms, and sector gears. His technical achievements were recognized in the *International Library of Technology, Cyclopedia of Textile Work, Yearbook and Calendar of Textiles (Leipzig),* and *Transactions of the New England Cotton Manufacturers Association. Scientific American* featured the device in an illustrated article, and the *Century Dictionary* included a drawing of it in the definition of the term "knotter."

knot-root (not′röt), *n.* Same as ★*knob-root.*
knotter, *n.* 2. In *textile-manuf.*, a hand-device for mechanically tying together two ends of yarn or thread. —3. The mechanism in a harvester and binder which ties the knots in the binding-cord.

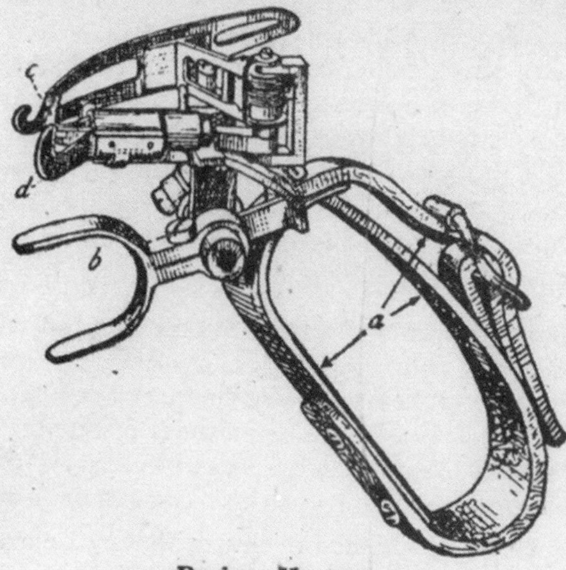

Barber Knotter.
a, strap for fastening on the hand; *b*, thumb-piece; *c*, knotter and cutter; *d*, thread-guide.

knotty-horn (not′i-hôrn), *n.* An American cerambycid beetle (the cloaked knotty-horn), *Desmocerus palliatus*, dark-blue in color, with the basal part of the elytra orange. Its larvæ bore into the stems of elder. *Comstock*, Manual of Insects, p. 570.
knotty-pated (not′i-pā″ted), *a.* A doubtful term, either genuine and meaning 'having a knotty or lumpy pate,' or, simply, 'having a hard (wooden) pate,' or a mistake for *not-pated*

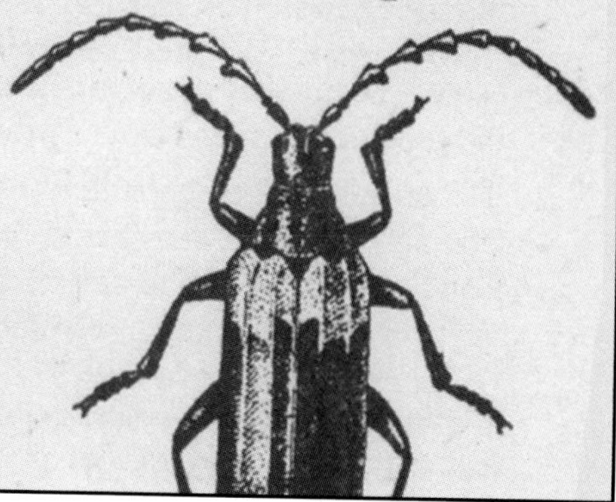

The name "Barber" became synonymous with hand-knotting in the first decades of the 20th Century as result of the Barber machine's near-market monopoly. This entry is from the 1909 edition of the Century Dictionary.

Colman worked hard to establish his business overseas, visiting England and the European Continent for a second time, in August-September of 1902, with his wife and mother-in-law in tow. To judge from Bertha's journal, Howard was an infrequent companion on the trip, joining the women mostly at meals in the evenings and spending the rest of his time in talks with mill owners and salesmen like R.H. McCullagh. A Barber and Colman branch office had recently opened in Manchester's Royal Exchange Building, where agents bought and sold yarn, cloth, and textile equipment on a daily basis, a nearly ideal location for a hand-knotter outlet in the British Isles. Colman concluded his trip with quick visits to Brussels, Cologne, Dusseldorf, Mainz, Heidelberg, and Paris in hopes of establishing contacts that would lead to the hiring of future Barber and Colman sales representatives on the Continent.

In September Colman returned to Rockford to take charge of his expanding knotter business and to oversee the transfer of machines and tooling from Spengler Brothers to Barber and Colman's new Rock Street factory, as agreed upon in their contract. The pressures of meeting a demanding production schedule, hiring several dozen men and women into the organization, and creating a staffing plan to accommodate future sales were such that he needed to be in direct control. January 1903 was a turning point for the partnership. Barber and Colman became a prime manufacturer of machine tools for the first time, no longer solely an invention business with affiliated contract houses like the Spenglers and Cornish, Curtis & Greene. Colman had his own sales and office staff now, his own machinists, his own building and equipment, with all the attendant opportunities and responsibilities. Harry Severson was asked to supervise the business's administrative functions, including purchasing, payroll, and accounting, while Colman went out onto the production floor to deal with fabricating and assembly problems as they arose. Somehow, amidst the challenges of managing a busy machine shop on the run, he still found time to conduct experiments on the top floor of his new factory, which had filled up with the odds and ends of earlier projects: the D.I.M., drop wires, reeds and harnesses (heddles), gear trains in different configurations and different stages of assembly, tying bills connected to pivoted levers and slides, guide bars, and an assortment of steel tables and frames, some of which were used as work benches and others which served as the bases of undisclosed works-in-progress. New to his test floor were a system of pneumatic cylinders for collecting lint and loose threads and a standard spinning frame with rows of empty bobbins.

According to Barber and Colman records, Louise Culver was the second person to be hired into the new factory after Harry Severson. Given the official title of "cashier," she worked as Severson's assistant and assumed most of the clerical duties in support of the knotter operation. (Culver and Severson were later married.) The first Barber and Colman "shop employees," John Skorberg, Martin Johnson, and Martin Noling, were one-time Spengler apprentices who had spent much of the previous year working on knotter assemblies and who had been hired by Colman as a part of his transition agreement. Noling, especially, proved to be a diamond in the rough, a practical improviser and workaholic of exceptional value to Colman. Known within the factory for his ingenious mock-ups of Colman's inventions, Noling used wires and rubber bands to join and test the parts of small assemblies before committing resources to a "final" design. (Colman referred to rubber bands as "Noling Springs" with a mixture of sarcasm and affection.) Noling's children would later remember their father sitting quietly in church, tying knots and manipulating metal parts in his lap while listening to the sermon.

Other early hires of significance were Earle Parker and Bert Peterson, who came aboard as draftsmen within seventeen months of each other after the factory opened its doors. Both men moved quickly from mechanical drawing into different areas of new product design; and it was their versatility and enterprising ways that soon persuaded Colman to establish an "Experimental Department" as an official arm of the business. Parker was promoted in succession to "chief draftsman," "engineer of products," and "factory manager." Peterson, who showed himself to be particularly adept at envisioning the elements of new devices and at formulating plans for their laboratory trials, was given the title of "chief experimental engineer" and allowed to work semi-independently under Colman on a variety of textile projects. Contemporary accounts of the size of Barber and Colman's payroll at the end of 1903 vary from 30 to 54; but it's apparent that the Rock Street building itself was rapidly running out of room, as knotter production reflected the activity of new sales representatives in Atlanta, Dresden, and Lille (France), and additions to the staff in the Boston and Manchester branch offices. Plans were already underway to move the latter from the Royal Exchange Building to a factory in the Manchester suburb of Brooklands, to begin fabricating and assembling machines there, and to set up a separate English corporation, Barber and Colman Ltd., as a means of avoiding import duties and gaining a bigger share of the British market.

Martin Noling in his twenties.

Anticipating the demands on Colman's time in the weeks after the wedding, George and Adella Maguire had earlier offered to house their daughter and new son-in-law at 623 North Main Street, allowing them to proceed at their own pace in finding a house or apartment. The offer was accepted as a practical necessity; and when Bertha learned that she was pregnant at the end of the summer of 1902, she was grateful for the security of her parents' home. Thus, when the honeymoon and trip to Europe concluded, the Colman newlyweds took up housekeeping in the Maguire mansion amidst the familiar surroundings of Bertha's childhood and under the semi-scrutiny of her parents. If the arrangement was less than ideal from Howard's point of view, it at least had the advantage of occupying Bertha's time while he attended to his business. Out of consideration for his wife and the approaching birth of their first child, he kept silent and threw himself completely into the start-up of the Rock Street factory.

After a son, Walter, was born on May 12, 1903, Colman made up his mind to move out of the Maguire home. Bertha was intent on staying, however, and used a series of excuses - the lack of suitable housing, the inconvenience of moving, the baby's welfare - to delay their departure. By late fall Howard was nearing the end of his patience. Good manners could only partially disguise the sadness in his note to Bertha of November 17, which was written from the Boston office of Barber and Colman during a New England business trip:

> Hope you are ready to go about making a nest of our own for just us three as soon as I return and [am] very sorry that you have not written me that such is the case. It is the only possible way for us to live happily, and delay only makes it harder.

How and when the impasse was resolved is unclear. According to later anecdotal Colman family accounts, Howard gave Bertha an ultimatum: he intended to move into his own apartment at the end of December, with or without her, though he wished with all his heart that she would see fit to join him. At some point Adella Maguire is also said to have intervened on her son-in-law's behalf and to have convinced Bertha that her place was at her husband's side.

Early in the new year, according to the *Rockford City Directory*, the young Colman family left the Maguire home for rented quarters on Church Street in Rockford. We know that a second son, Edwin, was born there on March 19, 1905, and that the couple subsequently moved into a duplex at 523 Fisher Avenue. Two years later, on June 12, 1907, Howard and Bertha celebrated the birth of a third child, Ruth, and began looking in earnest for a permanent residence to accommodate their growing family. Howard hoped, if possible, to find a house along the Rock River, preferably close enough to the Maguires to satisfy his wife and far enough away from them at the same time to suit his needs for independence; and his delay in moving from Fisher Avenue may well have been related to the lack of available property that met his special requirements. By 1907 it clearly had nothing to do with his ability to afford a new home. After five years of steady expansion,* evidenced by four separate building additions to the Rock Street factory and the opening of a large branch office in Greenville, South Carolina, his textile equipment business was booming and gaining an ever-increasing share of the American and European markets.

On the 9th of August, the headline of an article in the *Rockford Morning Star* announced:

H.D. COLMAN BUYS PRICE DWELLING
Is One of Rockford's Most Beautiful Homes
Has 240 Foot Frontage

According to the article, the sale was among "the most important real estate deals ever made" in the city. The property had been on the market for several years, the newspaper said, but because of the high asking price, estimated at more than $41,000, and the scale of the house and grounds, it had attracted few qualified parties. While it was known that the seller, Mrs. H.W. Price, had received offers for portions of the land, she had refused to subdivide it. She told the *Morning Star* that Colman himself "had been negotiating for the place for some time," though we are left to guess if this meant weeks or months or years. The Price house (929 North Main) was an elaborate three-story, neo-Gothic wedding cake fantasy, with peaked towers rising from the roofline and iron cresting along the ridges accentuating its verticality - a style whose ecclesiastical overtones could hardly be expected to be to Colman's taste. Yet its riverside location was nearly ideal for his purposes, the building interior commodious, and the ample grounds attractive to a father of three young children. The house was also an easy five-minute walk from the Maguire residence, an important consideration for his wife, but separated from its neighbors by ample grounds and set back from North Main Street by a long winding gravel drive. Colman told the *Morning Star* that he planned to make "needed changes"

* The collapse of the U.S. textile market in 1907 had little lasting effect on Colman's machine sales, which rebounded by the middle of the following year.

to it and take actual possession in the fall; but records show that, for unknown reasons, the Colman family did not actually occupy the property until the summer of 1908, eleven months after the sale.

Colman's anticipated house remodeling was apparently not the reason for this delay, since at least two of his children, Edwin and Ruth, would later remember living in the Price home for a short time before it was "converted." A possible reason may have been the pressures of work at the Rock Street factory and elsewhere, as Colman was then busily engaged in expanding his textile operations, both domestically and overseas. During the year, we know, he hired technicians in Italy, France, and Russia, incorporated Barber and Colman G.m.b.H. in Munich, and leased office space in New York, Detroit, Milwaukee, and Chicago for sales representatives.

Colman lived at 929 North Main for more than a quarter century. It was here that his second daughter, Dorothy, was born (March 1, 1913), and here that all four of his children grew to maturity. When he first moved into the house, Colman occupied a bedroom at the west end of the second floor, while Bertha slept across the hallway from him in her own quarters (according to Ruth Colman Tower, her parents never shared the same bedroom). Later, as part of his remodeling, Colman had a bedroom, bath, and drafting room constructed for himself on the third floor of the house, in a high-ceilinged attic area overlooking the Rock River. This end of the floor was thereafter considered to be off-limits to his family, especially when he was working. It was typically Spartan in its furnishings - only a bed, desk, chair, dresser, and drafting board - and free from any other kind of convenience that might prove to be distracting. Dormer windows, facing east, provided the only source of natural light, the only contact with the outside. Behind a single opening in the northwest corner of the roof, Colman labored in his drafting room on a myriad of technical details, ideas that fleshed out his concepts and found their way into the two-dimensional line drawings that were the beginnings of working models.

ii

Because of the Barber knotter's commercial success, we tend to overlook the role that that it played in the development of Howard Colman's later textile inventions. The knotter's rotating tying bill, in particular, proved to be an efficient and flexible joining device with other uses in the warping process, and Colman would later see and exploit these possibilities in the creation of a warp-tying machine and automatic spooler, though it

Howard Colman's bedroom and third-floor study ("drafting room") in his home at 929 North Main Street were located behind the dormer windows on the east side of the building, facing the Rock River.

took him longer to do this than he originally reckoned, even given his many painful lessons from years of working on the D.I.M. He knew instinctively that the knotter, as much in demand as it was commercially and as far ahead of its competitors in the field as it seemed to be, was still a manual device, an apparatus worn on the back of the hand, and that sooner or later, probably sooner than he thought, someone would come up with a way to connect the tying bill, or an apparatus like it, to a power source. It was typical of him that he was already envisioning the knotter's demise as he developed his working models. If someone were going to make his invention obsolete, he promised himself, he eventually would be the one to do it.

Colman had his eyes on a prize that was bigger than either the knotter or D.I.M. As early as October 1900, in the midst of testing a hand-knotter prototype at the Beaver Dam Cotton Mills, he had started turning over in his head the possibilities of a new mechanism to replace the conventional commercial winder (warper) that he saw operating on the factory floor. "When at B. D. Cotton Mill [sic]," he wrote William Barber, "wish you would take especial notice of the process of warping (i.e. winding off from spools on to the 'section beam'). I have a project in mind in regards to that I wish to talk over with you" (10/8/00). A month later, while involved in hand-knotter trials at the Merrimack Mills in Massachusetts, he had written Barber on the same subject. Colman said that he'd been discussing his "warper plans" with an industry expert there and had been told about the Draper and Sons' efforts to perfect a similar winding apparatus in the past; the man had predicted "emphatically that 'there are millions in it if we can do it' " (11/5/00). The challenge was reminiscent of Colman's earlier conversations with mill men on the D.I.M., and it's apparent from his subsequent patent applications, in 1902 and 1903, that he was designing and testing a winder/warper device even as he finalized plans to mass-produce the knotter.

With the advantage of hindsight, we also know that he had something called a "doffer" in the works, a mechanism for replacing empty reels or spools of thread (bobbins) on the mills' spinning frames. Doffing machines and warpers had both existed before Colman came along; but like many other devices in mills at the time, they worked imperfectly and were often less efficient over the course of a working day than a good manual operator. We know that Colman planned to take an existing commercial doffer, reduce its size and weight, and limit the number of moving parts that went into the feeler arms that "doffed" (removed) and "donned" (replaced) the bobbins. He apparently did not get a satisfactory prototype developed for several years, since his earliest doffer patent application was submitted in 1908. But according to the records of the Barber and Colman partnership and his own later testimony in the U.S. District Court of Massachusetts, he had a "temporary and experimental installation" of a doffing device in the Olympia Mills of Columbia, South Carolina in 1903. This meant that his incredible balancing act at the time of testing the hand-knotter, starting a machine shop, hiring staff, purchasing equipment, scheduling production, and working out the details of a practical winding device included the additional self-imposed burden of getting a doffer off the ground.

Colman's ambition knew no limits. He continually amazed his associates with his capacity for innovation just as he surprises us today with the range of his investigations, the number of experimental irons he had in the fire at any one time. He routinely tested himself with conceptual puzzles, envisioning the ways that manual devices might be mechanized and integrated into a larger system, while projecting his schemes forward in time and weighing the future consequences of the changes he envisioned for his competitors and himself. In the case of the 1902 winder, his big idea, his radical scheme to make "millions," was to skip the spooling process altogether and to wind yarn directly from the bobbins onto the section or warp beam. This had never been done before successfully; and the fact added greatly to the excitement in undertaking it and to the imagined rewards. His 1902 winder patent application was carried forward in revised applications in 1903 and 1913; and the last revision, incorporating the main features of the previous two applications, finally passed to issue in 1914. Nevertheless, Colman continued to be dissatisfied with his working model, making 16 further applications for refinements in the mechanics of winders, automatic winders, and automatic cheese winders between 1903-19.

Perhaps the best way to understand the range and direction of Colman's textile experiments at the time is to visualize them in the context of the standard milling process that created or "filled" cotton yarn. As a rule, raw cotton arrived on the loading docks of the factories in bales after being "ginned" in the fields to separate the seeds and fiber; these bales were broken open and the contents dispatched on conveyors to be cleaned, shaped, and tightened into the tiny strips that eventually went into the warp. Matted fibers were drawn through screens to remove lint and foreign matter and fed between rollers with minute surface combs, which straightened and aligned the strands. The stock was then pressed into the shape of a small rope or cord and fed between other sets of rollers, which were engineered to turn progressively faster in sequence, the second set turning faster than the first, the third faster than the second, and so on, with the result that the fibers were stretched to a pre-determined length and thickness. Typically, two strands of cotton were drawn and twisted together to give them the desired strength. At the end of the filling process, these strands were twisted again, tightened on a spinning frame, and wound onto bobbins.

The challenge that mill owners faced from this point forward was getting the finished yarn into shape for weaving as quickly and efficiently as possible. Each of the previous steps in the filling operation contributed something to the value of the cotton stock, made it cleaner, straighter, thinner, stronger; but after the bobbins were removed from the spinning frame, there was a final warping stage that was purely logistical. This was where most of the mills' manual laborers were employed and where the majority of the companies' weaving problems originated, as has already been discussed in this book in the accounts of the early D.I.M. and Barber knotter. Not coincidentally, it was also the area of the factory floor - between the spinning frame and power loom - that Colman laid claim to as an inventor, since he regarded all the points of human involvement in the warping process as opportunities for automation, as chances to reduce costs and improve efficiency through the development of labor-saving devices.

In the cotton mills of Colman's day, high-speed rotary machines were used to wind the bobbin threads onto larger spools or "cheeses," the individual strands being tied end-to-end to form a continuous length. The finished spools, 300-400 at a time, were then mounted on the spindles of a steel-framed "creel" and wound again onto barrel-like metal cores that became the warp (loom) beams. How many thread ends were actually taken up and wound onto the beams, and how many turns the beam cores made in winding the yarn had to be determined from the specifications of the cloth; and these changed from job to job.

After the threads were given a starch bath to toughen the fibers, the warp beams were taken to a drawing-in or "reeding" station, which was the last stop before the loom itself. The purpose of this operation was to fit out the beams with the loom elements - harnesses, reeds, and back-stop motion wires - that were needed for the next job; and these were determined by the kinds of materials (cottons, woolens, worsteds, synthetics) and the intricacies of the patterns to be woven. The reeding station itself was staffed by operators, "drawing girls," who were responsible for pulling the individual thread-ends through openings in the loom elements with tiny needle-like hooks. Colman had been fascinated by this operation as a schoolboy on his tours of the Beaver Dam Cotton Mills and had envisioned the D.I.M. as a mechanical substitute for this kind of nerve-wracking work. The standard drawing-in process, both in the initial preparation of the warp beam and in the later renewal of threads after they ran out in the loom, was a logistical challenge for mill owners that required exceptional patience and concentration on the part of the workers, the precise positioning of openings in the loom elements, and a capacity for rapid changeovers on the production line between one job and the next.

iii

By the summer of 1903, Colman had his hand in the development of labor-saving devices in every phase of the warping process and had begun to envision ways to blend the different functions into an integrated mechanical system. As he later disclosed in court testimony, his attention had been focused on three "fundamental questions" underlying the coordination and timing of his machines' moving parts: 1) the best means of selecting and joining the threads, 2) the best means of positioning the thread-handling mechanisms, and 3) the best means of actuating these devices. How was he going to generate the complex mechanical motions associated with winding, drawing, and tying? What kinds of engagement would be needed between the teeth of his gear trains to give him precise pattern control? And how would he engineer his cams to balance the speeds and thrusts (torques)? When he moved into the Rock Street factory, he had set up and begun testing a prototype of his winding device and had entered into negotiations with the owners of the Olympia Mills for the installation of his doffing machine there: two important pieces of a larger conceptual puzzle. He had also completed, or nearly completed, an attachment to the D.I.M. that was designed to handle the drop wires of the Draper-Northrup loom; but his work on the machine had eventually stalled because of nagging concerns about the relevance of the drawing-in process, especially in light of the tying bill's demonstrated capacity for close precision work. The debate in his mind over the relative merits of "drawing" and "tying" had been going on for some time - at least since his 1899 visit to the Merrimack Mills in Massachusetts and several months before his original knotter brainstorm:

> ... I have become more impressed with the feasibility and desirability of a tying-in machine, especially in view of the fact [that] the part of our machine which handles the threads has proved, in the experiments here, much the most satisfactory part of the machine. A tying-in machine would be more simple, I think, than our present machine and would have

> the advantage of having a wider range of work, because it would be [useful] to anything having a plain warp, and be independent of the kind or number of harnesses available.
>
> This is an important consideration. It would not draw in new work, it is true, but the D.I.M. operates rather dubiously on new harnesses because of the tendency of the eyes to stick together. Very likely both kinds of machine will have a field, but I am not sure but what it would be easier to start with a tying-in machine ... A great deal of the fancy work now is tied or, rather, twisted in (8/24/99).

Colman continued to mull over the possibilities of a warp-tying machine for several years after this and incorporated thread-handling systems into his designs of the knotter and first winding prototypes that were loosely based on the principle of tying or twisting in. When the concept of a fully-fledged warp replenishing mechanism finally came to him in the fall of 1903, when he was able to visualize, or sense, the features of a practical device, he was returning to Rockford on a train from Columbia, South Carolina after conversations with the manager of the Olympia Mills there about his experimental doffer installation. His thoughts had been elsewhere, and his goal in boarding the train had been mainly to endure the tedium of the long trip home; but engaged by sights and sounds along the way and stimulated by the motions of the speeding car, he had begun daydreaming, and upon his arrival in Rockford, had "devised the [tying-in] machine substantially as shown in the drawings of the [eventual patent] application" (U.S. Patent Office Depositions, 1915). As usual with Colman, the concept was entirely in his head, and he needed to translate it to paper as quickly as possible.

The next day Colman sought out Earle Parke at the factory and pressed him into service, discussing the details of his hypothetical device with the help of pencil sketches. Parker would later remember the morning as much for his own condition at the time as for the disclosure of the warp-tying machine:

> I had a very strenuous day before, took a trip to Chicago, arriving home the next morning about 5 o'clock; I only had a short time for rest before reporting for work, where Mr. Colman came and explained to me the new machine he was going to build. I remember distinctly that it was a very hard subject to swallow in the condition I was in at the time, being very sleepy, and have thought of this a great many times in connection with the warp-tying machine (U.S. Patent Office Depositions, 1915).

Colman told Parker that he wanted his mechanism to use "the same uniting means as … on our hand knotter, rotating the bill continuously instead of reciprocating it," and that this knotting element should be mounted on a carriage traveling across the warp bed. The carriage included "selectors, feed levers, and other mechanisms for bringing the threads from each warp to the uniting mechanism." Colman began laying out the relative dimensions of the machine, all from his head, in an assembly drawing and worked on this design steadily over the course of the next few days, consulting frequently with his machinists and assemblers and making numerous changes. "Part of the time I stood behind Mr. Colman," Parker recalled, "and made sketches as he put in the lines, and he would measure the drawings and give dimensions to me. Then I would take these sketches and make detail drawings from them."* The first prototype parts were rapidly machined according to Parker's specifications and laid out for assembly on the floor of the Experimental Department. Colman insisted that the new machine be put together as soon as the parts arrived and "run under power until it was running freely." Warp sections were then brought to the device, a rubber hose supplied as an exhaust system, and the first warp-tying tests begun.

"As these experiments progressed," Parker said, "complete dummy warps were tied, and the results were so satisfactory that we rushed the work on the second machine." Most of the parts from the original model went into "machine No. 2," while the rest were modified to address problems revealed in the assembly and initial trial runs. Tests on small sections of warp continued with the new machine, which turned up additional problems, and almost immediately, "we were designing and starting to build machine No. 3." Colman was encouraged enough by the experimental

* Colman described the following steps in the assembly and testing of the early warp-tying prototype: "The machine was built from the detail drawings just as rapidly as possible. The details of such pieces as the bed and others that would require the most pattern work were made first and each detail as fast as it was finished was put into the shop … Some parts were purposely omitted from the general drawing because I could design them better after the rest of the machine was completed. This was done immediately, and the parts were added, and the machine was operated during the latter part of January. I ran it both by hand and by power at that time and observed its action; it appeared to tie the warps as it was designed to do. However, at this time I used only sections of warps clamped in each frame without any harness and reed or loom beam attached to these sections. Before the general drawing was completed, it became evident to me that more space was needed in some directions. The two warps were too close together and more space was needed crosswise of the machine. Before the machine was completed, I had already begun drawings to make changes in accordance with these ideas, and after the experimenting with the machine above referred to, I rebuilt it, incorporating these ideas" (U.S. Patent Office Depositions, 1915).

results to purchase and set up two high-speed looms to approximate milling conditions. The entire development cycle of engineering, fabricating, and testing lasted five months, from December 1903 until the following spring. "About the middle of April 1904," he noted, "we tied in a warp behind the loom and drew the knots through the harness and reed and wove cloth out of it" (U.S. Patent Office Depositions, 1915). Eager to test his machine in actual production and gauge the reaction of cotton manufacturers to it, Colman arranged in July to have the No. 3 prototype shipped by express rail to the Olympia Mills, where it was put into operation along with his doffer. Two months later a fourth prototype ("No. 4") was also completed and shipped to the factory.

iv

When Colman installed the No. 3 machine in Columbia, South Carolina, he had no immediate plans for sales, let alone mass production. He told the mill superintendent, Edward Thomas, that he did not want it "exhibited to visitors" and instructed his own sales staff to tell anyone asking about it "that the machine was not in their hands for sale and that they could give no information about it." He insisted that all other inquiries be referred to him personally. His precautions were due not only to a lack of intellectual-property protection - his warp-tying application to the U.S. Patent Office ("Machine for Operating upon Warps") had just been submitted in May - but also to the Rock Street factory's continuing struggles to keep up with its worldwide knotter sales. He intended to put the No. 3 and No. 4 machines through an extended production run during the summer and fall and to use this time for refinements in the system, especially in the design and integration of auxiliary devices such as a loader, beam truck, and overhead frame; but as in the case of his early hand-knotter experiments, events soon overtook him.

In many ways Colman was a victim of his own success. He had downplayed the machine's capabilities in persuading the Olympia Mills to take it, primarily to avoid attention and guard against raising false expectations. Operators in the factory quickly discovered, however, that the device was a huge time-saver in renewing the warp, increasing productivity in the weave room by as much as 30%. At top speed it was capable of tying 250 knots a minute, a nearly blinding pace in an industry still dependent on the work of "drawing girls" (a.k.a. "drawing-in hands") for the majority of its warp beam preparation. This was really astonishing news, and Thomas could not be expected to keep it to himself. The presence of a new tying device in the Olympia Mills "became known to the men connected with cotton mills in the South very shortly," Colman remembered, "and prominent men, friends of Mr. Thomas, came from a distance to see it and he did not feel he could refuse them."

> Some of these ordered machines immediately, without even inquiring as to the price, and some ordered without going to see the machine in operation. About the time that machine No. 4 was installed I removed my objections to visitors being admitted and, in many cases in answer to letters of inquiry from mills, we stated that they could see the machine by going to Olympia ... Many mills asked us as to the capacity of the machine and the help required to operate it, but at that time we declined to give any information on that point but preferred to have them form their own judgment by seeing the machine in operation (U.S. Patent Office Depositions, 1915).

Colman could not speak authoritatively about the machine's capacity - the range of warp threads it was able to handle, its compatibility with different commercial looms, its staffing needs, its maintenance issues, and its optimum operating speeds - because he was unsure of them himself. While the responses of mill men in the South were highly gratifying, he knew that a good deal of further testing was needed to determine, specifically, what the machine *could not do.* He had used a standard 28-size yarn up to that stage in his tests; and with this as a starting point, he "felt" his "way in both directions, finding out by experiment how far the machine would go [in handling different sized threads] and increasing its range by refinements." He soon discovered that finer and coarser qualities of yarn could be handled simply by adjusting the knotting bill's size. "Our whole policy was based on the idea of understating rather than overstating what the machine would do," he said, and on flexible contract terms. The company planned to accept future orders with the stipulation that it would experiment on the required warp-thread sizes before shipping the machine and cancel the order if the experiments turned out unsuccessfully (U.S. Patent Office Depositions, 1915). The biggest obstacle to mass-producing the warp-tying machine, however, had nothing to do with the product:

> At the beginning of 1904, we had a comparatively small shop, which was sufficient for manufacturing our hand knotters and for doing the machine-building necessary in our experimental work ... This shop was, of course, wholly inadequate for the warp-tying machine business ... (U.S. Patent Office Depositions, 1915).

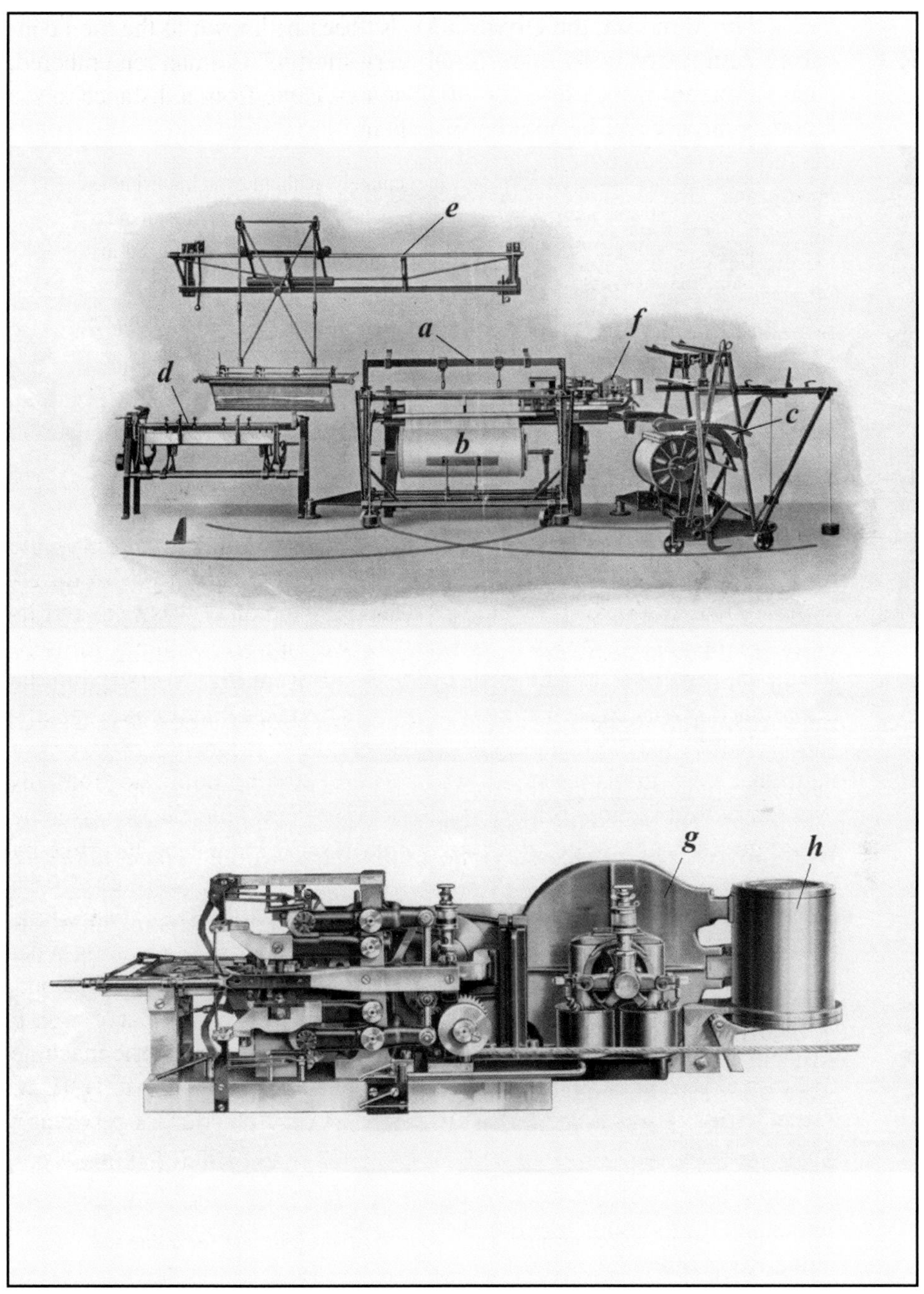

(Top) The accessories of the Barber warp-tying machine (a) included beam trucks (b and c), a loader (d), and a wall-mounted overhead carrier (e) for conveying old warp from the loader to the machine. The use of two trucks allowed operators to prepare one warp beam while the other was being tied. (Bottom) The Barber machine's motor-driven carriage, which is shown in the top illustration (f), used a suction fan (g) to hold threads in position for tying. Waste ends were removed to a centrifugal collector (h).

To raise money for a building addition and to purchase the fabricating equipment necessary for mass production, Colman issued 500 shares of capital stock at a par value of $100 and created a new Barber-Colman corporation to absorb the assets of the Barber and Colman partnership. He purchased 265 of the shares himself and sold 235 to Barber; a single share was reserved for Harry Severson. Colman became president and treasurer of a three-person board of directors (along with Barber and Severson) and assumed the duties of company's general manager, though the day-to-day operation of the business remained exactly the same as in the partnership (see "From Partners to Shareholders," pp. 360-64). In October 1904 construction began on a three-story, $25,000 addition to the Rock Street factory. More than $100,000 was allocated to "equipment" and "production" expenses in the company's warp-tying *pro forma*, all this to be provided by cash-flow from the anticipated machine sales.

The price of the new "Barber warp-tying machine" (the name reflected Colman's continuing esteem for his friend and colleague) was initially set at $3,000 and then raised by $500 increments until it reached $5,000 early in 1906; prices were even higher for machines operating on warp beams with widths greater than the standard 46 inches. When auxiliary devices such as loaders, beam trucks, and overhead frames were figured into the price, total system costs approached $8,000. Colman devised an "advance payment plan" that offered $200 worth of extra parts to early purchasers; but demand for the machine was so strong that special incentives proved to be unnecessary: most mills were willing to meet the terms that Barber-Colman proposed simply to guarantee their place in line. With little more than word-of-mouth promotion and a single demonstration site in South Carolina, Barber-Colman received orders for 19 warp-tying machines in the final two and a half months of 1904 (this was in addition to three systems that had already been leased to the Olympia and Granby Mills in Columbia before mass-production started). Another 31 machines were sold in 1905, and 23 more in the first six months of 1906. Barber-Colman's Rock Street plant was soon out of space again, and plans were made for the construction of what would later be known as Sections "No. 3" and "No. 4" of the factory, three- and four-story building additions immediately adjoining "Section No. 2" (1904-5) and advancing southward along River Street.

The Barber warp-tying machine was heralded in the world of textile manufacturing with fanfare equal to that of the Barber knotter.

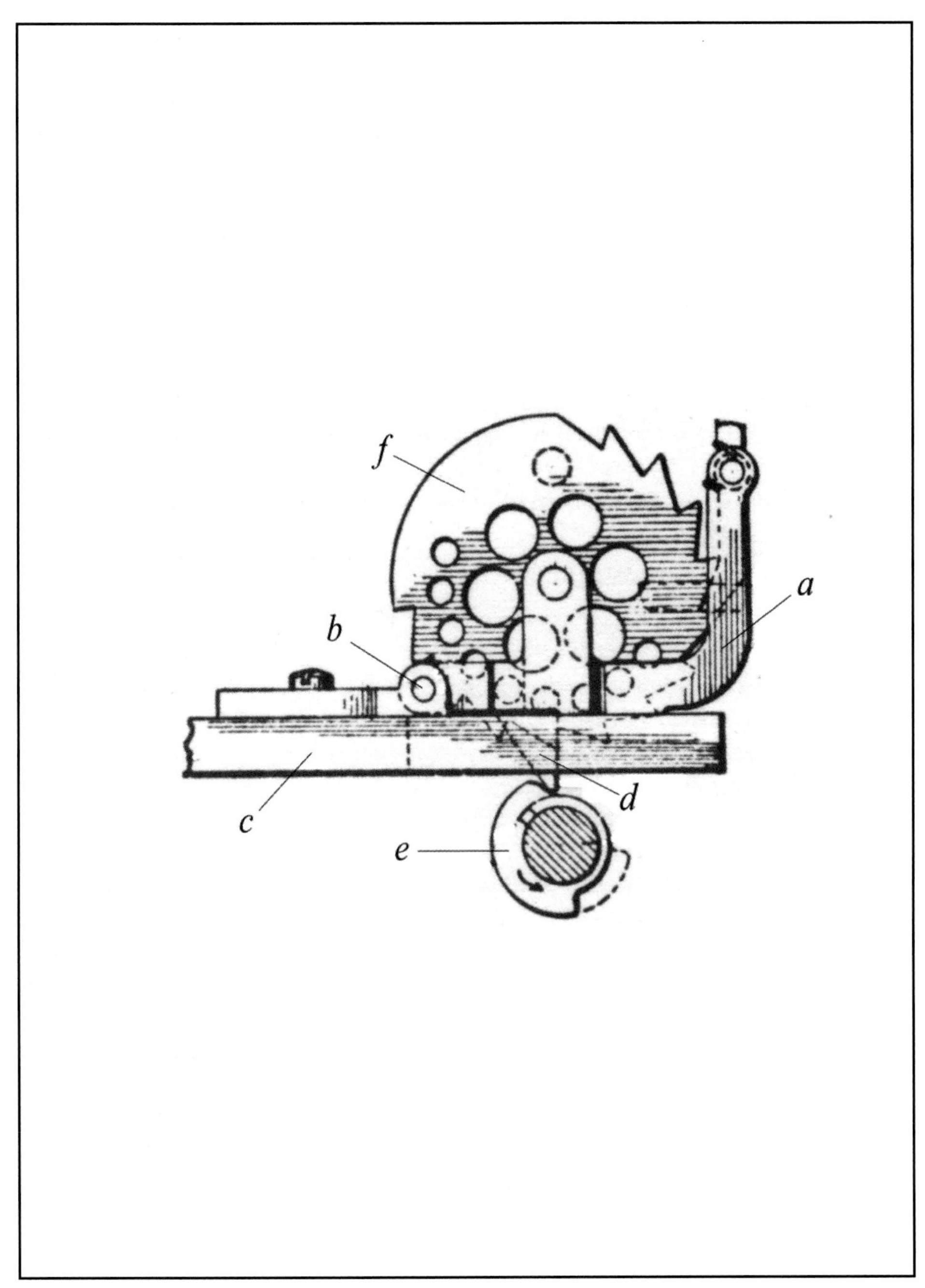

The Barber warp-tying machine contained a "try-again mechanism," which allowed the thread-selector to make repeated attempts to pick up a thread if it failed on its first effort. The selector rode on a bracket (a) that was connected pivotally (b) to a slide (c). A long tooth (d) extended downwards to engage a cam (e) on a shaft, which supplied the mechanism's motion. When the cam rotated, it moved the slide backwards one notch so that it could go through the motion, again, of grasping the next thread.

Thomas H. Rennie, an executive of the Pell City Manufacturing Company (Alabama) and the ex-president of the American Cotton Manufacturers' Association, said that it was the first successful mechanism of its type in the history of the industry. Joseph Cloudman, the Draper Company's agent in the South, called it "a great invention," anticipating the positive impact it would have on the country's cotton production and, in particular, on the sales of his own Draper-Northrup loom. The Barber warp-tying machine was a workhorse, tying 12,000 knots per hour and turning out new warp beams every eight-nine minutes; a single installation matched the previous output of three dozen drawing-in operators. Barber-Colman's first warp-tying customers were all from the South (South Carolina, Georgia, Tennessee, and Louisiana); but in December 1905 orders were received from the Edwards Manufacturing Company of Augusta, Maine and the Massachusetts Cotton Mills of Lowell, and this was the beginning of sales to New England, the Midwest, Great Britain, and Europe. For the next 15 years, the Barber knotter and warp-tying machine would be the staples of the Barber-Colman Company, its two best-known commercial offerings and the primary sources of capital for its experimental investigations.*

The Barber warp-tying machine's success changed Colman's view of the D.I.M. and its place in the process of warp preparation. His tests showed that the warp-tying machine was three times faster than existing models in long production runs, the only measure that really mattered in mill owners' estimation of equipment. Except when the loom elements needed to be individually threaded at the beginning of new jobs, when weaving patterns changed, tying was much better in renewing the warp and less likely than drawing-in to break or damage the yarn. As Colman had predicted to William Barber, "both kinds of machine" would eventually have their "field" in manufacturing (8/24/99). Mill operators would learn to use one to start new patterns and the other to keep them going.

In the case of tying work, mill operators needed to make sure that three-four feet of yarn remained in the heddles and reed after a loom beam was exhausted. The tying machine would then be brought up to the side of the loom (or the beam itself taken to the side of a stationary device), and the warp threads brushed out to make them as straight and parallel as possible. These would be stretched and clamped in the tying machine's "upper warp frame" and a new beam similarly prepared and clamped in its "lower frame." The frames had to be carefully positioned, one above the other, so

* Altogether, 802 Barber warp-tying machines were sold by Barber-Colman in the first decade of production (1904-14). The estimated value of these sales was $6.5 million.

Barber-Colman's exhibit at the 1912 National Association of Cotton Manufacturers' Convention in Boston included demonstrations of the Barber knotter and warp-tying machine. A warp beam and portable tying machine are visible in the lower left of the photograph.

that the thread ends were nearly touching. When the tying machine was activated, its motorized carriage traveled along a track between the two sheets of threads and rapidly joined the ends from each in succession. Afterwards, the clamps were taken off and the newly joined threads pulled through the harness eyes and reed dents to start the new beam unrolling. It was a practical solution to the problems of warp replenishment that avoided the headaches of drawing in and enabled operators to complete an entire loom beam in less than ten minutes.

V

The sudden and dramatic entry into the market of the Barber warp-tying machine was a shock to existing equipment manufacturers, particularly makers of drawing-in devices, since the sales of the new Barber apparatus could legitimately be perceived to be coming at their expense. An early visitor to the Olympia Mills in 1904 was the manager of B.B.& R. Knight Company of Providence, Rhode Island, one of the country's largest combination mills and an important customer of the American Warp Drawing Machine Company (AWDMC) of Boston. The manager's enthusiastic reports soon reached the ears of the Edgar F. Hathaway, one of the AWDMC principals and the owner of an early drawing-in patent himself. Hathaway was worried enough by what he heard from the Knight Company to go to Olympia Mills to see Colman's device in person, and his visit quickly confirmed that there was a new and formidable competitor in the field. On Hathaway's recommendation, AWDMC filed new patent applications for a drawing-in machine (March 6, 1905) and a "twisting-in" apparatus (February 14, 1906), with claims that were so sweeping that an interference with Barber-Colman would be all but inevitable. Hathaway knew that this would force the disclosure of Colman's tying application and prevent it from passing to issue. AWDMC hoped to tie up Barber-Colman in the courts, entangle it in legal maneuvers, and make the commercialization of the warp-tying machine as difficult and costly as possible. AWDMC lawyers set out to learn everything that they could about the Barber-Colman Company and pored over the details of existing patents that had a bearing on the case.

Hathaway's company, which was chartered in Maine, had purchased a number of older warp-drawing patents and applications and had gone into business, in 1899, with a composite machine that incorporated features from several different inventions. Though it owned the rights to the expired Moore patent, which had previously blocked the sale of the D.I.M. to Draper and Sons in 1896, as well as the designs of

Millard F. Field and Charles D. Lanning, two of New England's better-known textile inventors, the company had an uncertain intellectual property position because of Colman's still-pending 1894 D.I.M. patent application. Rather than contest the pioneering status of their respective machines in the courts, AWDMC chose to shift the burden of proof in the proceedings to the validity of Colman's 1902 D.I.M. application renewal, an otherwise routine continuation of the 1894 paperwork. AMDMC argued that it had discovered a serious "irregularity" in the 1902 application that disqualified it from further consideration: the papers had not been properly amended, within one year of the first filing, as stipulated by the regulations of the U.S. Patent Office. It was not Colman's originality that AWDMC wished to challenge, only his place at the head of the patent-application queue.

Colman was informed of the AWDMC lawsuit on September 12, 1906, when he was busy with the build-out of the Rock Street factory ("Section No. 2") and hurrying to fill new tying machine orders. Whether or not he regarded it in the beginning as anything more than a nuisance is uncertain, but after the initial interference proceeding in Washington was decided against him, the contest with AWDMC became deadly serious, degenerating into a series of trials and appeals that absorbed his time and money and effectively halted further warp-drawing and tying experiments. The D.I.M., newly-furnished with an attachment to handle the drop-wires of the Draper-Northrup loom, was mothballed once again, this time on the advice of Luther Miller, who feared that sales of the machine might lead to financial penalties if the initial judgment against Barber-Colman in the Patent Office proceedings was upheld. AWDMC addressed a similar concern on its side by leasing warp-drawing machines to customers, though Colman was under no such compulsion in regards to the Barber warp-tying machine, where he felt his legal position was more secure. "We were perfectly willing to continue a profitable business," he testified in court, "notwithstanding the pending and existing interferences" (Proceedings of the U.S. District Court of Massachusetts, 1919).

In the early phases of the lawsuit, AWDMC's campaign of harassment proved to be successful, forcing Barber-Colman to suspend its efforts to sell the D.I.M. and burying its drawing and tying patent applications in enough red tape to call their eventual approval into question: all provided that AWDMC was willing to continue to bear its mounting legal costs. Charles Lanning, a co-owner with Millard Field of the company, pronounced himself well-satisfied with the progress of the case, at least, in a confidential memorandum that was later discovered by Barber-Colman and admitted into evidence: " … as regards the Barber machine," he wrote, "we have a lot of stuff in the Patent Office that I think ties them up completely."

From the beginning AWDMC's strategy seems to have been to force Barber-Colman into an out-of-court settlement that would allow AWDMC to specialize in the manufacture of drawing-in devices and Barber-Colman to continue its sales of warp-tying machines. According to this plan, Barber-Colman would either give up its D.I.M. patent application or assign it to AWDMC in exchange for an end to the lawsuit; Lanning and Field doubted that the Rockford company would have the resolve and financial resources to continue the fight indefinitely. AWDMC first presented its case to the Patent Office's law examiner, then to the board of examiners-in-chief, and finally to the assistant commissioner of patents, all who decided in its favor. Barber-Colman, which had appealed each ruling, now took its case to the commissioner of patents himself, who reversed the decision of the assistant commissioner and chastised AWDMC for its "piecemeal prosecution of interferences" and waste of the Patent Office's time. In response, AWDMC proposed that the interference proceeding be remanded to the examiner-in-chief and by him, if necessary, to the law examiner. Luther Miller countered that the petition was a delaying tactic intended to tie Barber-Colman up in procedural knots:

> If a motion to amend was granted and new claims based on Colman's warp-tying machine were suggested to and adopted by Colman, it would be necessary to declare a new interference, file new preliminary statements, make new motions to amend and dissolve, and, after the form of the interference is finally settled by the primary tribunals, to take three successive appeals to higher tribunals; and all this in a case which has once been specifically and finally determined by the Patent Office, and which involves only questions which have been repeatedly litigated between the parties (Barber-Colman Brief in Opposition to AWDMC Petition).

The AWDMC lawsuit was mean-spirited, Miller said, and its sole purpose was intimidation: "It is difficult to understand the mental attitude, which prompts the presentation of a petition like this."

What Lanning and Field failed to take into account, however, was the mental attitude of Howard D. Colman. In matters of right and wrong, he was absolutely unyielding; and AWDMC seriously underestimated his determination to defend his intellectual property rights, especially in regards to the youthful invention that had started him on his career and to

The Barber-Colman model K warp-tying machine. Despite his protracted patent dispute with AWDMC, Howard Colman continued to refine his warp-tying product offerings, introducing this lightweight portable model K in 1913.

which his originality was clearly established in time, at least in his own mind. He was ready to spend thousands of dollars in defense of his position, but not a single penny in tribute. AWDMC eventually appealed the decision of the patent commissioner to the Court of Appeals of the District of Columbia, which ruled in its favor on January 14, 1919; Barber-Colman then took the case to the U.S. District Court of Massachusetts, which upheld the ruling of the Court of Appeals. Undeterred by either judgment, Colman immediately notified AWDMC of his intention to appeal the ruling of the District Court and to carry the dispute forward for as long as was necessary to establish his legal claim to the D.I.M. Lanning and Field, in turn, renewed their appeal for an out-of-court settlement, arguing that the protracted legal dispute was hampering both operations and having a paralyzing effect on innovations in the warp-replenishment field. A deal was finally struck in the summer of 1919 that led to the consolidation of the two companies' warp-drawing and warp-tying businesses, though the arrangement was the opposite of what AWDMC had envisioned when it first tried to block Colman's patent applications.

"We feel that Barber-Colman employees will be interested to know," the *Barber-Colman Association News* announced, "that the company has recently completed a transaction by which it acquires the entire warp-drawing machine interests of the American Warp Drawing Machine Company, domestic and foreign." According to the agreement, Barber-Colman would be assuming immediate ownership of all AWDMC drawing-in machines on lease to cotton mills throughout the world. It would also be undertaking the manufacture of "repair parts" and doing "rebuilding" work on some AWDMC equipment, though new production was not then being contemplated. Barber-Colman employees were told to anticipate the addition of a "considerable number" of salesmen and installers, who would have the responsibility in the future of "looking after all the machines now in use." While the terms of the acquisition were not disclosed, the article said that the transaction ended a "series of complicated interference proceedings, all relating to the same subject matter and, taken together, constituting one of the most elaborate and extensive litigations … ever conducted in the Patent Office (October 1919)."

But Colman, despite the satisfaction of having eliminated AWDMC as an adversary, was not yet finished as a petitioner. His purchase of the company's drawing-in interests still left in place the judgment of the Massachusetts District Court; and he was anxious to settle, once and for all, the question of the D.I.M.'s originality. It was hardly a coincidence that the following news release found its way into the Rockford press shortly after the public announcement of the AWDMC acquisition:

> HOWARD COLMAN INVENTED FIRST WARP DRAWER
>
> It seems that an erroneous impression has been obtained from a newspaper article relating to the recent purchase of the American Warp Drawing Co., by the Barber-Colman Co., of this city. The impression obtained that the Barber-Colman Co., had infringed upon other patents by the manufacture of a warp-tying machine, and the purchase was made to avoid litigation. The very opposite is true. Mr. Colman invented a warp-drawing machine several years before the American Co., began business and discontinued the machine because the warp tier proved more satisfactory. While there has been constant legal friction between the companies, ... it is assumed that the purchase was facilitated by the prospect of a victory for the Rockford company. In the deal the Rockford company acquired no plant in Boston; only the warp-drawing interests were purchased (10/26/19).

The article was a kind of manifesto, a declaration of rights, which announced Colman's forthcoming petition to the Massachusetts District Court to "continue" its review of the interference proceedings between AWDMC and Barber-Colman. Although there was no opposing party this time, Barber-Colman argued that it should be entitled to receive the pioneering patent for the D.I.M. if the Court "adjudged" the "facts in the case" in its favor. As an indication of the lawsuit's importance to Colman, Luther Miller was authorized to work with three of the nation's leading patent attorneys - Livingston Gifford, Charles Neave, and Edward Rector - in preparing his brief. Miller also took the extraordinary step, with Colman's approval, of hiring AWDMC's former legal team as consultants, unwilling to leave any stone unturned. It was an extraordinary conclusion to an extraordinary patent litigation. "Notwithstanding" Barber-Colman's "common ownership" of all the patent applications under review, Miller wrote, the company was determined to prosecute the "proceedings to final determination in order that the courts may finally determine the question as to who is the first and original inventor of the inventions in controversy." The oddity of the petition was that Barber-Colman now assumed the role of both plaintiff and *de facto* defendant in the case, and that by eventually establishing the legal "priority" of its D.I.M. and warp-tying patent applications, it lessened, if not effectively destroyed, the value of the patents and designs it had purchased from AWDMC (Proceedings of the U.S. District Court of Massachusetts, 1919).

10
Winding and Warping

The development of the Barber-Colman automatic system practically eliminated the human element in spooling. The operator of the spooler is required only to place bobbins in position to be handled by the automatic mechanisms and to remove full packages. Machines are not subject to such human characteristics as fatigue, carelessness, indifference or the errors that are frequently found on manually operated machinery. The operations performed by the workers on these machines are extremely simple.

- Barber-Colman product brochure (undated)

i

During the years of the AWDMC lawsuit (1906-19), Howard Colman devoted most of his experimental time to the development of winding devices. His work in this field, his plan to perfect a mechanism that would wind yarn directly from bobbins onto the warp beam, was sidetracked, however, by the Barber tying machine's commercial success and the need to equip his factory for mass production and, later, by opportunities in the field of gear manufacturing. To judge from his patent applications in 1906-07, his attention was mostly given to refinements in the knotting mechanism - better clamping and loop-forming features and a means of staggering knots on adjacent warp threads - and to the design of a new "hook-and-spear" yarn selector: all which addressed problems in the operation of the tying machine. By 1908 a slump in the economy and suddenly serious legal problems with AWDMC caused him to reassess his business options. Rather than put all his eggs in one experimental basket, depend on textile products exclusively, he decided to branch out into jobbing work by making components for the Duntley gasoline motor-driven railroad section car and by manufacturing a limited number of end mills and milling cutters for general sale.

Colman had purchased a commercial gear-making machine to help him design and test his first hand-knotter; and out of necessity he had

The drafting area of Barber-Colman's Experimental Department in 1917. The company built seven additions onto its original manufacturing facility (River and Loomis Streets) between 1904-12. The construction of a six-story structure at the corner of Rock and Loomis was interrupted by the Financial Panic of 1907, and a temporary roof installed on the fourth floor. Eventually, in 1912, a fifth floor was added to the building, and the Experimental Department moved into this space.

rebuilt the main elements of the device, retooled the indexer, spindle, slide, and supports, and adjusted the bearings to give him more precision in developing his gear profiles. This led him to construct several machines for his in-house gear production, assembled in true Colman fashion from parts of existing commercial models (castings, motors, arm supports) and a number of his own specially-engineered components. To get the kind of close fit between the bearing surfaces of his gears that ensured the efficient transmission of power to the tying machine's thread selector, Colman had to make himself the master of gear geometry, gear-cutting, and finish-grinding. This was done through trial-and-error and careful observation, with no other goal in mind than being able to apply the lessons of gear-making to the design of mechanisms that selected and united tiny pieces of yarn from adjacent warp beams.

Gear design was critical to the performance of Colman's textile inventions. If it's fair to say that his tying machines would not have been perfected without an extensive knowledge of cam engineering, it's also true that his gear experiments needed the stimulus of practical thread-handling challenges - different speed ratios, less vibration, closer spacing between gear teeth, faster rotary motions - to be successful. Colman essentially reversed the process of gear production in his mind, moving backwards from gear cutters to the machines and tools that made them, to the precision methods and tolerances used in the design and manufacture of the machines and tools. Much of this was instinctive, given his natural fascination with root causes and habit of looking backwards and forwards at the same time: on one hand to the technologies that contributed to the existing state of the art in gear manufacturing, and on the other to new models or configurations of these technologies.

Two years after Colman started making and selling end mills, he launched the Barber-Colman "Machine and Small Tools Division" with the rollout of a proprietary hobbing machine* that incorporated the lessons of nearly a decade of in-house experiments. The gear machines of Colman's day were an evolutionary development of the pattern-makers' craft, which began with hand-formed wooden teeth being set in cast-iron blanks and progressed, under the demands of 20th Century mass-production, to the automated milling of steel cutters. Hobbing machines were a step beyond this, designed for durability and high-speed operation, and featuring a continuous cutting action that brought several teeth at once into contact with a blank; as the rotating hob fed forward, it produced a complete gear.

---

* A device using "hobs," or threaded cylinders, to cut teeth in gear blanks.

A close-up of a Barber-Colman hob (a) engaged in generating a gear (b). The pitch of the tool's cutting edges was determined by precise geometrical calculations.

This was a powerful tool in the hands of someone like Colman, who saw it as a means of making improvements in a variety of products. One of his most important innovations was to heat-treat the blank before cutting it (a standard practice today), reversing the traditional step of hardening the metal after the teeth had been formed and thereby eliminating problems of warping and distortion in the finished profile. The problems of precision-machining a hardened gear blank had been considered to be insurmountable at the time; but Colman solved them with a grinding process that increased the gears' pitch capacities and became one of the signature features of his hobbing device.

In his fashion Colman refined each of the products in the Machine and Small Tools Division by taking them through what the company's literature called "a severe and expensive process of development." He made his hobbing machines more accurate with better indexing, increased their speeds and feeds, and purchased castings of hardened crucible steel to enable them to process heavy, large-diameter automotive parts. He extended the hobs' slide travel and improved the depth and uniformity of the cutter's feed-in. Inevitably, the traveling hob slide of his device mimicked many of the features of the Barber tying machine's motorized carriage, and the lessons of one enriched the other. Over time Colman would expand his line of small tools into milling cutters, involute gear cutters, angular cutters, metal-slitting saws, helical milling cutters, straight-shank and taper-shank cutters; undertake the production of various sizes and styles of hobs, ratchets, square shafts, spline shafts, and reamers; and design and manufacture hob-sharpening and reamer-sharpening machines to maintain the surface finishes of his cutting tools.

During the rollout of the Machine and Small Tools Division, Colman submitted several applications to the U.S. Patent Office for "improvements" to the doffer and supervised the reorganization of the company as a co-partnership. William Barber, who was then in his late sixties and living in semi-retirement in central Wisconsin, made the decision to liquidate his stock in Barber-Colman in 1909, and a new shareholder plan was formalized at the annual meeting of the company on January 8, 1910. According to this arrangement, Colman purchased the majority of Barber's stock and increased his interest in the business to 75%, with Harry Severson and Luther Miller dividing the remainder of the shares. In the early days of the knotter production (1901-02), Barber had withdrawn from an involvement in the company's operations, content to let Colman take over both the daily management and tactical strategic planning.

His infrequent trips to Rockford in the years after this seemed to be as much about Colman's family as the state of the business (the latter continued, in spite of occasional downturns in the economy, to show remarkable growth). The Colman youngsters habitually referred to him as "Grandpa Barber" and later compared the excitement of his visits to those of Henry and Lucinda Colman and the elder Maguires. The inventor never ceased to revere him; and when Barber died in Warrens in 1912, Colman lost his best friend and most stalwart supporter, the one person in his life, above all others, who understood his special gifts.

If patent applications are an indicator, Colman had resumed his winder experiments in earnest in 1907-08, addressing a series of problems that surfaced during the construction of the first winding-warping prototype in 1902-03, an ungainly-looking device that used an endless mechanical chain - a kind of miniature ferris wheel with bobbin-holders for seats - to feed threads onto a section beam. The original model apparently performed well enough for Colman to go to the trouble of seeking patent protection, though it was never a practical device. It merely demonstrated the principle of bobbin-to-warp-beam winding. It failed to show that it could do this consistently, without stops and broken threads, and at a rate of speed that would make it attractive to mill owners.

In spite of these obstacles - or perhaps precisely because of the challenging nature of the obstacles he encountered in developing his early winding device - Colman continued to be intrigued by the possibility of an automated thread-handling system between the spinning frame and loom. It was characteristic of him, as the history of the D.I.M. shows, that once he understood the limitations of an existing manufacturing process and began to envision an alternative, once he got to the point of designing and testing an actual study model, he found it hard to abandon the concept. His extensive doffer trials at the time (see his patent applications of July 22, 1908, November 5, 1908, and November 7, 1910) led to the development of a transfer mechanism that removed full bobbins from the spinning frame and replaced them automatically with empty cores. Colman modified the Barber tying machine's traveling carriage to vary its propulsion and enable it to deal with irregularly-spaced bobbin spindles, and he mounted a sensitive thread detector on the slide that measured the bobbins' build-up and determined when they were full. This was really "winding" under a different name, just as his winding ("spooler') patent application of November 11, 1907 was really about the use of constant and varying yarn feeds to doff exhausted bobbins.

There was little apparent rhyme or reason to the winder applications that Colman submitted to the U.S. Patent Office after 1907. Most were formulated during routine trials of his study-models, following plans that were determined as much by the failures of these models as their successes. In Colman's mind, the best way to know whether something worked or not was to model it, put it through a series of tests, analyze the results of the tests, correct the failures, and test again. He was surrounded in the Experimental Department now by many different prototypes and trial assemblies, and he had the help of an experienced group of Barber-Colman designers, engineers, and machinists to carry out his design ideas. A few entries from the "daily notes" of Martin Noling, selected here more or less at random from the machinist's project writings, give us an idea of the systematically unsystematic approach to discovery that characterized a typical Colman workday:

> Today I found that the trouble we had with the relief finger was due to the center of the clip bowing upwards and the center-back intermediate disk did not get on top of the clip. I pointed this out to Mr. Colman, who suggested that I cut the points off from the center disc so as to be able to run the machine without the danger of the clip being caught, the points on the center discs not being necessary until we operate the fingers from the clip pins. This being done, the machine ran without any further trouble …
>
> Mr. Colman suggested that we experiment with the springs until we get a weight that will permit the clip to pass through without being raised off from the center intermediate disk. He said he will figure out the speeds according to the amount of tension on the finger. He said that we could make other changes later on, since the mechanism he has in mind and wishes to use on it has a four-tooth intermediate disk instead of the existing nine-tooth disc …
>
> The study model was ready to run, and Mr. Colman came over to witness a demonstration, which was very satisfactory. I pointed out to Mr. Colman that we have not as yet put a feed mechanism on the machine, which may make some difference in the actual running. To this Mr. Colman suggested my having this mechanism put on …
>
> Mr. Colman suggested using an endless band to represent the mechanism and to insert soft lead blocks in the holes of the band. We will punch

> slugs from 1/32" thick wire stock and insert these into the holes in the steel band, as would be done if it were made as per Mr. Colman's idea of the finished machine. Part of the scheme disclosed by Mr. Colman was to extrude the material that was used in place of the fuse wire …
>
> The differential study model was completed today and the power applied. It ran only about ½ minute at the rate of 40 r.p.m. on the cam shaft before the short end of the dog broke. Mr. Colman came to see the study model just a minute or so after it had broken, and he suggested that we put a friction member on the ratchet shaft controlled by this broken finger, thereby permitting us to continue the test using only the one finger on the dog. After this change, Mr. Colman watched it start, and we ran it at a speed of 200 r.p.m. on the cam shaft. Mr. Colman spoke of changing the entire design of this unit …

Invention, for Colman, was always unexpected. As often as not, it proceeded from his reactions to shop-floor trials, from perceptions of design flaws and process weaknesses, and led to the formulation of certain assumptions about the solutions to these problems and the ways to incorporate them in mechanical devices. Like a chess master engaged in multiple matches, Colman made regular daily rounds of the Experimental Department to witness the tests firsthand. Whenever appropriate, he made suggestions for design changes and system modifications, while also weighing the effects of the changes and possible alternatives to them.

Among mill owners at the time, winding was regarded as the next important developmental stage in the manufacture of cotton cloth, since it was the phase of production where automation had had the least impact up to that time and where manual labor was critical to the quality of the finished warp. The system that Colman observed in the Beaver Dam and Merrimack Mills was a hodgepodge of different motorized and belt-driven devices. Winding was done at low speeds and shepherded by diligent operators who cleaned, knotted, and repaired the threads, starting and stopping the spoolers when breaks occurred, and adding and removing yarn packages, as needed. Winders filled the air with lint, the faster the rotation, the greater the clouds of microscopic fiber that fell on the machines. Tiny ravelings, invisible to the eye in the rapid feed-out of threads from the bobbins, coated the yarn surfaces and created gouts and kinks in the finished cloth; fluff likewise embedded itself in the corners of the spools, gummed up the gears and contacts, and threw off the cores' rotational balance.

Sometimes this led to an uneven build-up of thread on the spools, which would wobble and vibrate in feeding the warp beam. Broken threads were frequent, with the loose ends quickly "buried" in the surface of the rotating beam (these were hidden by rows of new threads and later revealed as blemishes as cloth came out of the loom). Perhaps the greatest nightmare of all for mill owners was the prospect of multiple breakages, a chain reaction of popping threads, backlash at the spools, and a runaway warp beam, a not-infrequent occurrence when winding speeds were increased.

Knotting was an additional problem, even when labor-saving devices like the Barber knotter were employed. While the knotting bill had simplified the task of joining thread-ends during the spooling stage, it had proved to be less than ideal when the same threads were wound onto a warp beam. The reason was that the knots it tied - round or spooler's knots - tended to loosen or pull apart under the strain of high-speed winding (if the knots held up during the threads' run-out, they were sometimes undone in the weaving). The delicacy of the yarn, which was formed by twisting and compression, placed its own limits on the pace of mill production and determined the kinds of devices (and kinds of gearing) that could be used to wind the threads. The spoolers and warpers of the day left a lot to be desired in this respect; they were slow, cumbersome, and subject to frequent breakdowns. The industry had been forced to compensate for these problems through the training of skilled operators ("spooler hands") and had come to see the existing level of mechanical winding technology as making the best of a bad situation.

It was a simple matter of cause and effect. To boost cotton production, mills needed to wind faster. To wind faster, they needed to keep enough pressure on the threads to ensure a steady feed, and to do this without drag or friction. Too much pressure weakened the threads, made them taut and brittle, and led to breakages in the loom; too little pressure created backlash at the spools and send the threads ballooning. The highest-quality yarn retained a suppleness and elasticity throughout the warping and weaving stages; and the winder of the future, the machine that transformed the industry, would have both higher speeds and lower tensions, rapid-fire rotations that were light as air.

In the history of Colman's winder patent applications, 1913 stands out as a watershed year, a point in his experiments where he apparently abandoned plans to wind threads from bobbins directly onto the warp beam in favor of a much more conventional arrangement of separate spooling and warping devices. On June 28, to be sure, he sent to Washington his most ambitious and highly-evolved winder application to-date, which included 57 pages of detailed drawings and a self-declared goal of bringing the "greatest possible degree of automaticity" to bear on winding "as commonly practiced." Colman claimed in his application to be able to unwind simultaneously 280 bobbins, arranged side by side in vertical tiers or columns on a large steel frame; according to his design, the strands of yarn were fed from the bobbins through a series of rollers and combs and onto the sides of a beam. His device contained a tying mechanism for joining the thread ends of the exhausted bobbins to those of full replacements (the old cores were discharged through openings in the bottom of the holders after the threads were tied). On the same day, we know, Colman also submitted patent applications for a new high-speed warping apparatus, complete with individual brakes for its yarn packages, and a creel, which was intended to be used in the warping device. Two days later he submitted yet another patent application for a warper creel with removable or modularized sections. And on December 31 he sent off an application for a patent on an automated method of winding yarn from bobbins onto spools or cheese cores; the application included a motorized winder-tending mechanism that traveled the length of the machine to join the ends of yarn, the same device that he described in his application of June 28 for the revolutionary bobbin-to-beam winder but now appropriated for a traditional spooler function.

Colman was heading in new directions. We can only guess at why he finally gave up his plan to build a single automated winding system between the spinning frame and loom and turned instead to the manufacture of spoolers and warpers. It may well have had less to do with an inability to demonstrate the feasibility of his winding concept than it did with unexpected technical breakthroughs in his development of spooling and warping prototypes, since Barber-Colman records show that the company made arrangements for experimental installations of both devices in a half dozen mills in the South, Midwest, and New England, beginning in 1912. It's unlikely that Colman would have been willing to do this without first conducting exhaustive tests in-house, which means that he was probably working on winding devices and study models of spoolers and warpers for a number of years in parallel. Typically he would have purchased at least one commercial spooler and one warper for use in the Experimental Department as a means of focusing his thoughts on the development of the bobbin-to-beam winder. To supplant an older system, he needed to be able to visualize the working parts - understand, internalize, its mechanisms. Here, one guesses, the usual process of feeding his imagination with ideas from an older, under-performing commercial model worked in reverse, and the lessons from the new system, the advanced mechanism he was in the process of designing, triggered something (or some things) in his understanding of the older configuration that made it seem to be the more promising alternative and caused it to go forward.

Whatever the reason, Colman turned now to the development of spoolers and warpers full-time, hoping to prove up an advanced winding system that would replace the "old-style" operations of most American mills. He systematically addressed weaknesses in the leading commercial spooling and warping machines, improved the efficiency of the working parts, and added features that he hoped would lead to higher winding speeds and greater warp-beam output. His existing library of patents, designs, and study models, his winder/doffer prototypes especially, were invaluable in this respect. The motorized winder-tending mechanism described in his December 1913 patent application, a device that was closely modeled on the Barber warp-tying machine's traveler, seemed tailor-made for the spooler's long steel frame. Colman redesigned the thread-handling unit to include a bobbin-holder and swinging mechanical arm, and mounted it on a carriage that continuously circuited the frame, manipulating yarn packages in its path. As the winder-tender approached each package - there were 30 or more cheese cores suspended in rows on each side of the frame - it used suction ("air friction") to pick up the loose thread end on the cheese's surface and draw it downwards into the jaws of the knotter, which simultaneously engaged a loose thread end of a bobbin in a holder below. As soon as the cheese and bobbin ends were tied, the line was cast off the winder-tender and the slack taken up by forced air. The mechanical arm holding the cheese then retracted, like a raised hammer, and swung into contact with a revolving cam drum at its head. This drum fed the line into a narrow groove ("traversing channel") on its surface, which immediately began to draw thread off the end of the bobbin and onto the core of the cheese.

After the bobbin was exhausted, the winder-tender cut the thread and moved on to the next yarn package in its path, working its way around the spooler frame according to a timed schedule. Colman used a spring-activated "thread detector" to measure the build-up on the surface of each

A close-up of the automatic spooler's thread-handling unit shows the bobbin-holder (a), cheese core (b), and rotating zigzag drum (c). Here a full cheese (d) is suspended at the end of a flexible mechanical arm.

cheese and to withdraw the cheese from the drum as soon as it reached a standard thickness. If contact with the drum was interrupted, either by a full cheese or broken thread, the bobbin remained in a "reserve position," poised diagonally in the holder. This signaled the operator, who was walking behind the traveler, to remove the cheese and replace it with a "starter" core. When she did this, the empty bobbin below it was automatically ejected from the holder onto a conveyor and taken to a sorting table at the end of the machine.

Colman's most important innovation in the development of the spooler was his use of a weaver's knot. In the Barber knotter, he had chosen to tie a round knot because it seemed best-suited at the time to a manual operation - the thumb lever could only activate a simple mechanical motion - but in the case of a spooler, which was motor-driven, he was able to tie a tighter, more compact knot and dramatically increase his winding speeds. The superiority of the weaver's knot in warp preparation had always been acknowledged by industry experts, but Colman was the first person to incorporate it successfully into a high-speed mechanical spooling system and take this device to market. "Every knot a weaver's knot" became the motto of the Barber-Colman automatic spooler, featured throughout its product literature and displayed graphically in the drawing of a knot joining the threads of a cheese and bobbin, which served as a kind of logo. If he could prove that his tying bill worked, tied a true weaver's knot, Colman knew he could make a case for the spooler:

> More uniform distribution of the mass of the knot around the yarn, less bulk, and decreased tendency to slip allow the weaver's knot to pass more readily through harness eyes and reed dents, which results in loom stoppage. In the same way this type of knot passes more freely through the eyes of needles when the yarn is used in knitting machines. Knots with short ends bury themselves more completely in cloth than those having long ends.

To attract attention at textile conventions, he decided to set up individual weaver's knotters in his exhibition area, connect them to motors, and run off knots continuously like strips of ticker-tape: demonstrations that proved to be as interesting to convention visitors as those of the spooler itself. When he began exhibiting the machine, he also realized that the spooler's success would ultimately be at the expense of the Barber hand-knotter:

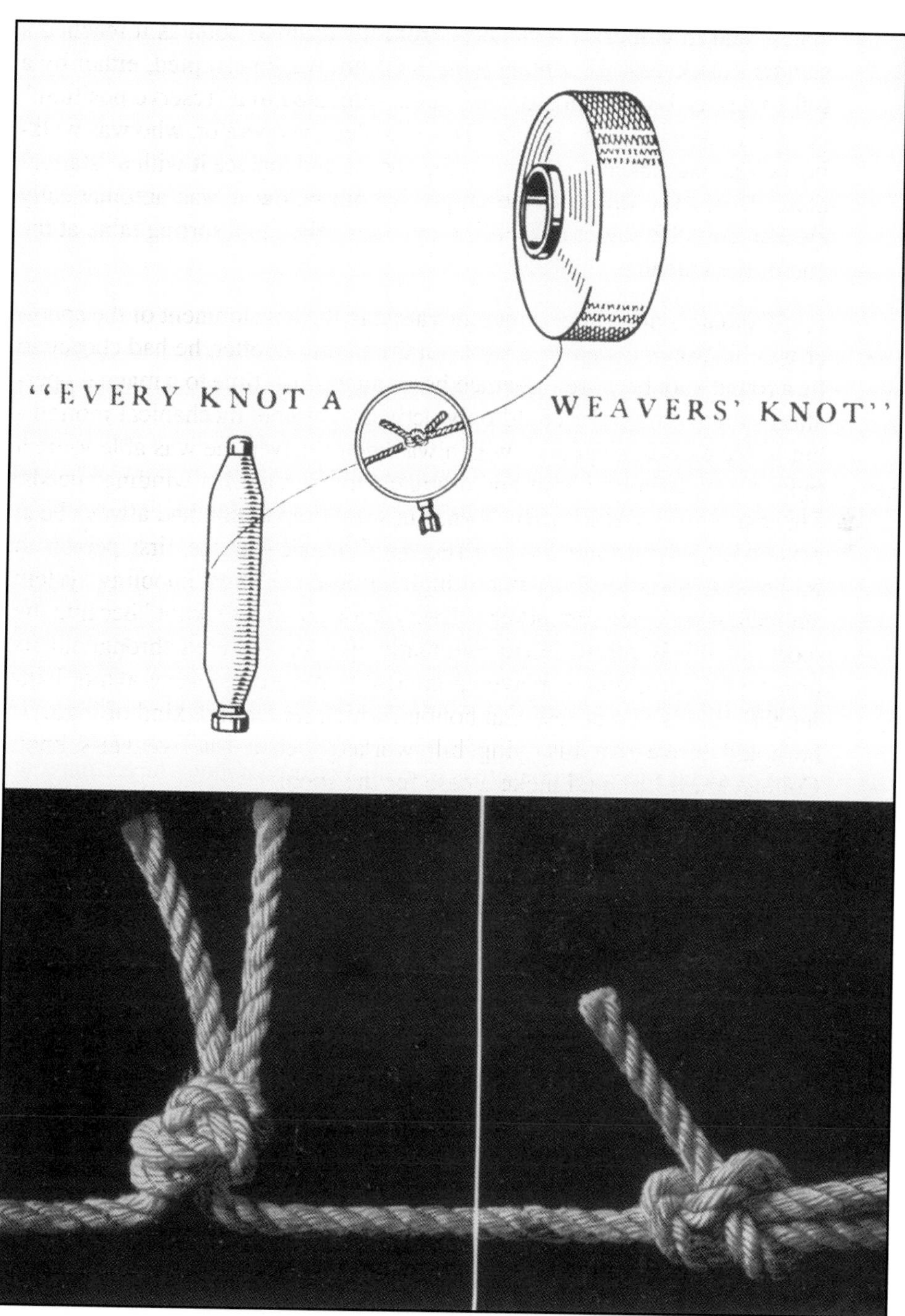
"EVERY KNOT A
WEAVERS' KNOT"

"Every knot a weaver's knot"(top) was the watchword of the Barber-Colman automatic spooler, highlighting one of the device's most important innovations. Besides its resistance to unravelling, the weaver's knot (bottom right) was more compact than the traditional spooler knot (bottom left) and formed closer to the thread.

> Careful spooler girls with hand knotters can spool yarn without making spooler kinks, but it is difficult to get them to exercise proper care to accomplish this. The automatic spooler eliminates the human equation, and extensive tests show over 90% less spooler kinks in yarn wound on these machines.

As always, Colman's objective was to "deposit human skills in the machine," expand its capabilities, build more and more intelligence into its sensors and controls. His inventions followed a natural evolutionary progression, and he readily accepted that what was once the state of the art (Barber knotter) would give way in time to a higher level of organization (automatic spooler), which absorbed and transformed its key elements.

Besides the weaver's knotter, the automatic spooler contained a number of novel features that helped to differentiate it in the marketplace. The combination of a pneumatic-suction head and an automatic thread-cleaning device known as a "snick plate," a narrow throatway or channel in the winder-tender that the line passed through on its run-out from the bobbins, removed foreign matter (gouts, kinks, loose fibers, wild ends) from the yarn and controlled the accumulation of lint. A zigzag channel in the surface of the revolving drum distributed yarn to the cheeses in a crisscross pattern, allowing it to build up, back and forth, on a headless spool and thus unwind more rapidly during the warping stage without the interference of metal rims; the crisscross feed also created a much larger mass on the core than then was standard in the industry, resulting in fewer line changeovers and hence more time on the machine that could be devoted to yarn production (see Colman's patent application of October 30, 1911, "Traverse Mechanism for Winding Machines"). The electric drop-wires from the D.I.M. and warp-tying machine were employed as thread-selectors in the spooler; and the tying machine's try-again mechanism was resurrected as a "retie device," which enabled the traveler to make repeated attempts to grasp a loose thread and operated according to the same principles of cam engineering. A "by-pass" sensor, likewise, told the machine when a cheese in its path was full and permitted it to move ahead to the next package.

Colman devoted a great deal of experimental time to finding exactly the right tension for the threads, the right run-out position for the bobbins, the right amount of mechanical actuation to ensure a steady, uniform winding motion (see his patent applications of February 1, 1913; April 7, 1913; July 15, 1914; February 1, 1915; and March 9, 1916). He studied different

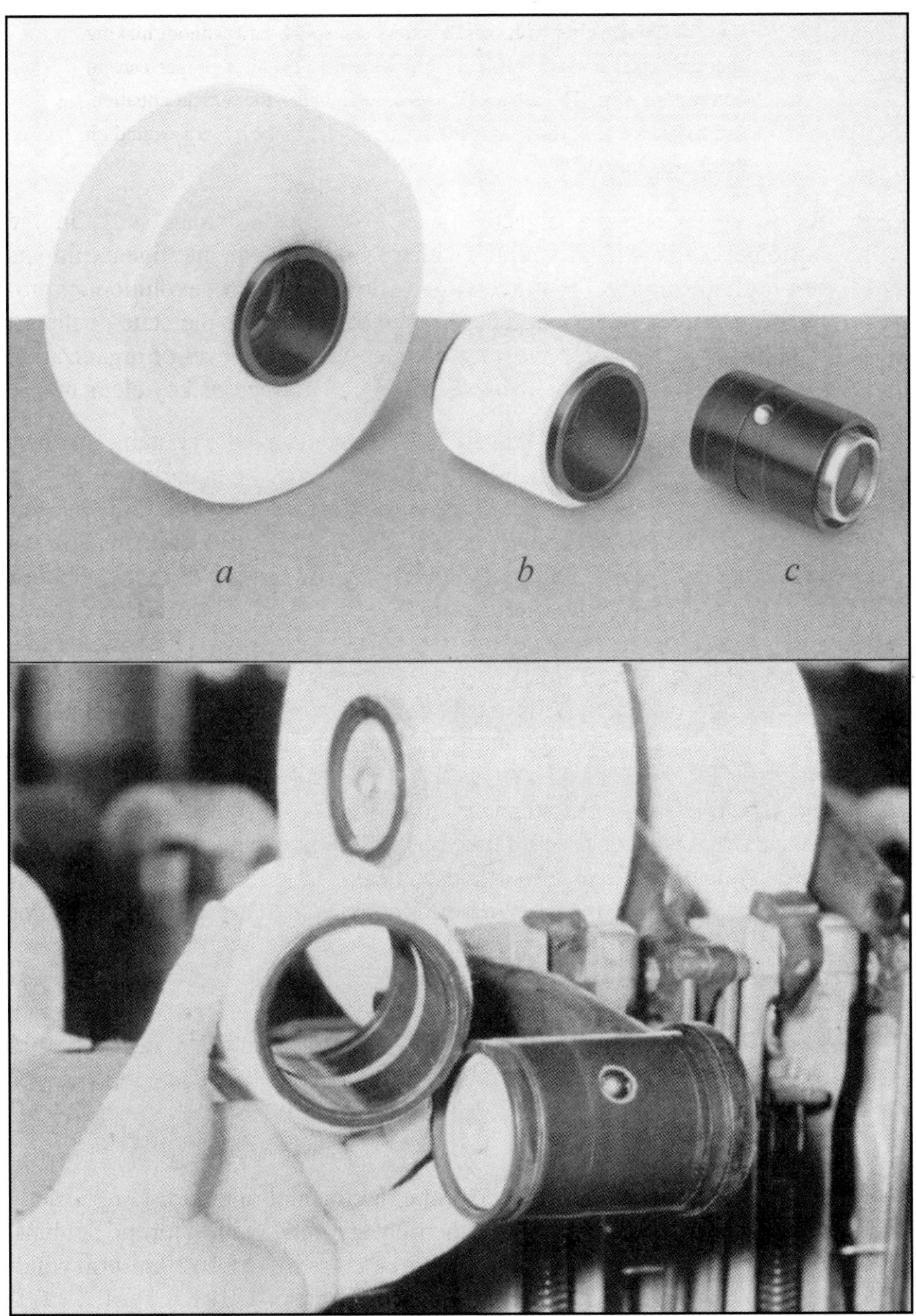

(Top) A full cheese on a sleeve (a), starter cheese (b), and spooler core with ball detent (c). (Bottom) An operator installing a starter cheese on the spooler core prior to winding. The interior groove, which engaged the sleeve's ball detent and held it firmly on the core, is visible in this photograph.

The automatic spooler's "traveler," shown at the end of the machine frame, was modeled on a similar device in the Barber warp-tying machine.

ways of producing air currents along the side of the spooler, investigated the designs of conduits, air ducts, and fan-blades, in order to prevent yarn from slipping off the edges of the cheeses while the slack was being taken up, and as a means of separating the running threads from adjacent threads (November 28, 1916). He perfected a bobbin skewer that held fast to its platform instead of turning and rising as yarn was drawn off the end (January 4, 1917). He placed ball bearings between the cheese spindles and cores to ensure a flexible fit; devised compensating systems of tight and loose pulleys, torsion and compression springs, to deal with eccentric actions of the yarn packages as they were being formed (December 23, 1918); and even cushioned the back-stops of his bobbin holders to give them additional play. When an automated conveyor for transporting cheeses from the spooler to his warping machine failed to work to his satisfaction, he scrapped the entire system and came up with the idea of a "trident table," a small portable truck that operators could push on a runway alongside the spooler while loading it up with cheeses. As simple as it was, the table would eventually become the industry standard for the conveyance of finished packages.

The Barber-Colman high-speed warper, which was co-developed with the automatic spooler, was always a secondary interest of Colman's, since the early tests that he conducted with commercial models of both devices convinced him that the opportunities for improvement, for greater output and higher-quality yarn production, lay mainly with the latter. "From the start, the goal was a spooler which would do mechanically as much as practical the work done by hand with the old machines," Barber-Colman reported, no doubt parroting Colman himself, who devoted the majority of his experimental time (and the majority of his patent applications) during this period to perfecting a spooling system. The two machines were closely associated in his mind, however, and embodied many of the same winding principles. Improvements in spooling, he found, also significantly reduced warping problems downstream. Better, tighter knots on the cheeses enabled the warper to run faster. More uniform distribution of yarn on the cores ensured a smoother feed. Less build-up of lint in the packages reduced gouts and kinks in warp surface, and fewer kinks meant fewer stoppages in the loom.

The spooler and warper were composed of a steel scaffold and revolving drum in their barest essentials; but whereas the spooler had a rectangular frame with individual winding units along the sides, the warper was V-shaped. The machine's basic winding units were vertical bars with round cheese receptacles - a rim, spindle, and spring detent for attaching the yarn package - mounted on the surface, nine to a column. It was as though Colman had folded the spooler frame in half and festooned the sides with hundreds of metal cans. Instead of using a traveler to make a circuit of the machine, Colman moved the bars around the structure in a motorized track like a carousel, connecting them to endless sprocket chains at the top and bottom of the frame. The spooler brought the thread-handling mechanism to the yarn packages; the warper worked in reverse. The V-shaped creel permitted yarn to be wound off both sides of the scaffold at the same time, while also allowing operators to replace exhausted cheese cores from the inside of the V while winding was going on.

Warping was done towards the nose of the creel, where a revolving barrel-beam, driven by a motor, was set up a few feet from the end of the structure. Operators, usually working in tandem, pulled threads off the ends of the cheeses and laid them over the top of a specially-designed saw tooth comb, which fed them in parallel onto the beam surface. As threads were drawn from the creel, the motion actuated electric sensors in the individual receptacles, raising tiny drop wires into a vertical or running position. If a thread subsequently broke during the warping, the drop wire would fall from the vertical position and complete an electrical connection through a magnet mounted on the top of the machine. This, in turn, would release a brake on the warp beam, bringing it to a stop in less than three seconds and enabling operators to repair the broken thread end without serious damage to the cloth. Colman engineered the sensors to be mutually-reinforcing. A broken thread not only shut the warp beam down immediately but disengaged the other receptacles; and this created enough tension on the strands of yarn to prevent kinks from forming during the run-out.

Based on fail-safe features such as these, Barber-Colman promoted the spooler and warper as part of an "automatic system" that dramatically increased weaving quality and efficiency. From its own mill tests, conducted over nearly a decade with every yarn type and size and every piece of available commercial winding and warping equipment, the company was able to document an average reduction of 25% in its loom "stops" per day through the use of the new models, 92% of which was directly attributable to improved spooling techniques. Colman liked to say that this reduction translated into an immediate savings of one-tenth of a weaver's wage.

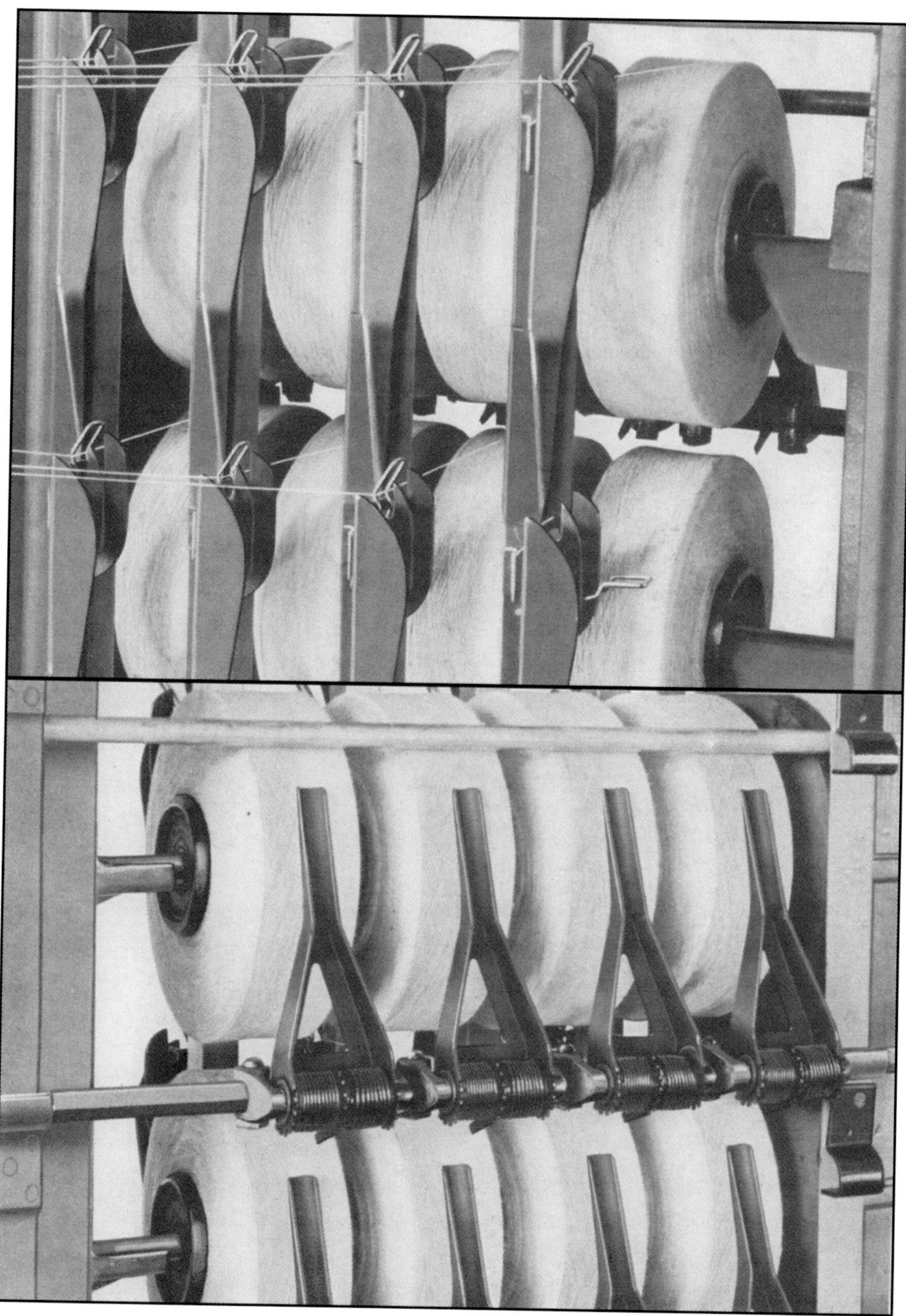

The Barber-Colman high-speed warper employed an electric drop-wire system (top) to monitor broken threads. Spring-actuated brakes riding on the surface of the cheeses (bottom) were engaged when wires on the other side of the machine fell from the vertical position.

In the mills' spooler and warper rooms, he believed, employee numbers could be cut in half through the use of the machines, and the amount of yarn-in-process lowered by as much as 75%. The high-speed warper showed that it could do the work of nine "old-fashioned" machines, processing 500 yards a minute, which was by far the fastest output in the industry.*

With its drawing-in machine (D.I.M.), warp-tying machine, Simplex hand-knotter, automatic spooler, and high-speed warper, the Barber-Colman Company was able to offer cotton manufacturers in the early 1920s as complete a range of warp-replenishing equipment as any then available in the world. Over the ensuing decades, the company would increase its share of the American market to a point, where, on the eve of the Second World War, more than 85% of the looms in the country were weaving from warps prepared by Barber-Colman automated machines.

* Colman later achieved an output of 900 yards per minute with the super-speed warper.

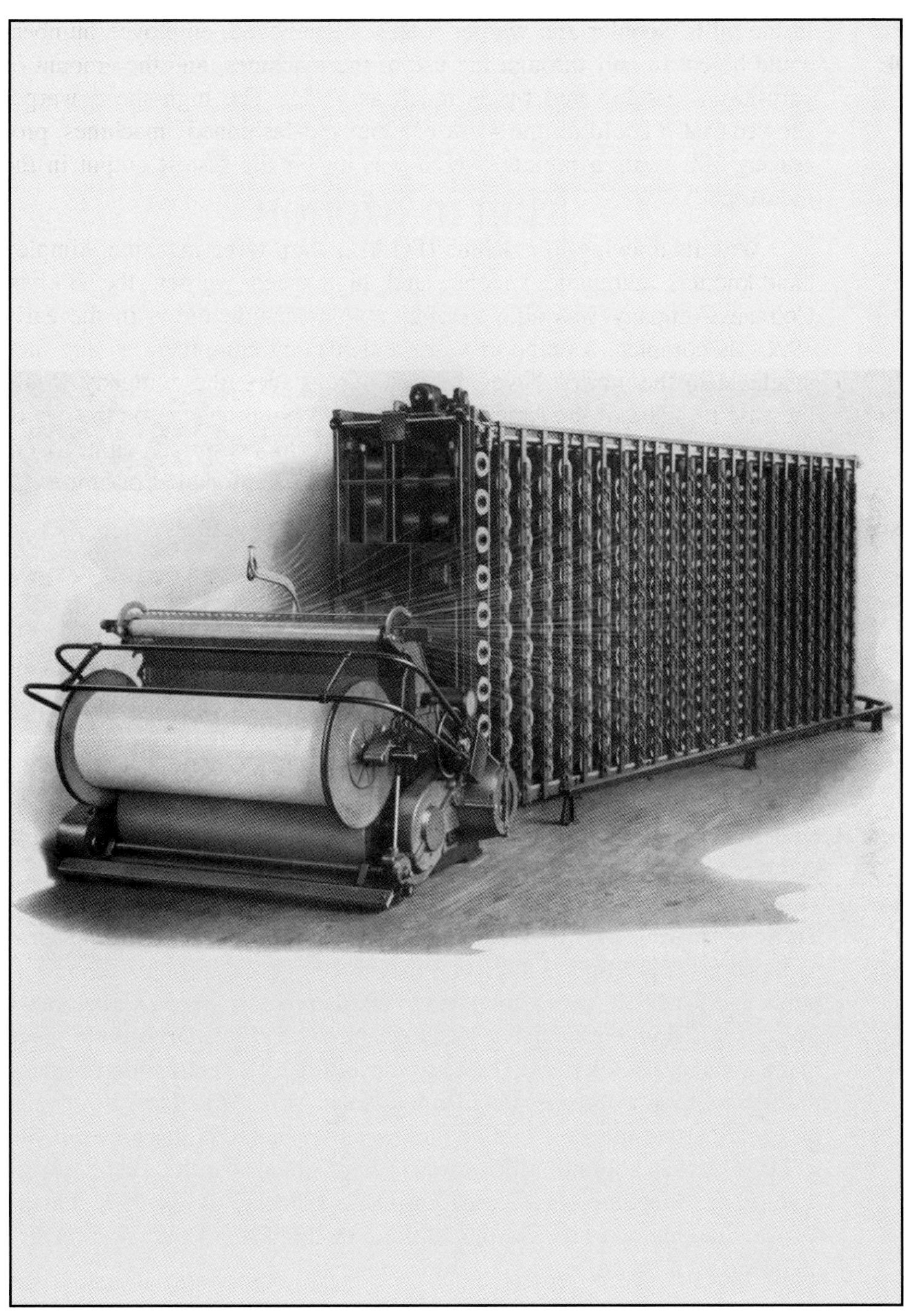

A motorized warp beam in the process of winding threads from the sides of a Barber-Colman high-speed warper.

11
Man in Motion

Father worked whenever he wanted to, and that was most of the time.

- Ruth Colman Tower

i

For the sake of convenience, Howard Colman's career as an inventor may be divided into two distinctive experimental phases, before and after the year 1921. The first period, beginning with the creation of the D.I.M. and continuing through the years of the First World War,* was mainly devoted to cotton manufacturing: in particular, to the automation of yarn processing between the spinning frame and loom. Colman started his textile investigations at Wayland Academy with no other resources than an active imagination and a working knowledge of basic mechanisms that he'd gained from fashioning homemade devices; and by building on this knowledge through trial and error, he gradually made himself the master of four automated processes that were fundamental to improved warp production: drawing, tying, winding, and warping. Of his first 95 patent applications, only three - his very first three submissions for the check pump and water lift - were unrelated to textile projects. His hobbing interests, his decision to establish a Machine and Small Tools Division for gear manufacturing in 1908, was initially an effort to diversify his business through jobbing work after the Financial Panic of 1907 and had its origins in a gear-cutting machine that he purchased for hand-knotter experiments in 1899. It was not until 1923, in fact, that Colman sent his first application for a "Machine for Generating Gear Wheels" to the U.S. Patent Office, drawing upon the lessons of more than a dozen years of commercial contract work to perfect his initial designs.

---

* Howard Colman's experimental work was interrupted in 1917-18 by America's entry into the War and the conversion of the Rockford factory to military parts production.

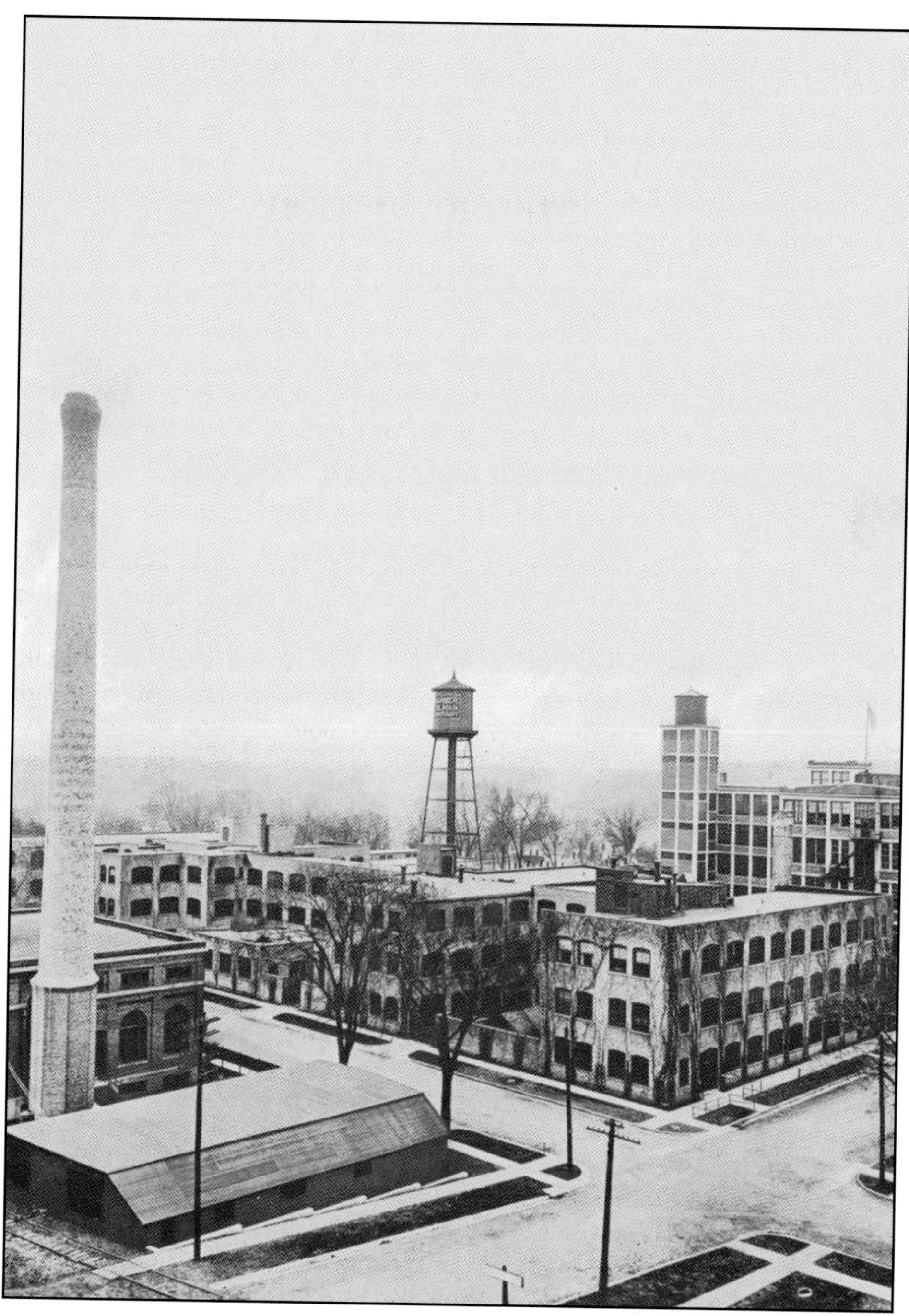

The Barber-Colman factory in the 1920s, as seen from the northeast. The original 1902 structure appears at the intersection of River and Loomis Streets in the foreground.

A second, largely non-textile phase of Colman's experimental career may be said to have begun in 1922-23, after a period of convalescence which, according to his own testimony, lasted from "July 1921" through "the greater part of 1922," and resulted from "poor health" (memorandum, 1/17/23). It's unclear what exactly contributed to this extended sabbatical, whether it was overwork and exhaustion or some more serious kind of psychological depression, and we know only that he was ordered home by his physician in the summer of 1921 and told to stay away from the Barber-Colman factory until he regained his strength. Work was forbidden. He was to give up his existing projects, have nothing to do with company business. But human nature abhors a vacuum, particularly an intelligence as restless and inquisitive as Colman's, and in this void a new set of interests and speculations eventually generated themselves and pointed him in a different experimental direction.

This was the beginning of what would later become known as the Barber-Colman "Electrical" or "Electrical Apparatus Division," the third of the company's major business units, and the primary focus of the inventor's scientific investigations after 1922. Though Colman would continue to work sporadically on textile adaptations and improvements in the succeeding years - better carriage feeds and reed controls, a simplified thread-handling mechanism, a device for lacing silk skeins, and so on - these were mostly retrospective interests, leftovers from earlier projects, and not radical changes in the state of the art. After 1922, in fact, he submitted only eleven new applications to the U.S. Patent Office on textile-related topics, six from 1923-26 and four from 1927-28, before developing a final proposal for a friction clutch in 1938, a device linked to the redesign of a warper-drum mechanism.

Colman's patent applications from the Machine and Small Tools Division were similarly limited in number and scope, the results of lessons learned from customers in the field as well as the fruits of the company's own engineering studies, particularly its designs of differential gear trains in electric controllers and motor-driven operators. Besides his 1923 grinder proposal, Colman submitted applications for advanced gear-cutting machines in 1924 and 1925, and perfected a new grinding and actuating concept for tools and gear-dressing elements in 1928. A 1927 application for an overload release mechanism, which featured specialized speed-reduction gearing, was formulated from his experiments with radiant energy and only secondarily related to projects in the Machine and Small Tools Division. A posthumous filing in the 1940s for improvements in spur gearing, an application that was put together from his study models and project notes, was only the fifth or sixth of his gear-related applications, depending on whether we classify the overload release mechanism as a part of the Electrical or Machine and Small Tools Division.

ii

For most of his adult life, Howard Colman was hampered by physical and emotional ailments - headaches, indigestion, sleeplessness, fatigue, depression - that seem to have been directly related to the progress of his experiments and the ebb and flow of his creative interests. As a scientist and inventor, he distinguished himself not only by the originality of his ideas, his ability to see and formulate new things, but by his single-minded attention to the details of these projects and by the blocks of time, day and night, that he routinely committed to the resolution of problems. It was customary for him to devote several days of continuous work to jump-starting an experiment, proving it up, when he was inspired by a concept. During these periods he usually slept very little (if at all), making a habit of dozing next to the machines in the Experimental Department for an hour or two at night even before he thought of building a rooftop bedroom at the Barber-Colman factory. He was driven by dreams and ideas. The pursuit of an intriguing concept was its own reward for him, and the excitement of making headway in the development of a new idea, of seeing it incorporated in a working prototype or study model, more powerful than any of its later commercial phases. He lived intensely through his experiments. His letters to William Barber testify to his exhilaration during the development of the early D.I.M., his first-of-a-kind successes in the automated drawing of "perfect warps" and the "millions" of dollars in sales that he envisioned when the machine was eventually commercialized. As an inventor, he believed that he could out-think and out-perform most of his contemporaries. As an entrepreneur, he felt, he could probably outwork the rest.

But the emotional pendulum swings both ways; and the same letters that document Colman's experimental successes and buoyant commercial expectations also record his darker moods and sudden changes of heart, the times that he was in the doldrums ("in the dumps") because of severe headaches and "protracted nervous strain," the occasional results of business and experimental reverses and the natural, inevitable outcome of the frenetic pace of his investigations. People wear out, lose their creative edge. When Colman's productivity on a project declined, his worries and anxieties mounted; and these tended to upset his stomach, sap his energy, and dull the "condition" of his "thinking apparatus." His letdowns at the end of experiments, even successful ones, also took their toll on his nerves. He needed to express himself creatively, engage in regular productive activities, to maintain an emotional balance. Like caffeine, invention was a stimulus, a cure for the "blues," and the best way to ensure that his energies continued to be channeled in a positive direction. His feelings were thus keyed to the level of his creative output, and maintaining it in force became essential to his physical and mental health.

Colman complained about digestive problems all his life and preferred a bland diet - roast beef and potatoes; corned beef; lamb chops; rolls, breads, and pies, the latter specially prepared for him by his Swedish cook Christine - as a means of calming his stomach. He typically had two formal dinners a day, six days a week, at noon and in the evening, in the privacy of his Main Street home, where he controlled the menu, company, and conversation, and was well-protected from random intrusions. He went home every day from the Barber-Colman factory and avoided the company lunchroom. His main dietary indulgence, and probably his single greatest failing in the eyes of his children, was a passion for chocolate, many helpings of chocolate at a time, which he continued to enjoy in spite of his family's suspicions that these contributed to the migraine headaches that periodically laid him low. Vegetables, most fruits, stuffing, seasoned and spicy dishes, and cheeses, cheeses of all kinds, headed the list of foods he refused to eat. "Cheese was absolutely anathema to him," his daughter Dorothy said, remembering an incident when her father accidentally bit into a cheese-filled hors d'oeuvres and ran into the toilet to spit it out. Stuffing was allowed at the Thanksgiving table, somewhat reluctantly, for the sake of the children, and Colman made a point of passing it on "with great disdain, as though it were a particularly noxious substance." Henry Colman's diaries chronicled the many times that his son was "on the sick list" as a result of his dietary quirks, bothered by indigestion and coping with mysterious aches and pains that may have been, at least in part, psychosomatic in nature. We learn, in a telling entry, that Howard suffered on the train all the way home from Seattle simply "because he ate some plumb pudding to please the hostess at a dinner" (10/24/08). We see him "dieting, omitting meat and eggs, and taking bran" to compensate, in his father's eyes, for a long reliance on unhealthy foods ("He has taken more meat than is good for one," 10/24/13). The diaries record Howard's "back pains" and attempts to deal with the effects of a nervous condition that his physicians diagnosed, at least in the beginning, as "neuralgia," a disorder that Henry continued to believe was somehow related to his son's eccentric diet. A "lack of elimination digestively ... troubles him and probably in some way causes the back difficulty;" he eats "sparingly" but is not quite "fasting" (9/20/14). "Howard suffers much with the headache," he wrote in another entry. "I do wish he would try thoroughly Fletcherism. He might not be cured, but I do think he would find help" (4/9/14).

The earliest physician of record in Howard Colman's life was a "Dr. Phillips," whom the inventor visited in Milwaukee in January 1893 for the treatment of catarrh, an inflammation of the mucous membranes. The standard remedy for this at the time was cauterizing, "burning out" the nose; and Henry Colman's diaries indicate that Phillips regularly followed the practice and that his son found temporary relief ("Thinks that the specialist helps him.") "Howard is coming home to consult his physician," he noted four years later (10/21/07). "He doctors for catarrh with Dr. Phillips here, to whom he went first, when we first came to Oakland Avenue" (the location of the Colman Methodist parish in Milwaukee). We know from the diaries that Howard was still going to Phillips for the relief of his catarrh in December 1912, as well as using him for other medical needs, such as eye tests and reading glasses.

At some point in his forties, possibly as early as the fall of 1913,* and almost certainly in connection with his health problems in 1921-22, Colman began seeing a Chicago neurologist named Archibald Church, a specialist in nervous disorders who subsequently became, in the words of Dorothy Colman Wallace, the inventor's "primary counselor and confessor." "Father confided a lot in Dr. Church," she said. "He often went to see him in Chicago and stayed overnight at the Blackstone Hotel." Trained at the Elgin State Hospital, Church was regarded by his contemporaries as an expert in clinical depression. As Dorothy recalled:

> It was a matter of nerves rather than thoughts and feelings in those days. Psychology then was not much accepted in the Midwest. People considered depression to be physiologically-based, a disorder of the nervous system, and doctors treated it entirely with medications. So Father went to Dr. Church, thinking that he would do.

---

* "A Dr. in Chicago gives him orders," Henry Colman wrote of his son's treatments at the time (10/24/13).

The library of Howard Colman's Main Street residence, where he spent much of his time recuperating from illnesses in the 1920s and 1930s. "The library, above all, was Father's room," Dorothy Colman Wallace said. "He would lie on the sofa [left] to think. He also did much of his reading there. In fact, I can hardly remember him sitting anywhere except at the dining table or at his drawing board upstairs."

iii

According to Ruth and Dorothy Colman, their father's illness in 1921-22 was one of the two worst of his life, the other occurring eight years later (1930-31) after the failure of the Stock Market and the onset of the Great Depression. The first left him immobilized, physically spent, but still somewhat active imaginatively; the second led to a complete mental and physical breakdown, an emotional paralysis that made invention impossible for many months and prevented him from undertaking even the simplest household tasks. In 1921, Ruth was fourteen and Dorothy only eight, so they may have been less sensitive to their father's moods than they were at a later age. Neither could recall the exact circumstances of the 1921-22 bout of depression, how and when it started, and their assumption was, from what they remembered of the period, that the illness was less debilitating than its successor. By the 1930s Dorothy was much more attuned to her father's personality and could precisely describe the changes in behavior that occurred during his convalescence:

> Father didn't laugh anymore, and he didn't tell jokes. He was quieter than usual. He talked sparingly at the dinner table. He became frustrated with Mother, who irritated him as never before. He seemed to have lost his confidence. He would spend hours wondering about the weather, whether or not it was going to rain. He sometimes had trouble even getting out of his chair. He weighed the possibility of taking in boarders, letting rooms in the house, but in the end decided that this was greatly beneath his dignity and would send the wrong message to the bankers. When he finally came out of his depression, he did it quickly and for no apparent reason.

Whatever the causes of Colman's extended illnesses in middle age, they seem to have resulted in the same creative blockages, the same losses of inspiration; and we may choose to view them, for the purposes of this book, merely as part of a greater personal dynamic that played itself out in the cycles of his invention. Time and again his ailments and "attacks" prepared the way for breakthroughs, for important experimental insights. He would leave the factory to recuperate, to recharge his emotional batteries, and return to Barber-Colman with new interests that had been incubated while he was getting well. These sometimes started out as left-over problems, things remembered from previous investigations, and took flight after they were energized by ideas from his readings and conversations and solitary reflections.

Unlike other phases of his experimental work, Colman's abrupt change of direction in the 1920s, his turn away from textiles, is well-documented in the company's archival file. The inventor himself described a 1925 illness and a newly-found interest in codes, ciphers, and military communications - an interest that may have been influenced by the national fascination with wartime espionage, the infamous Zimmerman Memorandum and the code-breakers of British Naval Intelligence, then much talked about in the newspapers - in a study of telegraphy (4/28/25) that he deposited in the Experimental Department. Colman noted that he had had his son Walter look up an article on "Submarine Telegraphy" in the *Encyclopedia Britannica* and had read the "pertinent parts;" he had also recruited Duncan Stewart, a young electrical engineering graduate of the University of Wisconsin and a North Main Street neighbor, to help him explore the field: "... Stewart and I discussed code[s] extensively during my illness and read everything we could find on the subject, including an article regarding Colonel George W. Fabyan in the *American Magazine* ... entitled "He Solves the Secrets of Cipher Writing" by John Kidder Rhodes."

Two pieces of capital equipment that had been recently installed at the Barber-Colman factory, an automatic switchboard for telephone calls (*Barber-Colman Association News*, 2/21) and an electric operator for the two-leaf door on the company's executive garage, also contributed to Colman's slowly gathering brainstorm. As Robert Nethercut, Barber-Colman's public relations manager, recounted in a later history of the period, the electric operator was a device that could be actuated by "inserting a key in a switch mounted on a post at the side of the drive," allowing employees to stay in their cars instead of opening and closing the door by hand; although, as Nethercut noted, there was still a need to stop the car at the right place, "fuss around and get the key, open the window in bad weather, and find the key slot in the post" (2/22/66). Colman was intrigued by the mechanism and grateful for the time saving it provided but also frustrated by the occasional "fussing around." The obvious solution, the opportunity for innovation, was to find a way to open the door without opening the window, without using the key, and without stopping the car by the post. His flash of insight, his eureka moment, apparently occurred when images in his head of the electric operator merged with those of the special coding devices and selective signaling mechanisms. He decided that the answer would be to send a radio signal from the car to the garage-door opener and to vary the pulses of the signal in a way that approximated, conceptually, the serrated edges of a standard Yale key.

A "radio key," Colman believed, could be designed to raise the pins in a garage-door "lock" to a height that allowed its tumblers to turn, and the relative pin positions themselves varied enough from lock to lock to permit an almost limitless number of codal combinations, providing users with unique secret keys for their garages. Colman envisioned a scheme in which the tumblers of a standard cylinder lock were transformed into a rotary drum in the garage-door receiver, a kind of mechanical pincushion actuated by radiant energy. When the signal was picked up by the receiver, a switch would be closed and a motor started to operate a selector mechanism. As it turned, the drum would push surface pins forward through a predetermined cycle that was synchronized with the transmitter. The mechanical actions would be initiated by a centrifugal clutch and the power controlled by rack and pinion. Edgar Lilja, a Barber-Colman engineer and close working associate of Colman's in the Experimental Department, afterwards traced the inventor's thought processes in developing his signaling apparatus:

> About 20 years ago, when Mr. Colman's health had been impaired by over-work, he was told by his doctor that he must have a good long rest. While complying as best he could, his active mind conceived the idea of opening and closing garage doors by radio control. Typically, he wasn't the least bit interested in a simple control that would open the doors in response to a single radio impulse, because then anybody could open anybody else's garage and, worse yet, the high frequency oscillations produced by lightning would open the doors whenever it thundered …
>
> Mr. Colman's transmitting scheme was the equivalent of inserting a key in a lock at a uniform speed and sending a radio signal whenever a bump on the key would have pushed a plunger in the lock … At the receiver in the garage, the response to these signals was as though a duplicate key were being inserted simultaneously in a receiving lock. If the key fit the lock, fine. The doors opened … If not, no dice (4/8/43).

Colman initially employed a clockwork mechanism to ensure that the radio key moved at a constant speed, winding it by hand "as the transmitter button was pulled." In this scheme, the radio key was "stationary" and the lock, so to speak, "moved over" the key, which was the same thing in Lilja's mind as pushing a key into "a stationary lock" according to concepts of relative motion. (The receiver inside the garage also required a "constant-speed drive" to advance the "proper cylinder plunger" as "each radio 'bump' " or serration was registered.)

Using Duncan Stewart to help him on weekends during his convalescence and afterwards hiring his friend as a full-time personal assistant, Colman constructed a study model of the radio-controlled door operator and began experimenting with it, soon realizing, as Nethercut put it, that the concept was "so new and … startling" that it had to work flawlessly in its first public demonstrations to have a chance of acceptance ("If it did not, people would be apt to criticize it … [as] 'crazy' equipment.") To gather as much field data as possible, he installed prototypes in the home garages of Barber-Colman employees; and this led to the further recognition of the sheer variety of existing garage-door types - two-leaf outward swinging, two-leaf inward swinging, three-leaf inward swinging, four-five-and six-leaf inward swinging, horizontally sliding, sliding-abutting, single sliding left-and-right, double-sliding past, folding, and overhead - that the operator would have to manipulate.

In 1926 Colman undertook a market survey of the "better residences" in Chicago, Milwaukee, Cleveland, New York, and Rockford as a means of determining the most popular garage-door "styles." (As part of this study, he also hired his son Edwin and Addison Brown, a Rockford friend, to drive around Long Island during their college breaks and count the number of garages.) He realized that the survey results would significantly influence the designs of his mechanical linkages; the nature of his motor unit and safety devices; his operator's power requirements; the way that his doors opened, closed, and locked; and even the ways that receivers were mounted in the garages. To sell operators, he'd have to sell garage doors; and to sell garage doors, the easiest thing would be to partner with an established commercial vendor. Quite coincidentally, Colman learned that the Overhead Door Corporation, the nation's leading garage-door manufacturer, had been experiencing a great deal of difficulty with the performance of its own switch-controlled opener; and he wondered if the Corporation would be receptive to some sort of joint-venture proposition. "We approached them about an arrangement for supplying them operators [in exchange for discounted overhead doors]," Nethercut wrote, "but they were not interested." The rebuff eventually led to Colman's decision to start his own "Barcol" garage-door line and to put his money on the development of an overhead model, the likeliest style, in his eyes, to dominate the future market.

Colman believed that the key to the success of his radio-key operator was finding a suitable small electric motor to drive the transmitter and receiver automatically and to synchronize the signals between them. On the one hand, the operator required a low-sensitivity circuit to avoid being affected by commercial radio broadcasts and atmospheric disturbances, such as lightning; on the other hand, it required a fractional horsepower unit that could still get up to speed rapidly when actuated by a coded signal, a demand that exceeded the capabilities of all the existing commercial motors. "Mr. Colman found that there were [sic] none on the market small, cheap, and reliable enough," Lilja remembered, "with the power required to drive the lock." The inventor's reaction to this, according to Lilja, was fairly predictable:

> Did he quit then, and wait for some motor manufacturer to produce what he needed? Not at all. Instead, he set out to develop a new motor of his own that had the required characteristics. It was just part of the game.

Colman designed his new small motor by attacking one of the things that bedeviled the electrical industry in the 1920s: the vibration or hum that occurred in magnetic devices when they were energized by alternating current. The noise was commonly regarded as an acceptable nuisance, as the price of using electrical technology. People learned to put up with it. But Colman saw it as a possible means of increasing his machine's efficiency; and he decided to reconfigure the standard synchronous motor so that it converted the flux into additional output:

> Colman harnessed … [the] hum. He mounted a magnetic armature on springs, and tuned them so the armature vibrated violently at power frequency. He then arranged a pawl and ratchet so that each vibration of the armature caused the pawl to step the ratchet ahead one tooth … The power supply frequency was already controlled by the Rockford Electric Company, and therefore the ratchet would obviously be inched around in time with the transmitter.

It was a simple and elegant solution, one reminiscent of his earlier use of municipal water pressure to elevate rain water to attic tanks. By tying his signal cycles to the Electric Company's power supply, Colman brought the motors driving his transmitter and receiver into a precise phased relationship, even when they started at different times. The motions of each step in a cycle were always equal to, or exact multiples of, the alternating current frequency.

The Barber-Colman door-operator included a transmitter, receiver, and two antennas, one that was fastened to the underside of the car frame and the other that was buried along the center line of the driveway. By straddling this line with his car wheels, the owner of a door-operator perfectly positioned his vehicle to signal the garage. He pulled a knob on the dashboard. This actuated a timer and spark-coil unit by drawing current from the car's battery and sent out pulses through the transmitting antenna. The receiving antenna, which was wired to the garage, communicated these pulses to the door operator and closed a contact there. The contact started the motor, which opened the door:

> When the starting contact is made, a latch magnet - by means of an armature and spring-operated lever - releases a brake and closes the main motor switch at the lever end. As soon as the electric motor gets up to speed (usually in less than a half second), a centrifugal clutch engages and passes the motion on to a planetary differential. This differential forms the main part of the release mechanism. A pawl holds the ring gear fixed until the load exceeds a set amount. Then the pawl trips. The ring gear also runs free. And the motor, which continues to run, is disconnected from the driving pinion as necessary [i.e. if the garage door is obstructed]. The driving pinion, through a mechanism that varies according to the type of the overhead door, causes the door to open and close (Barber-Colman Catalog A).

Colman anticipated problems in every phase of operation. He used a cam shaft at the end of the door's travel to apply a brake and bring the door down without slamming. He installed a release chain in the motor so that the door could be operated manually after a power outage, as well as a re-set chain to re-engage the door opener when the power was turned on. He created a locking lever to prevent the release mechanism from tripping if someone tried to force the door open. A secondary control device allowed the garage door to move to an "open" or "partially open" position; and a delay-action device, similarly, allowed it to open for a fixed interval of time before closing again, automatically. When it was dark, his transmitter drew an extra pulse from the car lights and sent it to a switch in the receiver, which was designed to turn on the lights in the garage (during the daytime, when the car lights were off, no signal was sent).

Going into the door operator mathematically, Colman determined that the device's coding bars, in variable "on" and "off" positions, could produce more than 4,000 individual radio keys, an analysis that owed a great deal to his understanding of cipher machines and encrypted wartime messages. True to his habit of looking backwards and forwards at the same time, his analysis of the radio keys yielded some important insights into telegraphy and a means of improving it with better coding. In a prospectus on "Telegraph Signaling" (1925), he explained how his radio-key experiments became the basis of a whole new concept of remote-control communications:

> This idea was suggested by my work on "DO" [Door Operator] where we use a combination of pins pushed and not pushed to form a mechanical lock having many different combinations ... This work called my attention to the large number of combinations possible with a small number of pins, as shown by the law $N = 2^n$ where N equals the number of combinations, and n equals the number of pins.

Colman wondered why the coded messages or keys that actuated his door operators could not work just as well in telegraph signaling and thereby lower the costs of transmission. Telegraph charges were based on the length of time that it took to send a message, and this depended entirely on the number of impulses involved. The standard practice was to spell out every message letter-by-letter, with additional signals being employed for numbers, symbols, and punctuation, a laborious and entirely unnecessary system, in his opinion, when a telegraphic shorthand, a series of word and letter codes, might be better adopted. Along with his survey of the most popular garage-door styles, Colman conducted a study of common words in daily business correspondence, using letters from Barber-Colman's files to develop a statistical sample. He found, as a result of the study, that 2,000 of the most frequently-used words could be represented by a small number of positive or negative/current or no-current impulses, which were similar in nature to those in the telegraph's own Baudot Code. In fact, combinations of the eleven signal units yielded exactly 2,048 codal keys; and he believed that this was more than sufficient for 96% of routine business communication.

Thus if 100 words were chosen at random for a new telegraph message (this was assumed to be the *average* length of a transmission), 96 of these, statistically, would tend to fall within the group of frequently-used words and require 1,056 electrical impulses to be sent. The four other words would need to be transmitted letter-by-letter, using specially-devised, five-unit codes for this purpose (based on a hypothetical average of seven letters in each word, this would require 140 impulses). Colman assumed that spacing, code-changes, and an end-of-transmission-signal would have to have 31 impulses, and that the entire message would end up being some 1,227 impulses long.

Ad No. 1411—2 col. x 100 lines—Newspaper Adv.—Byrne Adv. Agency

OPEN AND CLOSE YOUR GARAGE DOORS BY RADIO

(*Looking up under the instrument board*)

When this box in your car sends out its call . .

"*Open the doors—the owner seeks admittance!*" commands this little box as you pull the operating knob on the instrument board. And the receiving set, or brain of the Barber-Colman Radio-Controlled Door Operator, decodes the message and replies in spirit, "*Identity checked! Let the owner enter.*" Promptly, the doors swing open. If it is night and your car lights are on when you enter, the Door Operator also turns on your garage lights. If you turn the car lights out when inside your garage, before closing the door by another pull of the knob on your dash, *the operator* leaves your garage lights on so that you can find your way about!

No other radio-equipped car will open your garage—only your own. Nor will intruders break the powerful electrically-controlled mechanical lock. Truly a marvelous mechanism. It may also be controlled by conveniently placed switches, if desired. Write for complete information today.

BARBER-COLMAN COMPANY
Rockford, Illinois

BARBER·COLMAN DOOR OPERATORS

Early Barber-Colman newspaper advertisements likened the radio-controlled door operator to a genie in the car's instrument panel.

To send the same 100 words by the standard Baudot Code, Colman observed, a telegraph operator would need to transmit 25 impulses per letter, or 2,500, and five impulses for the spaces between the words, or 500, bringing the message total to 3,000. This was two and a half times longer than Colman's proposed signaling method and a considerable waste of time and money in view of the alternative. "While any preferred method may be employed for coding and decoding the signals," Colman wrote in a 1926 patent application for "Telegraphy," "it is contemplated that automatic mechanisms will be employed for this purpose, but inasmuch as these mechanisms form no part of this invention, it is deemed unnecessary to illustrate and describe them herein." The automatic devices for the transmission of signals that he described were only then beginning to take shape in his mind; but he knew that his remote-control concept, the idea of uniquely-coded electrical messages, which had been proved up in his radio-key trials, was capable of being applied on a much broader scale and the advantages of a telegraphic shorthand demonstrated by moving telegraph messages much more efficiently through the system. Over the next two years, in a burst of experimental activity, he would put the pieces of this puzzle together in his largest single patent application - indeed, the largest single application received to that time by the U.S. Patent Office - and take up the cause of multiple messaging or multiplexing, proposing a new method of sending transmissions over the wire and of eliminating bottlenecks during their transfer from station to station.

iv

There's no clearer indication of Howard Colman's importance to the Barber-Colman Experimental Department, his level of involvement in each of its projects, than the fact that company's patent-application efforts ceased during the period of his 1921-22 illness. When he returned to work in the fall of 1922, the company's application production-line started up again in earnest, with several holdover projects, warp-drawing and gear-making experiments mostly, receiving his blessing after a review of the engineering reports. Between 1923-25 the company submitted a total of ten applications in Colman's name to the Patent Office, five for textile devices, four for grinding and gear-cutting equipment, and one, somewhat inexplicably, for a tiny fuel gauge to register gasoline levels in automobiles. Reflecting his ever-increasing interest in electricity and remote signaling, Colman sent in sixteen patent applications over the next three years, beginning with his submission for telegraph messaging

("Telegraphy") and concluding with a gigantic 464-claim proposal for multiplexing and multi-stage telegraphic transmissions ("System of Communications").

Two theoretical pathways, in telegraphy and radiant energy, thus began to appear in Colman's experiments in the late 1920s: the first a radically new approach to remote, high-speed communications, a big idea with little expectation of immediate commercial acceptance; and the second a much more down-to-earth concept, a practical use of radio technology with an opportunity for sales to millions of American garage owners. The latter pathway was defined by seven patent submissions within a period of ten months in 1926-27. Colman's proposal for a "Selective Signaling Apparatus" (7/6/26), the basic blueprint of his radio-key concept, was the first. Three months later he submitted an application for "Operating Means for Doors and the Like" (10/4/26) to stake his claim to a switch-controlled mechanism that opened and closed garage doors for pre-determined intervals of time and at variations of "open" and "closed" positions. Three applications for garage door fail-safe devices, an "Overload Release Mechanism," "Motor-Driven Operator," and "Motor-Control Mechanism" were submitted on the same day in February (2/5/27). Two other applications for improvements in Colman's radio transmitter ("Signaling Apparatus," 3/14/27, and "Radiant Energy Control System," 5/4/27) rounded out his submissions.

According to informal Barber-Colman accounts, the inventor's enthusiasm for his new electrical projects was equaled by the concerns of people like Luther Miller and Harry Severson that these were becoming a distraction from the real business of the company - in their view, the manufacture and sale of warp-production machinery - and a drain on its financial resources. As president and majority shareholder, Colman was basically free to do whatever he pleased, to indulge any interest; but he also tried to be sensitive to his friends' feelings, and he eventually decided to underwrite the electrical experiments himself until their actual commercial value could be determined. This meant that any patents received for the projects would be owned by Colman exclusively and not assigned to the company, and that a separate set of financial records would be kept for all electrical-related transactions. Duncan Stewart was placed in charge of the enterprise, working directly for Colman, a kind of free-lance engineer within the walls of the Experimental Department but outside the purview of its ongoing textile initiatives.

We may assume, to the extent that Colman discussed his electrical experiments with Miller and Severson, that the multiplex telegraphy was the most baffling of all his new projects. A combination cipher machine and electromagnetic switching relay, it used a variation of the door-operator's selective signaling apparatus to record and transmit telegraph messages, adopting the codal concept that Colman outlined in his patent application for "Telegraphy" but modifying it slightly here to spell out messages on a letter-by-letter basis and reducing the number of signal units from eleven to five in the interests of efficient storage. Like the door operator, the multiplex system employed both receivers ("recorders") and transmitters, as well as an endless storage chain, arranged in a series of loops, for the translation of electrical signals into mechanical representations and vice versa. The chain was essentially an open-ended memory device for deciphering and sending alpha-numeric messages. It was intended to offer users a virtually unlimited storage capacity, as messages, after being recorded in the chain by combinations of pins "pushed and not pushed" in each linkage, were shunted off to "secondary reservoirs," whose memory capacity could be expanded indefinitely through the use of blank linkages. The signals were preserved in various mechanical combinations according to the law $N = 2^n$. They remained in the secondary storage chains until new signals were received from the transmitter to convert them into electric impulses again and send them over the wire to the next relay.

Colman realized early on that his idea of a telegraphic shorthand would be worthless without a better way of handling coded messages in transit. Unlike the telephone with its single-stage connection between parties, the telegraph used a number of relay points or exchanges to transfer communications. This was done to avoid tying up trunk lines and to ensure that messages reached the right destinations; but it turned out to be painfully slow in practice because station attendants needed to print the messages and read the addresses before sending them on to the next exchange. To speed things up, Colman felt the only choice was to change the system: to give messages peculiar coded addresses that enabled them, automatically, to find the right relays without the need for human intervention. To do this meant installing signal-control mechanisms ("relays") at each exchange that could read the messages, select the succeeding electrical paths, and transmit over these lines.

The heart and soul of Colman's multiplex "system of communications" was his chain-linkage storage medium, and it may be worthwhile to describe it here in greater detail as a way of appreciating the nature of the technical challenge he set for himself. In appearance, his storage chains were not unlike sets of pulleys or block-and-tackle mechanisms hanging from a steel framework. Suspended vertically in four matching "supply" and "storage" loops, and closely-spaced one above the other, the chains advanced by shaft-mounted sprockets that were driven by synchronous motors. At the end of the supply and storage loops, along short lengths of chain drawn off the main circuit, Colman set up recording and transmitting points, with a single "blanker," a pin-setter mechanism for clearing the linkages, positioned after the transmitter. The short runs were intended to allow the chains to advance quickly, with low inertia, when signals came in or needed to be dispatched. Colman designed the recorder and transmitter with five-pin "pushers" that acted in timed relation to the electrical signals they received. At the recording point, the pins in the blanks were moved to one of two "set positions," either "in" or "out," in a fraction of a second; and they were transmitted in a similar fashion. It was Colman's hope to furnish the relay paths in his telegraph system with five separate circuits, one for each signal combination, so that messages could be transmitted and received simultaneously. In its optimal form, his transmitters would fire off signals as a group, and his receiving stations would be able to sort them out. The idea was clearly revolutionary in a world of successive, start-stop telegraph communications, but Colman noted, from his experiments with small motors, that it was already possible to synchronize a transmitter and receiver over short distances within the same municipal electrical service.

He had big plans. A declaration in his proposal to the Patent Office said that his claims went far beyond the "specifications" of the current application; he believed that his intellectual property rights extended to "all modifications and alternative adaptations falling within the spirit and scope of the invention." The multiplex telegraphy was merely a "preferred embodiment" of a new communications system, he said, a variation "within the art" that had suggested itself in the course of his ongoing experimental investigations. It was broadly indicative of a fertile field of inquiry that he intended to exploit in future applications. The projects he contemplated were all interrelated, part and parcel of the same conceptual puzzle, and he wished to place the Patent Office on notice of this fact.

The big idea in this was no less than the reform of the telegraph system itself. In the back of his mind, Colman envisioned a new national subscriber network of multiplex relay exchanges that served a variety of small, medium-sized, and large business offices. There would be at least three different classes of communications available to subscribers in this scheme - "deferred," "ordinary," and "preferred (multiplex) messages," according to the speed of transmission desired - and at least two levels of service: 1) a traditional start-stop, single-circuit trunk line; and 2) a new high-speed, simultaneous, multi-circuit network.

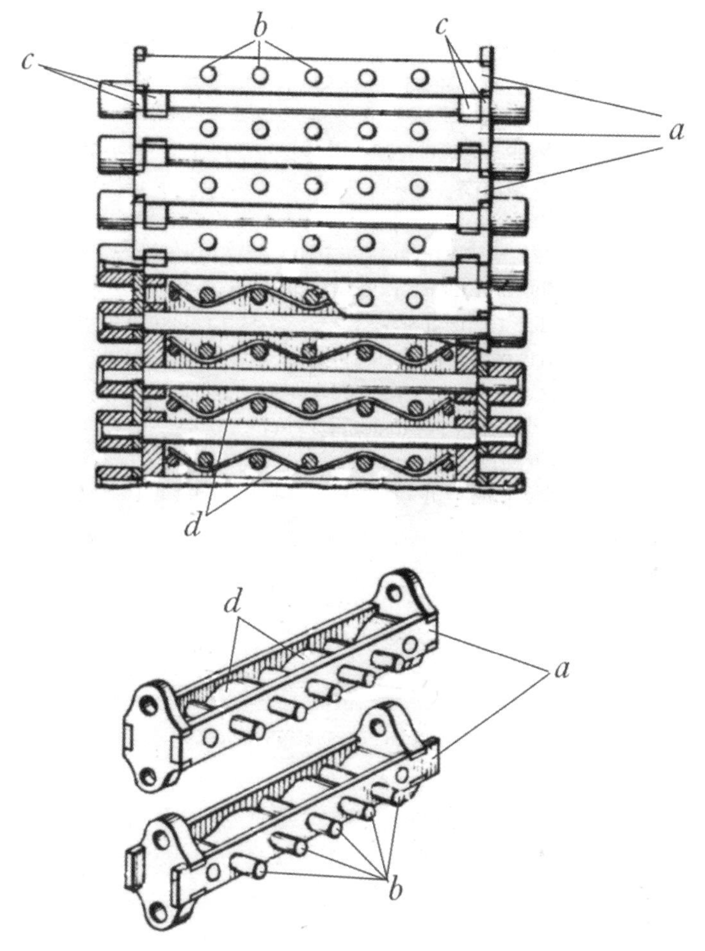

The storage medium of the multiplex telegraph, shown in two different perspectives (above), was composed of an endless chain of parallel metal bars (a), whose five-pin perpendicular "pushers" (b) were set in either "in" or "out" positions according to the coded message. Pivotal hinges (c) connected the bars. When pins were "coded," a thin metal strip (d) wrapped around them automatically to hold them in place until the messages were sent. The top drawing on this page is a frontal view of the chain. The bottom illustration is a profile of the parallel metal bars.

The schematic on the following page shows how the multiplex telegraph's "supply" (1) and "storage" (2) chains were incorporated into a electro-mechanical system of communications. Incoming electrical signals were received by the "recorder" (3) and converted into coded mechanical messages. When the storage chains advanced to the transmitter (4), these messages were re-converted into electrical signals and sent out across a telegraph wire. After the messages were transmitted, the storage chains passed through a blanker (5), where all the pins were cleared - i.e. pushed to an extreme "out" position - and prepared for the receipt of the next coded messages; blanked chains were routed into the storage loops in their progress towards the recorder (6). The chain lengths were suspended between a series of drive sprockets (7) and rollers (8).

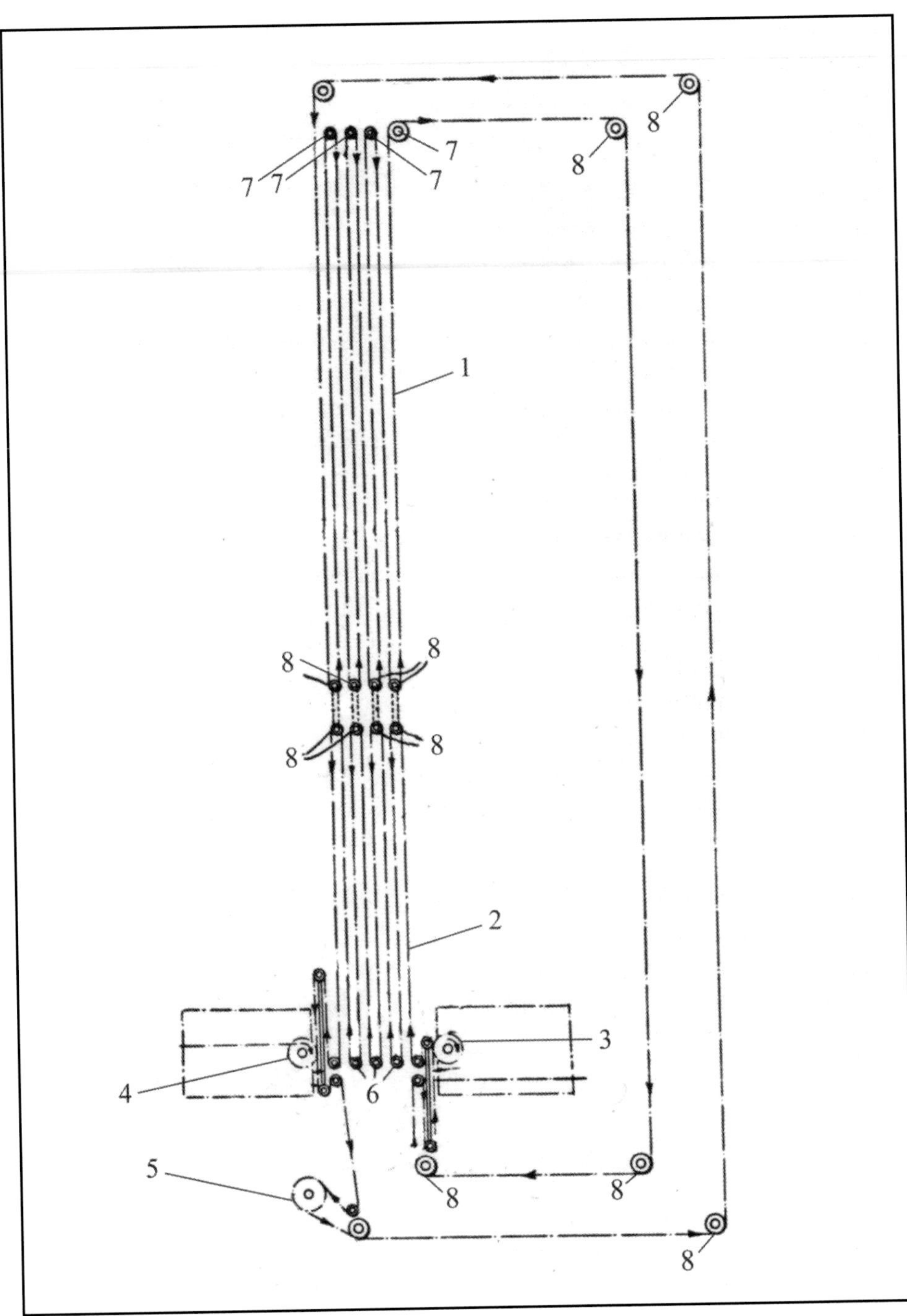
8
8
7
8
7 7
7
1
8
8
8
8
2
3
4
6
5
8
8
8

For a fee, subscribers would be given their own recording and sending devices and connected remotely to a multiplex central office, where messages would be received and transmitted electrically over available trunk lines. The central office would act as a traffic controller, an automatic switching relay (not unlike Barber-Colman's own commercial switchboard for telephone calls) that read and stored incoming messages and directed them to their final destinations.

To make his subscriber service a reality, Colman undertook the design of a manual keyboard transmitter ("storing transmitter") that recorded telegraph messages temporarily in a 250-link flexible metal chain, an adaptation of the coding mechanism disclosed in his system of communications. Powered by a small electric motor, the transmitter moved its memory chain around the inside of steel carrousel, where it passed recording, transmitting, and blanking points in succession. To aid in the transmission of traditional start-stop messages and to make his multiplex keyboarding more flexible, Colman next devised a high-speed page printer employing a dot-matrix arrangement of paper-thin (.003 of an inch) metal "ribbons" arranged as overlapping strips. Each strip contained clusters of tiny surface bumps or "anvils;" and these were shifted back and forth a few hundredths of an inch by a selector apparatus at the end of the row, according to the letters and numbers to be printed. Tiny cam-actuated push rods, which were spaced across the page, would then strike the paper and inked ribbons and press them against the anvils. An important feature of Colman's machine was the fact that it moved at the same pace between successive lines as it did between "successive characters in the same line." (There was no delay, as in a standard printer/typewriter, for the return movement of the paper carriage when it completed a line of type.) His close study of the mechanics of line and type spacing also bore fruit in two related inventions for the commercial printing industry. One was an internal space-counting system for typesetters that justified line lengths automatically in the process of composition (he called this a "totalizing register'). The other was a control-tape device (a "tabulating mechanism") that permitted commercial printers to anticipate the breaks in their line and type casting.

It was Colman's plan to turn the Barber-Colman factory into a test site for the multiplex central office. Since the Rock Street complex was already fully dedicated to high-volume machine production and crowded with materials, equipment, and works-in-progress, the decision was made to erect the storage and switching relay on the roof of one of his buildings.

Colman eventually chose the company's new (1927) five-story brick-and-concrete addition at the corner of Rock and Loomis Streets; this already housed an enlarged Experimental Department, and Colman designed his telegraph facility for the west side of the roof and connected it to the work area below by an interior stairs. With little concern for the appearance of the Rock Street factory exterior, he put up a two-story orange brick box between the building's two roofline decorative pediments. Fortress-like, with four tiny windows, the structure rapidly filled up with the mechanical memory chains that he readied for the launch of his communications project.*

V

The workhorse of Colman's early electrical inventions was his small synchronous motor. It was an integral part of the radio-key receiver, the multiplex recorder, and the different printing and storage devices that he had developed, but it was always considered in a supporting role, as a means to an end, an enabler of other technical schemes. What, then, were the motor's commercial possibilities in its own right? It was only a matter of time before Colman began asking himself this question and comparing the qualities of his machine, its power, size, and cost of production, to those of the current industry leaders. Edgar Lilja remembered that the inventor eyed one company in particular:

> At that time Minneapolis-Honeywell was making a "killing" in the newly-opened field of electric temperature control. Buyers paid as much as $125.00 for a simple furnace regulator or a valve operator. These units were driven by large motors of conventional design, and it seemed clear to Mr. Colman that if his new motor could be used there, the price might be halved and still leave a handsome margin of profit …

Colman's reaction was predictable. He went to work redesigning his motor for use in the controls industry, further reducing its size to make it

* Colman's patent application for a "System of Communications" (1928) was followed by submissions for a "Storing Transmitter" (1930); "Printer" (1936); "Selectively-Operable Mechanism for Typographical Machines" (1939); "Control-Strip Composing Machine" (1939); and "Automatic Multiple-Stage Telegraph" (1940). In addition, three posthumous applications were filed by Barber-Colman staff from notes on his experimental projects: a "Message-Intercepting and Relaying Circuit in an Automatically-Directed Message-Telegraph System" (1944); a "Message-Telegraph System" (1944); and a "Central Switching Point" (1947). The voluminous 1928 multiplex package, which laid the conceptual groundwork for most of the telegraphic inventions to follow, remained under review in the U.S. Patent Office for 17 years, finally passing to issue on July 31, 1945. The delay, in effect, prevented Colman from taking any of his multiplex schemes to market.

suitable to the regulation of small temperature-sensitive instruments. He built prototypes of thermostats, fans, valves, and dampers; put them together in a single motor-operated system; and field-tested different configurations of this system in buildings like the Rockford National Bank and Janesville City Hall.

Early results were mixed. While the system functioned automatically - it opened and closed the valves, started and stopped the fans, and accurately positioned the dampers on cue from the thermostat - the noise that it made in calling for heat and air conditioning, an annoying hum that reminded listeners of a swarm of bees, limited its commercial value. It might work for a garage-door opener, for a brief instant when putting a car away at night, but it was nerve-wracking in a house or professional office when controls were actuated in different rooms in succession. Colman went back to the drawing board and began to wonder whether his synchronous motor was really right for the job. Was this the best design? Could he buy or build a better motor?

Finding nothing appropriate on the market, Colman reached the conclusion that he would have to build his own device if he were going be successful. He knew that the attributes of the machine he was looking for - small, efficient, dependable, noiseless, inexpensive - led to a different kind of motor conceptually, most likely to a shaded-pole induction design; and he also knew these motors, invented in 1888, had been "worked to exhaustion" by the best engineering minds in the field (Lilja). No one had yet produced a model with the power and efficiency he needed for his temperature-control system. To understand the existing engineering literature and get some practical experience in the art, he conducted his own small-motor experiments, quickly determining that the features of the shaded-pole design that had been the most troublesome to engineers were exactly the things that he needed to improve it. What was lacking, apparently, were a fresh set of eyes:

> All of the commercial shaded pole motors had excessively large rotors, large gaps between the stator poles, and shading rings of small cross-section. It seemed reasonable that a large rotor should result in high torque. Gaps between poles should force magnetic flux to enter the rotor where it will be useful, instead of permitting it to leak around the rotor; and small shading rings should result in lower power losses than large ones. There was ample mathematical proof to support these simple theories, but each [previous engineering study] failed to consider all the factors

> involved. From the beginning, we flew in the face of all these theories, and this course paid dividends (Lilja).

The first shaded-pole motor that Colman designed had so little power that the oil on the bearings stopped it from running; the lubricant's drag disabled the rotor. "If a common housefly got on the shaft and braced himself," a Barber-Colman mechanic recalled, "the motor wouldn't start." So the inventor constructed a number of study models and experimented with the shading rings, the relative proportions of iron and copper, and different ratios between the shaded and unshaded pole areas. It came down to a matter of "cut and try," Lilja said, "more theory," and "cut and try" again. The approach played directly to Colman's strengths, for no one was better at improvising and theorizing, at learning from mistakes, and at formulating new designs from unconventional assumptions about the technical state of the art and the ways to supersede it. In this instance, his breakthrough notion was to reduce the motor's noise and speed by bridging the stator poles, an illogical move in the eyes of most contemporary engineers but one that subsequently yielded a shaded-pole design with "ten times the efficiency of the best commercial motors."

Colman thus found himself in possession of a low-voltage motor without equal in the industry. Inexpensive to manufacture, economical to run, and extremely durable in daily operation, its applications seemed unlimited. One of his first ideas was to incorporate it into a standard desktop fan (large industrial fans were used throughout the textile testing areas of Barber-Colman, and the commercial possibilities of a smaller-sized, home-and-office model would likely have occurred to him sooner or later.) Very little was required to scale back the height and weight of an industrial model to a six-inch blade diameter, furnish it with a Barber-Colman motor, adjust the blade speed to the electric power, and enclose the mechanism in a shiny bakelite casing to give it design appeal. Colman was able to interest the Eastman Kodak Company in using the motor for its new Kodatoy Movie Projector and eventually to sell it to manufacturers for inclusion in products as diverse as heaters, blowers, vaporizers, mixers, phonographs, pumps, timers, record-changers, business machines, traffic controls, voltage regulators, and small machine tools.

Nevertheless, the greatest opportunity for commercial development remained in the field of temperature control, where Colman could enter the market with the design of a unified electrical system, and where his motor would be part of every valve operator and damper controller that was installed. He knew that electricity was becoming ubiquitous, the "universal and widespread carrier of power" (Barber-Colman Bulletin B2), and he was determined to be the first one to apply it to all aspects of home and office temperature regulation, to every control instrument and means of air circulation. His chief advantage was his system's flexibility. Automatic temperature control required continuous adjustments to the changing levels of heat and humidity in a building, and this meant that his motors had to be able to stop when the desired temperatures were reached and reverse when they exceeded these limits. Colman's solution was to gear two uni-directional motors together and wire them to his thermostat in such a way that one "drove the controller when the temperature was too high, and the other drove the controller in the opposite direction when the temperature was too low" (Lilja). His pursuit of this kind of responsiveness led him to design an entire line of shaded-pole uni-directional, reversible, and synchronous motors that could be customized to buyers' needs.

Colman's entry into the temperature-control market was signaled by a handful of patent applications in the late 1920s: initially by the design of a new thermostat that responded to both manual and electrical signals (1928); then by plans for a fractional horsepower electric control unit (essentially his small vibratory motor with a miniaturized switch control and reconstructed magnet and armature) and a heat regulating system, which featured a thermostat and electrical relay for operating a series of heat-control devices, each with its own starting and stopping cycles (1929); and finally by an improved thermostat, with a novel bakelite casing that limited its exposure to dust, and by what he called a temperature regulating system (1930), which included the same basic mechanism as in the earlier heat regulating system, but which had been subsequently enhanced to manage different temperature zones within the same building and at different times of the day.

The temperature control system demonstrated, once again, Colman's talent for simplification, his ability to discover practical applications of new technologies by working backwards from the market, by focusing on existing commercial product lines and critically examining their designs and specifications. He put these products through a series of operating tests, both real and imaginary, as a means of justifying his own experimental plans. Usually he evolved a concept in his head, a sense of what

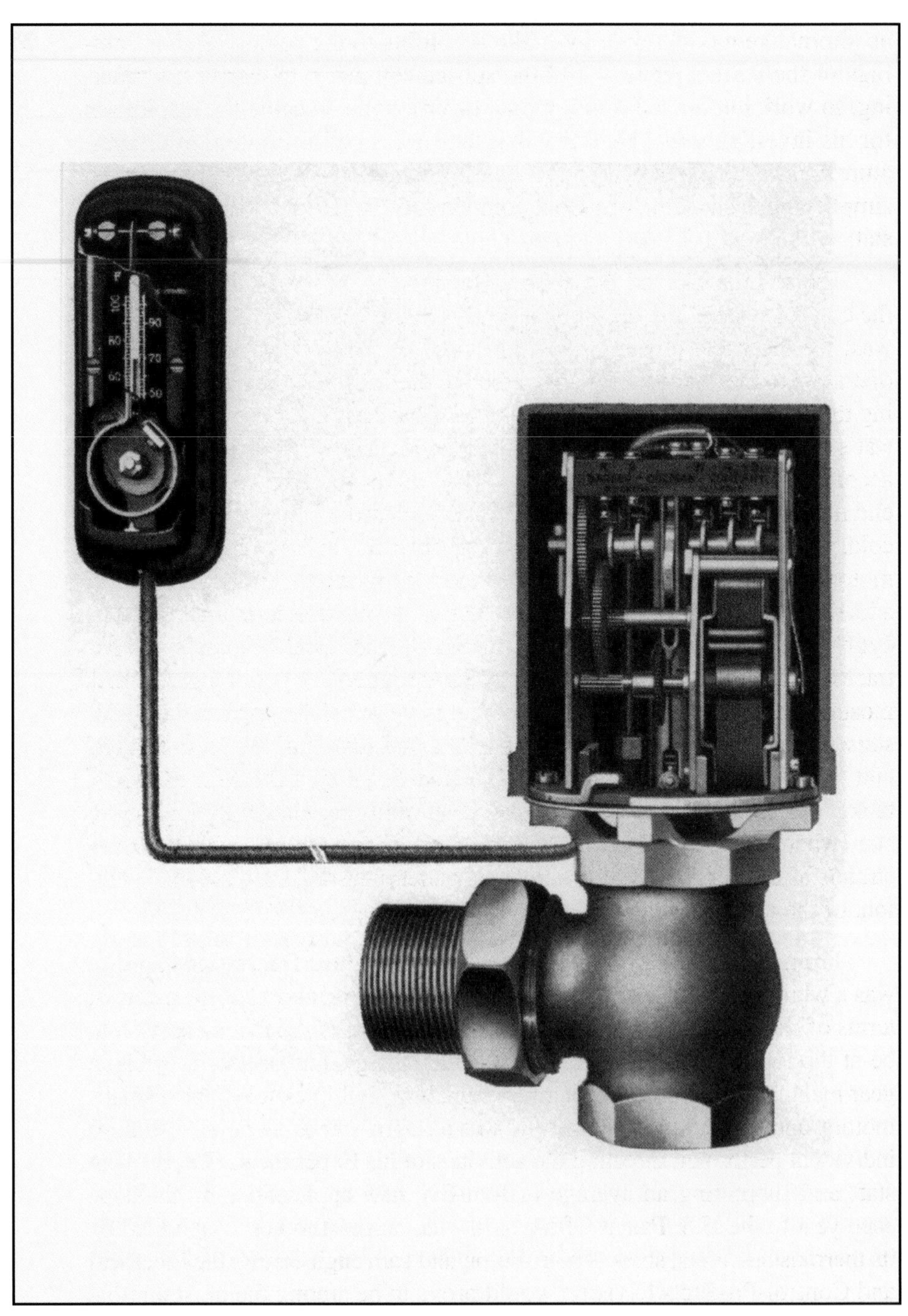

The "Barber-Colman electric system of temperature control" used thermostats to govern the opening and closing of motor-operated radiator valves. This illustration, which is taken from an advertising mock-up by the Byrne Agency, depicts the three main elements of the system (thermostat, motor, and valve).

an alternative model might look like according to the perceived shortcomings of the market leaders; and the subsequent effort to clarify his thinking, to work out his ideas in a model or prototype, became the inspiration for his investigations. He knew that the success of his system of temperature control would depend on its ease of operation, so he concentrated on simplifying each of the principal components, beginning with the thermostat.

Edgar Lilja likened the Barber-Colman thermostat to the "brains" of the control system, the device that always knew what the right temperature was; the electrical power to the "muscles" of the system; and the motor-operators to the "hands" that answered the thermostat's commands by starting the fans and opening and closing the valves and dampers. The thermostat's essential element was a little bi-metallic tongue that warped or bowed according to the room temperature. When it was too hot, the tongue's free end moved to an electrical contact point and closed a valve; when it was too cold, it moved to a different contact to open it. In each case, induction motors actuated the mechanisms by means of reduction gearing. Colman added another wrinkle to his thermostat to govern the humidity levels: a cylinder of seasoned maple, which, he discovered, would expand and contract in warmer and drier air. In time he designed a whole range of thermostatic products for the Barber-Colman system: two-temperature thermostats; duplex models with magnetic and manual switching devices; two-circuit "compound" thermostats; insertion-and-immersion units for air ducts, tanks, pipes, and vats; and an improved humidity regulation tool, a hygrostat, where his original block of seasoned maple was replaced by a few strands of human hair, which were even better measures, in Colman's opinion, of the air's moisture content.

From the mid-1920s to the early years of the Great Depression, Colman was a whirlwind of activity, enjoying the most prolific period of his career in terms of patent activity and new product development, and feeling himself to be at the top of his game creatively. Undertaking simultaneous projects in gear making, textile production, radio signaling, multiplex telegraphy, small-motors, and temperature controls, he was a ringmaster as much as a virtuoso individual performer, directing the activities of his Experimental Department staff and submitting an average of four-five new applications in his name each year to the U.S. Patent Office on a wide range of topics. Supported by its thermostatic tools, shaded-pole motor, and cam engineering, the Electrical and Control-Products Division would prove to be among the most durable of his initiatives. In 1931, to address an urgent need for working capital, he sold the division to the company on contract, insisting on full repayment for his investments and developing a formula for future "apportionments" of the division's net income that made him eligible for up to 25% of its profits (see "From Partners to Shareholders," pp. 360-64). The Electrical Division produced several spin-offs and collateral projects during the 1930s, including new plastic molded-products and air-distribution ventures, and, at the end of the decade, an aviation products initiative that brought Barber-Colman temperature controls, for the first time, into airplane cabins and cockpits.

vi

If there was one machine, one invention, that captured Howard Colman's imagination, epitomized the convergence of speed and power that had fascinated him since childhood, it was the automobile, a device that appeared on the American market at roughly the same time as his check pump and became an important social and commercial phenomenon in this country while he was consolidating his discoveries in warp production. It is little known, little remembered, that Colman was himself an automotive inventor - he submitted half a dozen patent requests in the 1930s for things like hydraulic brakes and self-adjusting brake actuators with clear-cut automotive uses and worked on other projects related to his interest in cars, such as clutches and clutch-controls - or that he was, in his personal life, one of the earliest and most enthusiastic "autoists" in the Rockford area, owning four-five cars at a time for most of his adult life. He grew up with the automobile as an inventor, used it as a kind of mobile mental laboratory or thinking space in which to incubate and refine many of his conceptual schemes. He would take off in his roadster on impromptu country jaunts for a few hours (or a few days) with no other object in mind than rejuvenating his spirits and meditating on certain ideas and problems at leisure. The open road, the changing scenery, and the vehicle's speed and performance were his tonics; they relaxed him, gave him a sense of well-being, like nothing else he knew. His usual routes were west and south of Rockford and, in the summer months, when he spent weekends with his family at the Colman cottage on Lake Geneva, in Walworth County of southeastern Wisconsin. Longer trips, occasionally with family members as passengers but always on his terms and according to his schedule, went to places like the Smoky Mountains, Rocky Mountains,

Ozarks, California, and Vermont. Riding on a train was boring to him, he told his daughter Dorothy. He was like the farmer boy who preferred to go fishing all day instead of turning the grindstone for half an hour: "I would rather drive an automobile for a week than ride on a train half a day" (11/17/36).

According to Colman family lore, Howard was the second person in Rockford to own an automobile (no one could say who the first person was), but this distinction seems unlikely, given the evidence of his letters to Bertha Maguire and what we know of Rockford's "automobile colony" at the turn of the century, when horseless carriages began appearing in the city:

> I did not leave Chicago until 8:30 and spent the whole day looking at automobiles. Took a fourteen mile ride in one and ran the thing about half the way myself. I certainly got quite a touch of the fever. Could get one (an auto, not a fever) at once and might have been tempted had I been sure of several things that I wasn't. I must have thought very hard about it if this headache was the result (7/16/01).

Less than a month later, a motorized vehicle was becoming a matter of practical necessity. As he told Bertha after a frustrating trip in his horse-driven buggy:

> ... Flora went lame worse than she ever has before, and I am not going to keep her or take her on a long drive again. Guess it'll have to be an auto next year - if the exchequer will stand it (8/8/01).

The difference-maker, the enabler, in 1902 turned out to be the hand-knotter, whose commercial success not only financed the expansion of the Barber-Colman factory but allowed its president to change his mode of travel about town and give expression to his automotive "fever" on a personal and creative level. The change was not without its practical adjustments. "Autoing" or "automobiling" was then in its infancy; and there were no traffic regulations, no formalized rules of the road, no driver's licenses, no speed limits. The earliest vehicles were as rough-edged as their drivers: noisy, vibrating contraptions that belched clouds of smoke and regularly broke down after encountering boulders, potholes, and other road obstructions. Drivers learned by trial and error. They cranked up the engine and climbed into the driver's seat. Like other early road warriors, Colman was forced to learn the hard way:

AUTO RUNS AWAY, STRIKES A TREE
Howard Colman's New Machine Comes to Grief
SWERVES INTO A TREE
Colman and Harry Severson Thrown
to the Ground - Auto Is Smashed
by the Impact - First Accident Here

This headline appeared on the inside pages of the *Rockford Morning Star* on April 1, 1902, April Fool's Day, recounting an incident from the previous night. The newspaper said that Colman had only recently received his new vehicle, "the largest ever used in Rockford," with an eleven horsepower engine and top speed of 30 miles per hour, and had taken Severson, "a draughtsman in his office," for an evening test drive. As the machine passed a brick crosswalk on North Court Street, it had suddenly spun out of control, "mounted" the curb, plowed down a hitching post, and smashed into a tree. The impact had separated the front wheels from the body and axle, and thrown Colman and Severson onto the ground, though neither was "hurt in the least," according to the report. Damage to the car was mainly to the front end and assumed to be repairable because of the low speed at which the vehicle had been traveling: "Mr. Colman was running it about six miles an hour, not wishing to exceed that speed until he had more experience with the auto."

In a bizarre way, the accident establishes a starting date for Colman's car ownership and driving adventures, as distinguished from his much longer fascination with automotive technology, which was apparent for many years in his experimental researches, particularly in his work with gasoline engines and gear trains, and in the record of his personal and business correspondence. We know from his family that the April accident and associated negative publicity embarrassed him a great deal and hardened his resolve to demonstrate his competency as a driver; he was simply unlucky, he felt, a novice driver among many other first-time autoists in a new national craze for personal motorized travel. The *Morning Star* said that his "broken" machine was hauled by a dray to the Barber-Colman factory, where it was expected to be reassembled. By the spring, we know, he had purchased a second automobile, an even-larger touring car from the Pope Motor Company, and the two vehicles soon became familiar sights on Rockford streets, still dominated in the third year of the new century by bicycles and horses and buggies. He ran the machines as often as he could, to and from the factory in the Water Power District, and increasingly on country roads near the Barber-Colman plant, though practice, it seems, did not always make perfect:

> HOWARD COLMAN'S AUTOMOBILE STRIKES
> A SOUTH MAIN STREET TROLLEY CAR
> And Gets Twisted and Smashed into
> Fantastic Bits of Brass and Iron Junk,
> While the Street Car Suffered No Loss Be-
> yond the Temporary Displacement of a
> Fender - No One Was Hurt.

This banner headline, from the front page of the *Rockford Register-Gazette* on April 9, 1903, gave Colman the distinction (ignominy?) of causing the city's first and second serious car accidents, though the seriousness of both was relative, in modern terms, in view of the lack of personal injury. The city's other newspapers, the *Morning Star* and *Rockford Republic*, reported the accident only as page-eight stories, which was perhaps more in keeping with its actual importance as a topic of local interest. Nevertheless, the focus on "Colman's Automobile" in the *Register-Gazette* headline and the fact that the driver is nowhere identified in the article beyond his full name - there's no mention anywhere of his occupation or street address - suggests that he was already well-known to the paper's readers. Yet well-known as a business owner and inventor? Or as a speed-demon behind the wheel?

> Howard D. Colman's devil-wagon came to grief this forenoon at the corner of Montague and West streets, in South town. Colman was coming in from the country along Montague street at a Nancy Hanks clip. His automobile was raising more dust than an April zephyr and neither Colman nor his companion nor the vehicle itself could be seen for the cloud of dust that was being thrown into the air. About this time a street car was dashing along West street down grade, and it reached the Montague street corner just in time to be enveloped by a seeming whirlwind of sand and dust, and when the atmosphere cleared it was found that there had been a mix-up between the big yellow-geared auto and the street car, the auto getting the worst of it by a Hutchins majority.

Beyond the reporter's purple prose, the article descends to a serio-comic level in its description of the damages. The street car lost its fender but was otherwise "merely bruised a bit," while the front end of the automobile was "smashed to smithereens." As in the case of Colman's 1902 accident, the front wheels were torn off his vehicle and pieces of the

Howard Colman (center) waits for a flat tire to be changed on one of his early automobiles (background); he is flanked here by his wife Bertha (left) and an unidentified female passenger.

machine scattered over the intersection. The *Register-Gazette* offered Colman its sympathies for his "misfortune" and congratulated him on a "fortunate escape from serious bodily injury," but also chided him for his reckless driving. The newspaper claimed that it had not been alone in seeing this coming:

> ... it was really the expected that happened this forenoon, as Mr. Colman has the reputation of letting his machine out to the limit, and predictions have been heard on all sides that the outfit would find itself up against something serious in time.

His driving adventures, in any case, were off to a bumpy start. One of the ironies of Colman's life is the fact that his name appeared in newspaper headlines on only a handful of occasions, and several of these involved car accidents and not his professional work. He was naturally shy of the limelight and took great pains to conceal his experimental activities at Barber-Colman, shield them from prying eyes; but he was transformed in the driver's seat and turned into a racer on the open road in ways that attracted attention and sometimes subjected him to unfavorable public comment. Was driving, in some ways, the emotional equivalent of his laboratory investigations, an expression of the same kind of imaginative excitement? It's tempting at least to think so, for his "dashing highway behavior," as he later mockingly described it,* seems otherwise inexplicable in the context of his usual personal and professional habits.

If it was hard to account for Colman's speeding, it was harder yet to slow him down. "Father's driving was a great source of worry for the family, both when we were with him in the car, and when he was in the car alone," his daughter Ruth said, though she also admitted that they were normally reluctant to discuss the subject with him or even hint at their concerns. He was not a person who submitted easily to others' strictures, especially those from his wife and children, and above all on subjects where he felt himself to have the advantage of superior knowledge. Confident in his abilities as a driver (he always maintained that the Rockford trolley *had hit him*), he claimed automobiles and automobiling as special areas of interest and asserted his right to tinker with gasoline-fueled vehicles - and personally to try out the machines that caught his fancy - with the same determination that he showed in staking out new territory in warp production, gear-making, and temperature controls. His response to the *Register-Gazette* article was to cancel his subscription and

* Letter to Dorothy Colman Wallace (7/11/39)

to devise an elaborate safety ritual for the benefit of his passengers in the weeks that followed the accident. When he came to a streetcar track after this, he stopped the car and listened intently for the sound of an approaching trolley; sometimes, for extra effect, he got out of the vehicle and peered up and down the track for several seconds with his hands cupped around his eyes.

Because automobiling was the most visible aspect of Colman's private daily regimen, it was the one that newspapers and curiosity-seekers tended to focus on during his lifetime and the source of many of the semi-humorous and apocryphal stories that made the rounds about him. Besides his habit of letting his machines out to the limit, people regularly commented on the size and variety of his motor-car collection and assumed, when a new and exotic motor vehicle appeared on Rockford streets for the first time, that Colman had something to do with it. They were often right. With Barber-Colman's earnings from the hand knotter and warp-tying machine at his disposal after 1903, he indulged his automobile fever by purchasing one-two new cars each year, keeping them in barns and carriage houses and the Barber-Colman factory itself, and trading them in after he had put them through exhaustive road tests or been attracted to newer models.

His family remembered that most of his "rare birds" (Dorothy Colman Wallace) were the early ones: Stevens-Duryea, Pope-Toledo, Haynes-Apperson, Locomobile - names that have now faded from general memory but all in their day popularly associated with innovative mechanical technologies. The Stevens-Duryea was the first commercially-produced motor vehicle in America, so Colman gets credit here as an early-adopter; the Pope-Toledo, with its characteristic peaked hood, was the premier model of the Pope Motor Company. The Haynes-Apperson, which was manufactured by Elwood Haynes, the inventor of stainless steel, pioneered the idea of left-side driving (another example, perhaps, of Colman's prescience). The Locomobile, considered by some people to be the American equivalent of the early English Rolls Royce, was widely recognized as a fine custom-made vehicle; the company refused to allow ready-made or mass-produced parts to be used in the assembly. Locomobile advertised its big, seven-passenger touring model as "as the exclusive car for exclusive people," but Colman bought it (he later owned several Locomobiles) because of the excellence of its mechanical systems and because there were very few people in Rockford who knew what it

Howard Colman at the wheel of his runabout (c. 1907).

was really worth. The car was used mostly for long trips with his family and for his wife Bertha's daily errands. Colman himself preferred the Locomobile's Gunboat Roadster, a much faster and sportier model that he ordered in battleship gray.

Across from his home on Main Street, on the west side of the road and at the end of a long driveway, Colman eventually constructed Rockford's first architecturally-designed, four-vehicle residential brick garage for his automotive fleet, complete with a gas pump. He engaged Cady and Crosby Architects of Chicago - a Rockford designer may have been too risky for him in terms of the local rumor mill - and told them to make the building look as much like an ordinary dwelling on the outside as possible. He planted lilacs in front and put frilled white curtains in the windows as a means of camouflaging its purpose. His children, who were unsure of what to think of it and hesitant to discuss it with their friends, referred to it simply as "our stable of automobiles."

While advancing age might have been expected to temper Colman's dashing highway behavior, it also supplied him with fleets of faster and fancier motorcars, Pontiacs, Packards, Chryslers, and Cadillacs, which he delighted in putting through their paces. His reputation for high-speed driving thus continued undiminished into his seventh decade. A popular story among Barber-Colman employees, probably apocryphal but reflective on a certain level of a peculiar psychological truth, told how he had been annoyed by a rattle in his engine and taken the car in to the factory to be serviced. Ralph Layng, the garage foreman, admitted to being puzzled when he returned the vehicle. He said that he'd been unable to hear the rattle and had had difficulty finding anything that was even remotely wrong with the transmission. Colman asked him if he had test-driven the car. Yes, Layng said; he'd not only driven it on streets near the factory but had taken it for a spin in the country, where he'd gone at least ten miles above the speed limit. But that's just it, Colman is supposed to have replied. You won't hear the rattle unless you go a lot faster than that.

For the Colman family, the consequences of these highway habits were more immediate (if less obviously entertaining). In the case of Dorothy Colman, who was married and living in Boston in the 1930s, it led to a refusal even to let her young children ride in the same car with her father whenever she returned to Rockford. She felt that she owed it to him to let him pick her up at the railroad station in his car, she said; she was willing to risk her own neck; but she simply could not bring herself, in good conscience, to entrust him with her children's safety, given his tendencies behind the wheel. She insisted (and Colman reluctantly agreed) that two cars be dispatched to the railroad station each time that she came home: the first, driven by Ralph Layng, to collect her children; the second, driven by her father, to pick her up. This awkward subject was repeatedly addressed in Colman's letters to Dorothy with a combination of earnestness and tongue-in-cheek humor:

> ... if you still do not care to trust your precious burdens to this paradox of highway excellence, I will send another [e.g. Ralph Layng] - a lesser light to be sure but still no mean luminaire (7/11/39).

> I agree with you in "thinking that the rigors of my trip home might be considerably reduced by flying," but I also think that there is a serious risk that they might be vastly increased. Although the recent record of air lines in regard to safety has been so good that the probability of fatal accidents is much reduced, nevertheless it is still much greater than it would be to trust your precious children in an automobile with your father at the wheel (4/30/40).

Colman never stopped trying to get Dorothy to change her mind. On her trips to Rockford, he always offered her the full-time services of his "best chauffeur:"

> The one I have in mind has had thirty-seven years' driving experience, and has covered over 500,000 miles in all the principal parts of the United States and some of Canada, and has always brought his passengers home without so much as a scratch or bruise (7/11/39).

Exemplary safety records notwithstanding, Colman's appetite for adventure, his willingness to risk life and limb on the open road had a lot to do with his ability to be in control, to be the driver instead of the passenger. His opposition to air travel, as surprising as it seems in the light of his documented interest in jet propulsion and passion for ever-greater speed and maneuverability in a motorcar, may have come down in the end to a matter of access. He did not, so far as we know, ever take up flying or consider learning to pilot an aircraft (even the thought of this, for his family, would have been impossible to bear) and simply learned to endure the feeling of helplessness on commercial flights.

> I suppose you know that it is a requirement that all passengers be strapped in their seats during take off and landing. This rule applies even

> in the fairest of weather, and when the weather is a little rough, the straps are necessary at all times, as otherwise you are liable to be thrown out of your seats and hurt. Much worse than this is the possibility that … you might be deathly sick, and what a mess that would be! On one of my trips to California, seven of the eight passengers were sick, and the weather was fair with nothing that could possibly be called a storm. It was merely a little bumpy (4/30/40).

This was not just a ploy to get Dorothy to agree to ride with him cross-country or a slightly exaggerated story to spice up his letter but a genuine and deeply-felt concern for his daughter's well-being. When the topic of flying came up in conversation, his response was always the same, regardless of the circumstances: "Traveling by plane is a reckless disregard of the dangers involved. I wholly disapprove …" (6/9/39).

Satisfied with the progress of his experiments and secure in the knowledge that Barber-Colman had weathered the worst years of the Depression, Colman spent his last years engaged in "new lifestyles and initiatives" (Dorothy Colman Wallace), the most important of which was his decision, in the fall of 1934, to separate from his wife Bertha and move to a new residence on Cunningham Road, several miles outside the city limits. The reasons for this were many and varied, and both partners no doubt contributed their share to the break-up of the marriage. They were, in fundamental ways, incompatible personalities: Howard, with his all-consuming work habits, dogmatic opinions, and Puritanical aversions to alcohol and tobacco; and Bertha, with her own less-obvious peculiarities, her continuing attachment to her parents after her marriage to Howard, her general indifference to the way she looked and dressed, and her objections, bordering almost on an anathema, to what she considered "wasteful spending" - to things that were new, stylish, and suggestive of upward social mobility. Her children remembered that she bought cheap straw mats for the steps of the Colman mansion and passed the day darning socks in the parlor. "Mother did not believe in spending money," Ruth Colman Tower said, "not on clothes, not on furnishings. When Father wanted new clothing, an overcoat or suit, he had to ask his Chicago tailor to make one that was 'exactly like' the existing article, so that Mother wouldn't know." Colman was not an easy person to live with in any event, and his workaholic tendencies became more pronounced in reaction to his wife's extreme frugality and willful control of the household budget. She had been born into wealth and had grown uncomfortable with its display and enjoyment; he had grown up in modest circumstances and had adapted quickly and easily to a patrician lifestyle as soon as he could afford it. Bertha and Howard seemed to pull apart unwittingly, reinforcing over time what was most objectionable in the other's personality. She would have liked to have had a glass of wine at dinner and to have been more active in Rockford society; he would have preferred a wife with a flair for style and design and an appreciation of the advantages that their lifestyle allowed. But he bore his frustrations in silence and did his best to be a dutiful husband and father. "Everyone understands the plight of a man with an extravagant wife," he told Dorothy after the separation, "but no one understands the difficulties of a man with a parsimonious one."

Nevertheless, Colman objected to divorce. He characterized it as "an arraignment of society" in a youthful letter to Fred Barber (6/8/93) and never wavered in this view in spite of his marital problems. Once he made up his mind to separate from Bertha, his main concern seems to have been to avoid disappointing his parents, particularly his mother, whose good opinion he treasured. When Lucinda Colman died in 1930, three years after her husband, this concern disappeared, though Colman's own illness at the time (1930-31), occasioned by the Stock Market collapse and the near failure of his own business, left him temporarily immobilized. After he found a new home on Cunningham Road, apparently with the help of Harry Severson, he moved out of North Main Street very quickly. He never divorced Bertha, but he also never spoke to her again; and they avoided each other after this when they appeared at the same public functions.

The Cunningham Road property, which Colman called "Hawthorne Hills" (and somewhat sarcastically his "triple ripple ranch," 1/13/40), was a 26-acre wooded estate with ravines and gently sloping pastureland that had been previously owned by a Rockford businessman named Milton Ellis, who built a single-story frame residence, with three bedrooms, at the top of one of the gradients. The house was invisible from the road and the entrance to the property mostly hidden by trees on either side of the drive, a setting that was perfectly suited to Colman's need for privacy. Aided by Paul Riis, a landscaper and general handy man whom he hired as a caretaker, Colman undertook an ambitious scheme to improve the property with a formal garden, tennis courts, and two-bedroom guest house. A stream on flatland near the highway was dammed to make a lake, and a sandy beach, diving platform, and small "bath house" (a changing room for swimming suits) were constructed. Later he put up what he referred to as a "sports house," with a fireplace that doubled as a cooking area for winter "skate-and-steak" parties, as well as a large stable on Meridian Road, which became the starting point for horseback rides through the countryside. In 1924, with Harry Severson, he had purchased a large

Howard Colman's "Hawthorne Hills" homestead was one of his chief sources of pleasure in later life. Besides using the grounds extensively for horseback riding, he created a lake by damming a small stream on the property and erected a "sports house" for swimming and skating parties. He also built a stable on Meridian Road near an area known as the "Dells," which he owned jointly with Harry Severson (Severson later acquired Colman's share and deeded the property to the Winnebago County).

550-acre wilderness tract southwest of Hawthorne Hills that was known as the "Dells;" and Riis was now put to work there building bridal trails through the woods and log bridges over the streams and gullies for the amusement of Colman and his guests. Colman's regular visitors were a mixture of family, friends, and business associates: his daughter Ruth and her husband Dick (Tower), his sister Laura from Milwaukee, Edith Barber from Warrens, Harry Severson and Earle Parker and their wives, Duncan Stewart, Harold Clark, Webbs Stevens, and Frank Edmison. His main horseback riding companions were Ruth and his stable master Clyde LaRue. "None of my guests ever fail to marvel at my good fortune in such a location …" he wrote Dorothy,

> and I marvel no less than they … So far at I can remember, there is not a thing that I have tried to do during the last six months which has not turned out to be pleasant and entertaining (4/1/35).

The only thing better than a cross-country jaunt in his car, Colman discovered, was a cross-country jaunt with a horse ride at the end. As he settled into Hawthorne Hills and carried out his property improvements, he also increased the number and frequency of his long-distance motor trips, particularly to the Smoky Mountains, whose natural setting fascinated him as nowhere else in America ("I am entranced with the trails and the country …," 4/25/39). He went to the Smokies regularly in the last years of his life, sometimes for several weeks at a time, in the "pursuit of happiness on the back of a horse" (10/9/39). He described for Dorothy the excitement he felt in negotiating the mountain trails:

> While the trails that I traversed did not run on the edge of any real precipice, still 200 or 300 feet is just about as final as 2,000 or 3,000, and the guides are not cowboys and do not carry ropes (as in Yosemite) for the purpose of lassoing falling tourists and bringing them back safely before they strike the bottom (5/13/39).

Occasional ridges of 5,000 feet were "steep enough to seem perpendicular;" and although he instinctively favored terrain with a wall on one side, he knew that it was irrational to worry about falling off "both sides at once." Horses often broke into a canter at the sound of a strange noise in the woods, and reigning them in risked starting an impromptu sideways dance off the side of the trail. Far better, he felt, to let them run ahead in the line of horses, trusting in their sure-footedness, and trying not to notice the way that the ground caved in around the hooves of the animals in front of him when they went too near the edge.

There was an unmistakable element of risk-taking in Colman's riding and driving adventures, though the appeal of these was mainly kinesthetic, the feeling of controlled energy and headlong movement that he got from being on the back of a horse and behind the wheel of a car. He dwelled on forces and motions in the development of his inventions, and his recreational activities, in this sense, were physical and mental rehearsals for his engineering work. One of his tricks was to record his outings on film and afterwards to play them back as a means of reliving (and re-imagining) the sensations:

> We have found the camera … very easy to operate and the results very interesting. We already have a number of scenes to entertain us and our friends: horseback riding, skiing, tobogganing, and snow-shoeing, as well as pictures taken through the windshield *while driving through snowdrifts higher than the car on each side* (emphasis added, letter to Dorothy Colman Wallace, 2/20/36).

He meant exactly what he said: he had filmed the snowdrifts while driving the car, with one hand on the steering wheel and the other on the camera, the vehicle's movement giving the pictures their quality of animation. He also took the camera with him on horseback and recorded sights along the trail, particularly deer and other wildlife, which he never tired of discovering, even in the same locales. It was the best way he knew, he told Dorothy, of stimulating his thoughts and preparing himself for a long day's (or night's) experimental effort.

As new roads and highways were constructed and older routes resurfaced, Colman's motor trips to Chicago, Milwaukee, and "other little stops between whiles" increased in frequency; he sometimes tracked more than 500 miles a week, visiting companies and attending meetings in the region and kept his vehicles running hot out of necessity ("I am afraid that if my new Pontiac should ever really cool off, it would have pneumonia …," letter to Dorothy Colman Wallace, 12/24/39). With America's entry into the Second World War, conferences on military parts production and armaments research replaced those on commercial topics. It was generally rumored in Rockford, in the Barber-Colman plant and the city at large, that Colman was involved in super-secret weaponry projects vital to the nation's defense, though the details of these were unknown and his exact role in the projects a matter of speculation. On June 25, 1942, he left for Chicago in the afternoon, driving alone, and "traveling," according to the newspaper, "at a high rate of speed" on country roads between Rockford and Elgin. Six miles west of the latter, "at the intersection of Route 47 and the Burlington-St. Charles blacktop road," his vehicle collided head-on with a truck from Joplin, Missouri carrying 30-gallon tanks of gasoline on the running boards. The impact ignited the fuel and swept both vehicles in a ball of fire. Colman and the truck's driver were killed instantly (*Rockford Register Republic*, 6/26/42).

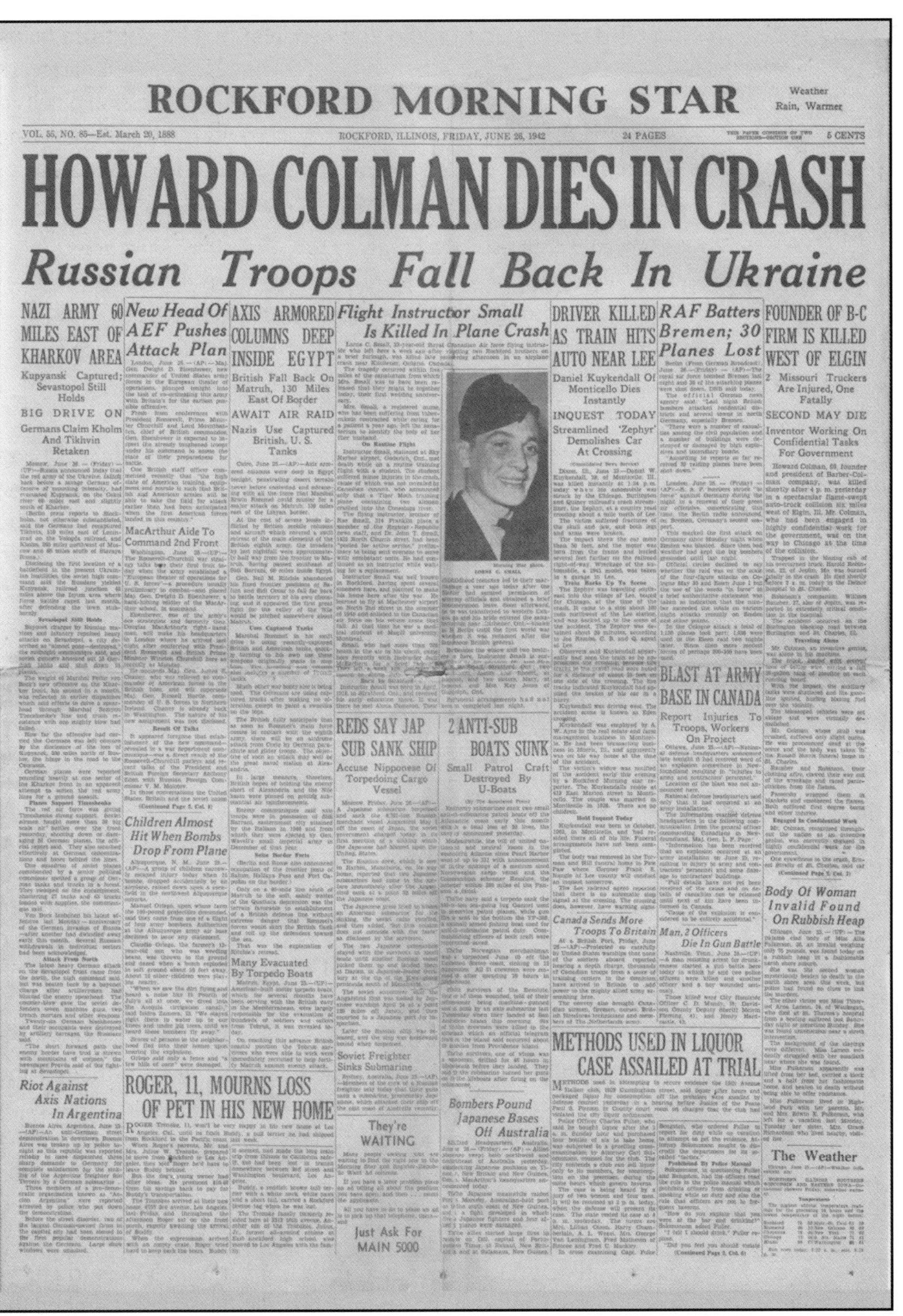

ROCKFORD MORNING STAR

Weather Rain, Warmer

VOL. 55, NO. 85—Est. March 20, 1888 ROCKFORD, ILLINOIS, FRIDAY, JUNE 26, 1942 24 PAGES 5 CENTS

HOWARD COLMAN DIES IN CRASH

Russian Troops Fall Back In Ukraine

NAZI ARMY 60 MILES EAST OF KHARKOV AREA

Kupyansk Captured; Sevastopol Still Holds

BIG DRIVE ON

Germans Claim Kholm And Tikhvin Retaken

New Head Of AEF Pushes Attack Plan

MacArthur Aide To Command 2nd Front

AXIS ARMORED COLUMNS DEEP INSIDE EGYPT

British Fall Back On Matruh, 130 Miles East Of Border

AWAIT AIR RAID

Nazis Use Captured British, U. S. Tanks

Flight Instructor Small Is Killed In Plane Crash

DRIVER KILLED AS TRAIN HITS AUTO NEAR LEE

Daniel Kuykendall Of Monticello Dies Instantly

INQUEST TODAY

Streamlined 'Zephyr' Demolishes Car At Crossing

RAF Batters Bremen; 30 Planes Lost

FOUNDER OF B-C FIRM IS KILLED WEST OF ELGIN

2 Missouri Truckers Are Injured, One Fatally

SECOND MAY DIE

Inventor Working On Confidential Tasks For Government

BLAST AT ARMY BASE IN CANADA

Report Injuries To Troops, Workers On Project

REDS SAY JAP SUB SANK SHIP

Accuse Nipponese Of Torpedoing Cargo Vessel

2 ANTI-SUB BOATS SUNK

Small Patrol Craft Destroyed By U-Boats

Children Almost Hit When Bombs Drop From Plane

Many Evacuated By Torpedo Boats

Soviet Freighter Sinks Submarine

Canada Sends More Troops To Britain

Man, 2 Officers Die In Gun Battle

Body Of Woman Invalid Found On Rubbish Heap

METHODS USED IN LIQUOR CASE ASSAILED AT TRIAL

Riot Against Axis Nations In Argentina

ROGER, 11, MOURNS LOSS OF PET IN HIS NEW HOME

Bombers Pound Japanese Bases Off Australia

They're WAITING

Just Ask For MAIN 5000

The Weather

The front page of the Rockford Morning Star on June 26, 1942.

12
The Elusive Mr. Colman

Howard Colman ... had a positive aversion to personal publicity. Challenged by a problem in invention, he would seclude himself and work it out. But he would not talk about his achievements ... Comparatively few people in Rockford knew him, though he lived here so many years ... I have heard persons say that he was one of the half-dozen men in the country in his field. That the Barber-Colman name is known around the world is evidence of it. And perhaps you have heard it said here and there that he was Rockford's most noted citizen. To which Howard would have said "Bosh." If he had listened at all.

- Frank Edmison, "Frankly Speaking,"
Rockford Morning Star, 1942

i

Howard Colman's life is a story of entrepreneurial daring and creativity, an extraordinary account of a Midwestern businessman who bootstrapped his company by imagining the shapes and motions of a long line of original mechanical devices. Was there an inventor more representative of the progress of American industry over the first half of the 20th Century? It's significant that Colman got his start in cotton manufacturing, the fountainhead of the Industrial Revolution, and tested himself with the development of a complex control mechanism for the preparation of warp beams, a project that confirmed his choice of a career and anticipated, conceptually, much of his later creative work. His setbacks in taking his D.I.M. to market, the trials of perfecting the apparatus and demonstrating it to potential buyers, and the disappointment of not being able to put it into mass production because of unexpected patent complications caused him a great deal of heartache, but it also taught him innumerable lessons in small-business management that served him well as the head of his company.

Colman grew up fashioning pieces of gadgetry long before he knew what it meant to apply for patents or mass-produce machines, responding

Howard Colman in his late fifties. This photograph was used as the frontispiece of a memorial booklet issued by the Barber-Colman Company (1942).

to a powerful urge for invention that was apparent even as a child. From his earliest days he showed himself to be a doer as well as a dreamer, capable of summoning the will power and ingenuity to translate his ideas into practical realities. Experience taught him to make the most of every situation, to exploit the commonplace. Knives, chisels, hoop skirts, rubber pillows, hazel nuts, and other household knickknacks had hundreds of uses in his young mind, most of them undiscovered and awaiting the trial-and-error of playful moments to turn them into something better: like jigsaw blades, water-wings, and the homemade cams of warp drawing-in machines. It was a prodigious feat of mechanical engineering to dream up the original D.I.M. as a schoolboy and an even greater feat of imaginative over-reaching to think that he could do it in the first place. Nevertheless, and in spite of the odds against him, he eventually succeeded in creating a number of original and highly efficient textile devices - knotters, warpers, spoolers, warp drawing and tying mechanisms - that established his company's reputation for innovation and solidified its position in the market.

Branching out from his textile investigations, Colman designed and manufactured a variety of commercial products that mirrored the changes in 20th Century technology: gear-making machines, reamers, milling cutters, radio-frequency door operators, shaded-pole induction motors, temperature controls, electric fans, furnace regulators, plastic molded products, automotive brakes and clutches, and a system of electro-magnetic communication known as multiplex telegraphy. Along the way he toyed with ideas for a jet engine, and during the two World Wars he led research groups at Barber-Colman in pioneering work in ordnance and armaments, filter motor-controls, gun director parts, tank-engine air conditioning systems, and airborne radar sets. It's well to remember that this was a person who was entirely self-taught, who made his first hand tools himself, and who used water power to provide the mechanical action of his original D.I.M.

Colman was fascinated by new developments in power technology. His work with piston engines, heat, and mechanical energy may or may not have led him to consider the possibilities of a turbojet system in the 1920s, but it's nonetheless typical of him that it was, at least briefly, a subject of serious interest. He had a broad practical understanding of gravity and hydraulics, the dynamics of forced air, electricity, light and electro-magnetic waves; and he parlayed this knowledge into the creation of countless experimental devices, some of which were later patented, and others which never progressed much beyond the prototyping stage, objects that merely helped to bring certain questions of utility into a little sharper focus. Given his penchant for risk-taking and making up things from scratch, he seems to have been undaunted by the challenges of exploring new and unfamiliar scientific fields.

Invention was in Colman's blood, a germ, a kind of "bug," as he once characterized his passion for experimenting to an examiner in the U.S. Circuit Court of Appeals. He really could not help himself. Indeed, the greater the obstacles to success, the more he was drawn to them. Free-lancing within his own Experimental Department, he followed his instincts, his inner compass, and routinely applied himself to problems and situations that got "his thinker working." Besides tending to experimental projects with his team of machinists and designers at the factory and meditating at night over a drafting board in his private study, he took regular morning walks, horseback rides, and automobile trips as a means of stimulating his imagination. Like most inventors, he was able to think both creatively and systematically; but creative thinking always preceded his critical analyses, and his most important insights were things that came as surprises, that he happened upon and experienced intuitively.

Beyond the impressive array of commercial products that he introduced during his lifetime, Howard Colman's most important legacy was his own example and the priority he gave to innovation as a driver of manufacturing success. While sometimes lacking the means to fabricate early gadgets to his satisfaction, he was never without his private workshops, his experimental areas, within the family parsonages, even when this meant, as it did in Beloit (1891), setting up for business in an unheated woodshed at the rear of the property. During the construction of his first factory (1902), he made sure that ample space was reserved on the top floor for drafting tables, workbenches, tooling, the D.I.M., and a rudimentary winding apparatus for his ongoing textile investigations, an investment in research that was unusual at the time in American industry.

The Barber-Colman Company (1902-42) was organized for the commercial development of "brand new ideas" (Roger Schuette), with the Experimental Department serving as the research and engineering hub of multiple production units. It was, in many ways, a smaller-scale Menlo Park, an invention factory no less committed to discovering the market applications of basic science than its celebrated contemporary. From the 1920s onwards Colman presided over a 22-acre industrial complex in Rockford that contained 38 different building sections (540,000 s.f. of manufacturing space), and employed more than a thousand full-time designers, engineers, planners, pattern-makers, machine operators, inspectors, heat-treaters, laboratory technicians, material managers, assemblers, blacksmiths, carpenters, salesmen, shipping clerks, truck drivers, maintenance workers, and general office staff. With the exception of raw materials and some castings and tooling, Barber-Colman was a largely self-sufficient enterprise, supplying its own power, heat, and light, and maintaining a state-of-the-art, high-precision fabricating capacity that had few equals in the country. Colman actively promoted a culture of innovation within the company by encouraging employees to become their own patentees, submitting applications to the U.S. Patent Office through the legal department and assigning the rights to these to Barber-Colman. He also created a comprehensive system of "daily notes" that honored individual initiative on different levels. The system routinely collected ideas and production details for documentary purposes and added these to the company's ever-expanding library of patents, prints, and models.

Colman viewed his diverse product offerings as assets, as a means of spreading out his operating risks and balancing ever-changing consumer demands. Each invention, each cluster of mechanical/electro-mechanical "instrumentalities" was a prototype that fed his imagination and offered the possibility of unlimited future refinement, how and in what forms he would eventually determine himself. More than numbers on a balance sheet, his devices were vivid visual representations of a world of forces and motions that he inhabited imaginatively. Colman would not have approved of the modern obsession with bottom-line business performance, the practice of hollowing out under-achieving production units and rationalizing assets in the short term at the expense of later commercial development. Because Barber-Colman was privately-held, its values and measures of success were different; and Colman, as the majority shareholder and chief executive officer, was able to make a determination of each product's importance to the company's earnings picture. Yet he was always sensitive to the opinions of Barber-Colman's other shareholders. When Harry Severson and Luther Miller raised objections to his proposed venture into electricity in the mid-1920s, he made the decision to finance the business on his own, setting up a separate "internal account" and hiring Duncan Stewart to lead a new engineering team. Later, when the venture had proved itself to everyone's satisfaction, Colman sold the business back to the company on a contract, along with the patents and tooling. He did this in 1931, during the depths of the Depression, and at a time when the sales of textile machinery had plummeted. His determination to enter the field of electricity not only preserved the assets and productive capacity of the textile division but saved the company itself from possible financial ruin.

With the advantage of hindsight, we can retrace the path of Colman's scientific investigations during his lifetime. The D.I.M. got him started, introducing him to issues of mechanical power transmission and the use of cams and gear-trains in balancing speed and torque; it led to the creation of a traveling warp carriage and several rudimentary feedback devices, such as an automatic stop and sensitive feeler arm, which were incorporated into his later textile inventions, and which contributed to his understanding of pattern-control technology. Though stillborn, the D.I.M. provided the basic framework for Colman's subsequent warp-replenishment experiments and awaited only the development of a better thread-uniting device, such as a rotating tying bill, to become commercially-viable. This gap was filled by the invention of the Barber knotter. Colman got the idea of mounting the knotter on the D.I.M.'s warp carriage and produced a tying apparatus that combined the best of both devices, a superior joining mechanism with a power-driven system. His interest in textile automation led him next to design a winding machine (spooler) and high-speed warper, adapting key elements of the warp-tying device to the mechanical manipulation of bobbins, spools (cheeses), and warp beams. His successes in tying and winding were made possible by a mastery of gear ratios. In 1900 he had purchased a commercial gear-cutter for the production of the knotter's tying bill and, almost inadvertently, developed an expertise in precision metal-forming. Colman realized that he was sitting on a gold mine. Convinced that he could produce better milling cutters than were then commercially available, he began doing selected job-work for customers on a trial basis and eventually entered the machine tool market as a fully-fledged manufacturer of hobbing machines, hobs, end mills, and form cutters.

Missing from this account is any mention of Colman's experiments with fluid power (1896-99), which led to the receipt of his three earliest patents. Though seemingly unrelated to his other investigations, his invention of the check pump and water lift may be viewed as preparing the way for his development of humidifiers and temperature controls thirty years later (1929-30). Nothing that he learned was ever wasted. An understanding of the behavior of fluids and gases under pressure and a practical knowledge of a spring- and cam-activated means of opening and closing of valves, which he acquired in developing the pump and lift, would have been an enormous asset in designing a heat and temperature regulating system. It would also have helped him in the creation of hydraulic brakes, bellows pistons, and hydraulic actuators in an even later phase of his experimental work (1936-37), a period that may have owed its inspiration to a love of motoring as much as it did to an understanding of fluid power. Nevertheless, Colman always drew heavily on his shop experiences in formulating designs, and the lessons that he learned in testing his inventions were among his most vivid memories.

Though they appear to be radical departures from his textile experiments, Colman's investigations of radio frequencies, signaling devices, and multiple-stage telegraph messages in the 1920s were really part of a continuing interest in pattern-control technologies. From the standpoint of a mechanical system, there was little practical difference between the sprocket wheels and rack and pinion gears guiding the movements of his warp-tying device and the use of memory chains in his multiplex telegraph to send and store messages. Both inventions transmitted motions and forces through the cams, gears, and linkages; both used special kinds of coded information, coded directions, to activate their parts. Where they differed was in the relative sophistication of the controls. Unlike the warp-tying machine, which had a limited number of sequential actions (an automatic stop turned the machine off if the actions varied from their prescribed course), the multiplex telegraph was capable of managing inputs, electro-magnetic signals, that were as various as language itself. The key was the telegraph's binary coding, and Colman's realization that he had to greatly simplify the controller logic in order to expand its range of operations.

In terms of functionality, the multiplex system was Colman's most versatile invention, the apex of his efforts, at the end of his life, to create an automated memory technology. It was a single piece in a considerable scientific legacy, a small group of inventions among the many patents, engineering drawings, and study models that he left behind him at Barber-Colman. When he died, the original multiplex application, a system of communications, was still pending in the U.S. Patent Office after 25 years of head-scratching and general befuddlement among the Washington examiners. (Colman's colleagues reckoned that the application, with 464 claims and 52 sheets of mechanical drawings, had simply been ahead of its time.) Though the patent was finally approved in 1945, the system never saw the light of day commercially. Nevertheless, the inventor's concept had a brief afterlife at Barber-Colman in the post-War years, and the account of this episode, previously lost to history, offers an interesting postscript to the Colman story.

The principles of binary coding in the memory system of Howard Colman's multiplex telegraph were similar to those in the controllers of his early warp-replenishing machines. "I think the thing that got him into computing," Roger Schutte told the Smithsonian (Computer History Project, 1972) "was getting into textile machinery and ... the warp drawing-in. [In] setting the patterns ..., they had these great big wide punched steel tapes that set patterns. It was thin, like a three-one thousands of an inch-thick (.003) steel sheet or band, with holes punched in it, so the rods could either pick up or reject a given thread." (Here a control mechanism from a 1960s Barber-Colman warp-drawing machine is shown with a continuous sheet of perforated metal directing the needle's actions.)

Harry Severson became president of the Barber-Colman Company after Howard Colman's death, and Duncan Stewart, who headed up the Electrical Division, subsequently took over Severson's old job as vice president and general manager. Stewart was then a member of the civilian-based National Defense Research Committee (NDRC), a group that advised the military on trends in science affecting the War effort. Generally he divided his time between committee meetings in Washington and Barber-Colman's own NDRC-related initiative to develop anti-aircraft, anti-submarine, and anti-tank gun artillery directors and servo mechanisms in Rockford. His committee appointment testified to Barber-Colman's reputation for technological innovation and his own stature as an experimental engineer. He had been a natural choice from the company, given its founder's well-known aversion to groups of this type.

One of the newer additions to Stewart's Barber-Colman research group was Roger Schuette, an electrical-engineering graduate of the University of Wisconsin who had begun working for the company as a test-laboratory technician. Schuette's reminiscences of the War and post-War years, recorded in interviews with the Smithsonian and the American Society of Information Processing Societies (1972), provide the basis for much of what follows. The rest is taken from a privately-published history of the same period by George Stibitz, *The Zeroth Generation* (1993),* which recounts (among other things) his work with Barber-Colman as an NDRC member and private consultant.

Barber-Colman's NDRC-sanctioned "anti-aircraft project" leaned heavily on the company's expertise in cam engineering. Begun in 1941, the project focused on ways of calculating an attacking aircraft's trajectory in space, its velocity and arc on the horizon, and on methods of checking these estimates in laboratory simulations. Barber-Colman built an apparatus known as a "dynamic mechanical tester" (1941-42), essentially a large cam-activated calculator that generated key experimental data for the preliminary design of the gun director. It used six, highly-finished steel cams, with maximum diameters of twelve inches, to produce variable signals to the director; rollers on the outer rims of each cam would rise and fall according to the estimated position of the moving target, rotating a shaft to the gun's hand wheel. How much Colman himself was involved in these experiments is impossible to say. We know only that they began

---

* The book's subtitle is *A Scientist's Recollections (1937-55) from the Early Binary Relay Digital Computers at Bell Telephone and OSRD to a Fledgling Minicomputer at the Barber-Colman Company.*

on his watch, that they bore his handprint, that he was the company's leading proponent at the time of this kind of automated calculation, as evidenced by his interest in the multiplex system.

George Stibitz, a scientist at the Bell Telephone Laboratories (Bell Labs) in New York and a member of the NDRC, worked with Duncan Stewart after Colman's death to improve the dynamic tester. Their first steps were to translate the tester's mechanical output into electrical signals and to replace the cams with electro-magnetic controls that employed paper and tape storage devices similar to those in the Bell Labs' existing telephone relay switches. Stibitz's experiments during the War with a teletype punch-mechanism, which recorded incoming signals as a pattern of holes in a paper tape and then read them out as electrical signals, mirrored work that Colman had been doing with storage mechanisms and binary coding systems since the 1920s.

Colman may or may not have met Stibitz in connection with the NRDC Project in Rockford, but they were clearly kindred spirits, all the more remarkable because of Stibitz's family background: he had also grown up in a household headed by a theologian and teacher of ancient languages. If he had known about it, Colman would surely have approved of Stibitz's homemade "model K" prototype "relay binary adding device," which had been assembled as an experiment in 1937 with two relays salvaged from a Bell Labs dumpster, two dry-cell batteries, two flashlight bulbs, and a primitive keyboard fashioned from strips of tin cut out of a tobacco can. With this small breadboard-sized apparatus, assembled on the top of a kitchen table (hence the choice of the letter "K"), Stibitz employed a binary electrical circuit to perform basic arithmetic operations. Each flashlight bulb on the breadboard represented a single binary digit. If the light was on, it was 1; if it was off, it was 0. Stibitz's test was to add up two one-digit numbers and show the sum through a combination of lights representing different binary values.

Model K contributed to the development of five subsequent automatic calculators ("models 1-5") at the Bell Labs between 1937-45, all which made use of logic elements in the telephone relay system, "the most thoroughly-engineered device of its time," according to the scientist Jerome A.G. Russell. The experiments coincided with Barber-Colman's work on the dynamic tester and anti-aircraft director, and data from the projects was shared back and forth as a part of the War effort.

Stibitz called Barber-Colman "one of the clients most important to me" when he became a private consultant after the War. A physicist and

Duncan Stewart.

mathematical engineer by education, he began working with the company in 1946 to perfect the "elaborate geometry of … [its] small-tool machines and other gear-making equipment." Much on his mind at the time were plans for a scaled-down calculator or mini-computer, which would be able to perform relatively simple computations, as opposed to the "large flows and through-puts" that had been standard in the Bell Labs machines. Could the wartime lessons of the big computers be applied to the design of more efficient, low-cost devices? Was there a commercial market for small computers that would justify their development? Eventually he got around to asking Duncan Stewart for Barber-Colman's help in exploring the "uncharted technical problems" associated with such a concept and went over with him what he thought were some of the important design considerations. Stewart became intrigued and signed a patent agreement with Stibitz. Roger Schuette was then asked to lead a small group of Barber-Colman engineers charged with constructing a preliminary computer model.

As it happened, Stibitz got more out of the arrangement than he had bargained for. Aware of Barber-Colman's engineering expertise from his days with the NRDC, he was pleasantly surprised on his first visits to Rockford by the company's large stock of "highly original [mechanical] components invented by the founder and president, Mr. Colman:"

> Even without the help of electronic technology, some of these components of fifty years ago were worthy of the present age of robotics. Among them was a completely mechanical thread-knotter which moved along a track from station to station where scores of bobbins were being wound. The thread-knotter monitored the threads being wound on the spinning bobbins. It automatically detected broken threads, picked up the loose ends at the break, and then tied them together in a "weaver's knot," a knot to test the skill of any sailor or Boy Scout.

Stibitz had been giving a good deal of thought to the technical requirements of a new dot-matrix printer for his prototype computer, a faster version of the teletype devices that had been used in the Bell Labs. He had begun to do the mathematical modeling for such a mechanism when he learned that Barber-Colman already had one in stock from the 1930s. The printer, moreover, virtually matched the speed of the computer that he was hoping to build:

> The printer was a high-speed - 60 characters/second - printer of a type that we now call a specialized dot matrix. The dot matrix of this printer

> was special in that it admitted only one dot in each of the horizontal rows of the matrix. As a compensation for this restriction, the matrix was provided with many rows. With each cycle during which it printed one character, the printer formed a row of 80 identical matrices of dots across the page, only one of which would be selected. The dots were formed by 80 small nipples on the edge of each of several sliding strips of metal.

Stibitz discovered that there were tiny hammers lined up behind the paper and ribbon; and when they struck the paper, they pressed the inked ribbon against the matrix of nipples. "The second character was then set up by sliding the strips, to form the second character, and activating the hammer at the second position which struck the paper at that position, and so on." Stibitz immediately decided to shelve the plans for his own printer and to incorporate the Barber-Colman machine into his computer configuration, marveling at the "breath-taking speed" that the device exhibited.

Between 1946-54 Schuette and his group of engineers planned and constructed two identical units of a prototype mini-computer according to sketches and schematics supplied by Stibitz, while nevertheless exercising a great deal of independent authority in the choice of the patterns. (Stibitz himself acknowledged as much in assessing the machines: "... all parts of the computers had been redesigned - in many instances, very extensively - by Schuette ... and other engineers of Barber-Colman Company.") To understand the role that Howard Colman's inventions played in the determination of the final model, it's necessary to turn to Schuette's account of the project.

According to Schuette, his engineers "borrowed a lot of what Colman had done with the multiplex telegraph," particularly its mechanical memory, and "combined this with vacuum tubes" to construct the two Barber-Colman mini-computers. Small in comparison to other computing devices at the time such as the 30-ton ENIAC ("Electronic Numerical Integrator Analyzer and Computer") machine at the University of Pennsylvania, the Barber-Colman prototype was still large by modern standards, occupying 25 square feet of space or approximately the size of a standard phone booth.

The sketches that Stibitz furnished, the preliminary designs, underwent extensive modification in the course of Barber-Colman's eight-year development phase, his initial proposal for a "rotating disk memory" being gradually converted into a device that used a "long shaft driven by a motor with toothed wheels on it and magnetic pick-ups." The storage tapes, which were modeled on Colman's multiplex memory chains and contained more than 5,000 feet of coded information, were activated by gears and a "synchronizing clutch;" Schuette and his group introduced a new wrinkle into the system that permitted users to access information randomly without having to read through the rest of the 4,999 feet, as was still the case with rotating-disk memories. Composed of "storage wires in a box," the boxes themselves stacked up like plates on a shelf and "pushed out" as needed, the retrieval device proved to be one of the earliest examples of a random-access memory in the history of the modern computer. It's perhaps worth repeating here that the same concept, if not the same application, had been anticipated by Howard Colman a quarter century earlier in his invention of the multiplex system. (Indeed, another prototype device, a knitting-control mechanism that employed a system of random memory, was designed even earlier for the B.Z.B. Company of Rockford, according to the evidence of Colman's "daily notes.") Given Stibitz's reputation as the "inventor of the first programmable digital computer in America" (National Inventors Hall of Fame), it's possible that future historians will wish to give some credit to Colman for his contributions to the design of Stibitz's most advanced model, the sixth of his prototype devices, the "Barber-Colman Computer."

The Barber-Colman Company had always impressed Stibitz as an organization that believed in its "ability to select and market products;" and during the course of the mini-computer's long development, it had formulated detailed business plans for the eventual manufacture and sales of the machine. "We were right to the point where we had to make a decision as a company," Schuette remembered of Barber-Colman discussions in the mid-1950s after the prototypes were completed. "Are we going to go into the manufacture of this thing? ... Here engineering has come up with a product. Now what do we do with it?" After much analysis, Duncan Stewart made the decision to walk away from the project and to explore "alternative licensing arrangements" with other businesses for the company's four patents, reasoning that Barber-Colman "would be really bucking the giants" if it entered the computer field. At the time IBM, Sperry Rand, Burroughs, and Royal were known to be investigating the same technology; and while Barber-Colman may have been farther along in its development than any of them, it had none of the distribution channels and service centers that would be needed for such a venture.

It's hard to guess what Colman would have done in the same situation. No doubt he would have been excited by the possibilities of the

Roger Schuette replaces a vacuum tube in the Barber-Colman's prototype computer (c. 1954). Because of what was described at the time as "financial reasons," the company's effort to commercialize this machine was eventually abandoned.

new electronic technology, for he had pushed his experiments with control devices as far as they would go in a strictly mechanical fashion. He had been exploring applications of binary coding since his earliest work with the D.I.M. and devising complicated memory systems even longer than inventors like Stibitz; and he may well have been willing to accept the challenges of developing a commercial computer rather than to allow its possibilities to pass him by. As forward-thinking as he was, he would have quickly recognized the revolutionary impact of computer technology on all his work. If it was a risky venture, it was certainly no more risky than his exploration of electrical devices had been in the 1920s and well within his personal means to bankroll if other company shareholders had objected.

iii

Howard Colman was first and foremost an inventor. His feelings of personal worth, his sense of identity, came from the expression of a remarkable gift for originality, for making new things and rediscovering the value of systems and devices that the market either passed by or ignored. He organized his daily affairs so that he could indulge his creative interests with a minimum of distraction, and he expected just about everyone within his immediate sphere of influence, his associates at Barber-Colman and family members above all, to observe protocols of behavior that respected his privacy and allowed him to concentrate on formulating the schemes in his head. Behind the free-hand doodles, sketches, mechanical drawings, calculations, study models, and prototypes is a man whose all-consuming passion for science plays havoc with our usual distinctions between "private" and "public," and whose elaborate self-protective stratagems present major headaches for a biographer. Alongside the richness of his many experimental projects, the continuous swirl of new ideas, his private life, such as it was, appears to have been a kind of minimal adjunct activity that served and sustained his more important scientific investigations. The man behind the mask turns out to be, more or less, indistinguishable from the mask itself.

Colman did an exceptional job of covering his tracks. Short and unimposing in appearance, with a reserved demeanor and soft clear voice that kept itself on an emotional even-keel, he wore dark three-piece suits that made few concessions either to fashion or the season and went through his days absorbed in the routines of his business. Everything about him, from dress to work habits, seems to have been calculated to avoid attention. Although Barber-Colman employees learned to watch out for him on his rounds of the Experimental Department and to anticipate his questions, it's likely that strangers took little or no notice of him in public. As a rule he engaged people in different ways, keeping a polite distance on the factory floor where issues were addressed with a crisp professionalism, and allowing himself a greater familiarity in private, where he revealed just enough of himself to permit others to open up. He was not always forthcoming, however, even to his friends, and sometimes proved a puzzle to his family with his moodiness and speculative projects that consumed days and nights on end. No one at home or the factory seems to have questioned his right to do exactly as he pleased, which ordinarily meant conducting experiments on any subject and in any manner he fancied. To become a pioneering inventor, to prove oneself as the originator of a useful electrical-mechanical property, the first of its kind in the country as determined by an independent governmental review of the state of the art was its own full reward for him, even if that originality was not widely acknowledged or resulted in an immediate financial gain.

Colman regarded publicity as a distraction at best, and at worst as a temptation to take himself too seriously. The amount of energy that he expended in bringing his concepts to fruition, in overcoming technical bottlenecks and experimental dead-ends, made him suspicious of journalists and the kind of glib analyses that appeared in the popular press, even when these were positive. As a result, he largely ignored his many opportunities for personal recognition and maintained a semi-anonymity within the ranks of Barber-Colman, where his name and photograph seldom appeared in promotional literature.

Colman is hard for us to judge. The reclusive inventor portrayed in his letters to William Barber, the mechanical drudge who worked through Thanksgiving and was apparently "all business" all the time in his early twenties, turns out to have been, during the same period, a member of an upwardly mobile group of young professionals in Rockford and an active suitor of Bertha Maguire, the daughter of a prominent local businessman. Although he grew up in modest circumstances and learned to get by on a dollar and a half a day when he began his experimental work, he quickly and easily adopted the lifestyle of a patrician landowner after the success of the hand-knotter and warp-tying machine. He purchased one of the city's most imposing riverside mansions and remodeled it to his taste by removing all the stained glass, bric-a-brac, and exterior trim that gave

What most of Howard Colman's Rockford neighbors knew of him was limited to things like the remodeling of his Main Street mansion, shown here before (top) and after (bottom) the building's decorative fretwork was removed.

the building its original architectural distinction. He had a Puritan's aversion to the trappings of ecclesiasticism, and the house's neo-Gothic fretwork was a painful reminder of his own religiously-constrained childhood. As his family grew, he hired a full-time nurse for his children, a full-time cook, a chauffeur ("driver") for his wife, and a groundskeeper; but when he later engaged a Chicago architect to design a new brick garage for his fleet of automobiles, he insisted that the building look as much like an ordinary house on the outside as possible and be built west of Main Street, away from his home, to disguise its real purpose. Judging from his letters to Bertha Maguire, he was involved in some the earliest social activities at Rockford Country Club, though it's not clear that he later used it for anything besides walking on the golf course and meditating on his experiments. Quoting Scripture from memory and enforcing a rigid code of behavior at home that forbid the use of tobacco, alcohol, and "naked toes" in women's shoes, he nevertheless refused to step inside a church and showed himself to be both a fan of popular plays and a hellion behind the wheel of a car.

The world of Colman's inventions was equally inscrutable. His model shop and development area were closed to visitors; and within the department he personally set the direction and scope of the experiments, monitoring the working prototypes and discussing possible improvements with his staff according to the statistical results. Any design change required his approval, even of minor features. Colman would revise the shop drawings for each project as he absorbed the lessons of the tests; and these, in turn, would guide the activities of the department's model-makers, draftsmen, and machinists. Inevitably, he became the filter for an enormous amount of conceptual detail. Concerned about protecting his intellectual property rights, he developed a penchant for secrecy and refused to discuss the status of his inventions outside of Barber-Colman. Even at home, the occasional dinner-table conversations about his work were sprinkled with semi-humorous references to entirely fictitious projects. "And how is B.S.J. today?" his children would ask. "And how is S.J.X.?" "And J.Z.E.?" No one knew what these abbreviations meant. They were codes, the short-hand equivalents of things that no one was allowed to talk about; and Colman coined them for this reason.

As puzzling as Colman's behavior sometimes seemed, his personal loyalties were unquestioned, and friends knew that they could count on his commitments absolutely. While he expected a great deal from his associates in the Experimental Department - they had to be able to work long hours, at a minimum, and to keep up with the headlong pace of the investigations - he rewarded them generously for their efforts. Whatever they gave him, he gave them back in kind. Peter Noling, the son of the Experimental Department foreman and chief model-maker, Martin Noling, remembered that his father sometimes received phone calls from Colman at home in the evening, and these were usually variations of the same message: *I'm at the shop. I've discovered something interesting. I thought that you might like to take a look.* Noling would stop what he was doing at the time - put down his work, get up from the dinner-table, or get out of bed - and go over to the Barber-Colman factory, often remaining there until the next morning. (On a few occasions he stayed away from home for several days, sleeping, it was assumed, whenever and wherever he could.) At the end of these impromptu meetings, Colman typically would send him away with a new vacation allowance. According to Peter Noling, he'd say, "Take the rest of the week off." Or "See you in a couple of weeks." * When Noling was bedridden with a bleeding ulcer in 1927, Colman looked in on him regularly and made sure that the company treasurer delivered a paycheck to his home on Wednesday afternoons. After six weeks of bed-rest, Noling apparently decided that it was time to go back to work; but as pleasantly surprised as Colman was to see him on the job, he took the precaution of calling Noling's personal physician for an update on his medical condition. Sensing from the report that Noling was rushing his recovery, and in spite of a huge backlog of experimental work that required his attention, Colman sent him away for three more weeks of rest. "If you bent a little in his direction," Peter Noling recalled, "he always took care of you. He was very predictable in those things."

In fact, Colman was very protective of all his employees and made the decision during the 1930s Depression to cut pay levels across the business rather than institute any layoffs. He not only tolerated, but encouraged, differences of opinion among his staff, especially in relation to the merits of projects. His reputation for fairness and evenhandedness in his dealings with employees was widespread. As George Stibitz recounted in his memoir: "Dunc Stewart once told me that Mr. Colman

---

* Noling's account of his father's eccentric work schedule at Barber-Colman is echoed in the recollections of Roger Schuette: "Mr. Colman, in his later years, was much more interested in development, and so he had his office up in the penthouse right above the development department, and he would spend his days and nights there. He had a cot up there. It was nothing for him to call the manager of the development department at three o'clock in the morning and say, 'I just got a brilliant idea. Come on down, and let's see if we can put this thing into effect.' Day and night he was working" *(Smithsonian Computer History Project, 1972).*

had never had a 'personnel problem.' His employees were people, and they might disagree with Mr. Colman's decisions, or among themselves, but they were still people, and not problems."

Family was also important to Colman, his parents and children above all. While he was a dutiful son and provided much of his parents' financial support in their old age, he inhabited an entirely different mental world, one that lacked a significant social, political, and religious dimension. He shared his father's fascination with curious knowledge but not his love of public policy, his mother's capacity for visualization but not her spirituality. In Colman's view, logic and reason defined the limits of everything worth exploring and being understood. What could not be mathematically deduced and empirically tested was simply beyond the scope of his interests.

Colman was, from all accounts (and probably against his better judgment), somewhat intimidating to his children. His sons, especially, felt the need to test themselves against his example, to measure up in their own ways to what he had accomplished. His daughters, who adored him and served as his closest confidants, were equally in awe of his talents and reluctant to stand up to him. Ruth recounted her many white-knuckle rides in the front seat of his automobile, cringing from the vehicle's high speeds and hairpin turns, but unwilling, ever, to ask him to slow down. Dorothy remembered how similar "motoring expeditions" sometimes led to awkward discussions of recondite scientific facts, such as the illusion of water on the highway and the law of accelerated gravity. She never knew what to answer when her father asked her if she understood what he had said on these subjects. To say no was to invite a more complex explanation. To say yes was to subject herself to follow-up questions, questions that she was unlikely to get right and thus force her to endure an even windier account of the topic at hand. "I didn't inherit the scientific gene," she recalled; and neither, apparently, did the other children, whose relationship with their father remained one of respectful affection.

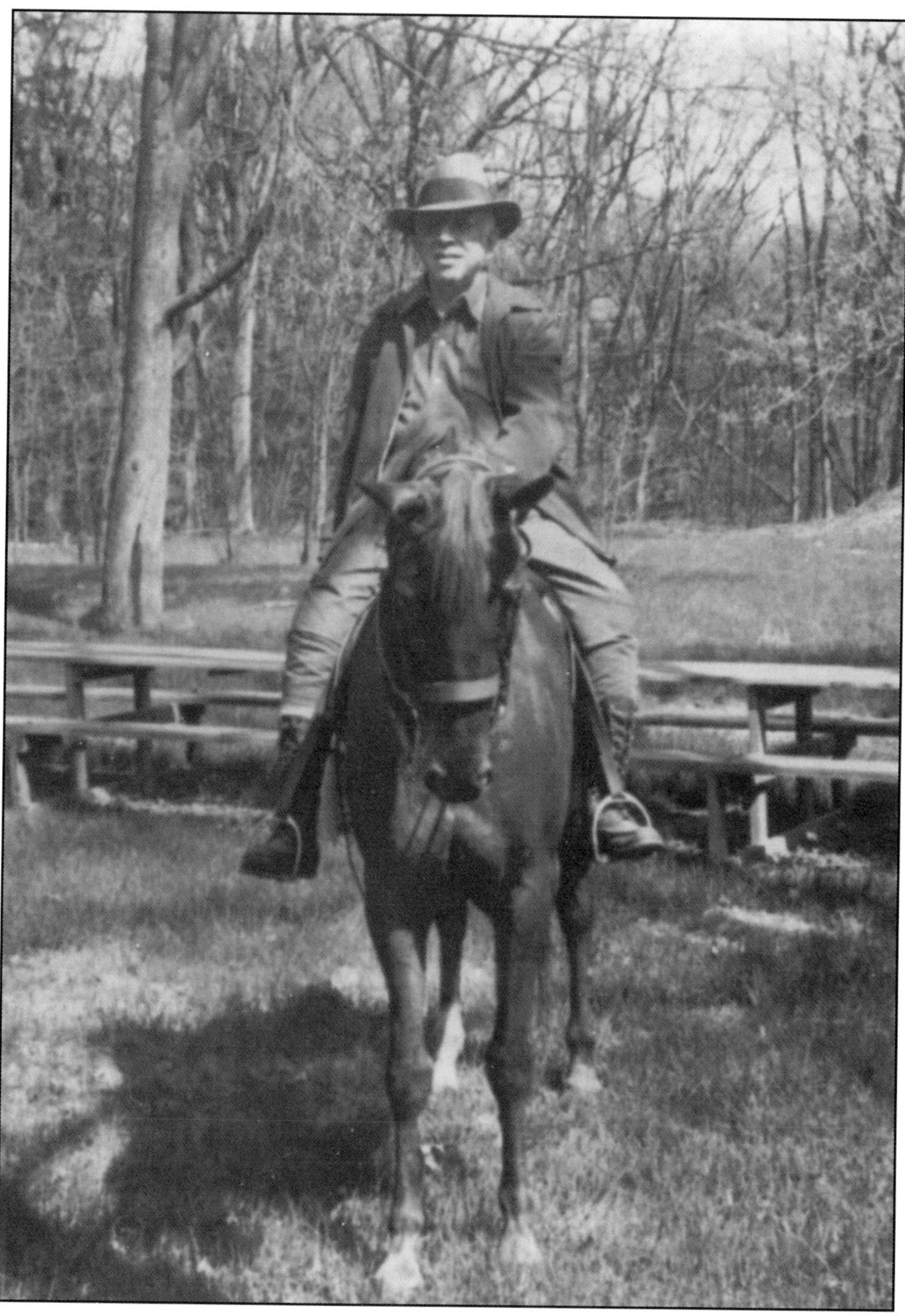

Howard Colman at Hawthorne Hills. "I often reflect on how extremely fortunate I am to have achieved such satisfaction in all the things about me so late in life ...," he wrote his daughter Dorothy (4/25/39).

In Colman's Own Words

Howard Colman's contemporaries remembered him as courteous, soft-spoken, and matter-of-fact in conversation. Few recalled seeing him angry. No one, not even his wife, ever saw him lose control of his emotions. He was cerebral rather than instinctive in his relations with people - the exact opposite, it seems, of his creative personality - and measured in his choice of words. When he talked, he focused intently on his listeners, and little of his inner imaginative world entered the conversation except through humorous asides. He admonished himself for a "painful habit of jesting," a flippancy and light bantering that appeared in exchanges with his family, but it's doubtful that many other people witnessed this tendency or credited him with a sense of humor. Like his mother, he loved word games, especially punning, and relaxed in the evenings at home by reading *Punch* and playing scrabble with his children, producing some strange verbal confections to test their wits. He also composed limericks about them when they were young that employed simple rhymes and inside jokes:

> There's a gink down home named Ed.
> Every hair on his dome is bright red.
> When he opens his face,
> The words start in a race.
> You're quick if you've heard what he said.

Colman's business letters contain little of his playfulness, and mostly go through the process of reviewing experiments, financial problems, patent issues, threats from competitors, production timetables, travel plans: exactly the sort of thing that one would expect to find in an active inventor's professional papers. We're interested in them, after all, because of the different ways that they reflect their author. Arranged chronologically, the following selections from Colman's personal and professional writings - family letters, business correspondence, experimental notes, random jottings - offer an impression of the man through the medium of his own words. Barring the discovery of a voice recording somewhere or a cache of private journals, this is as close to him as we are likely to get.

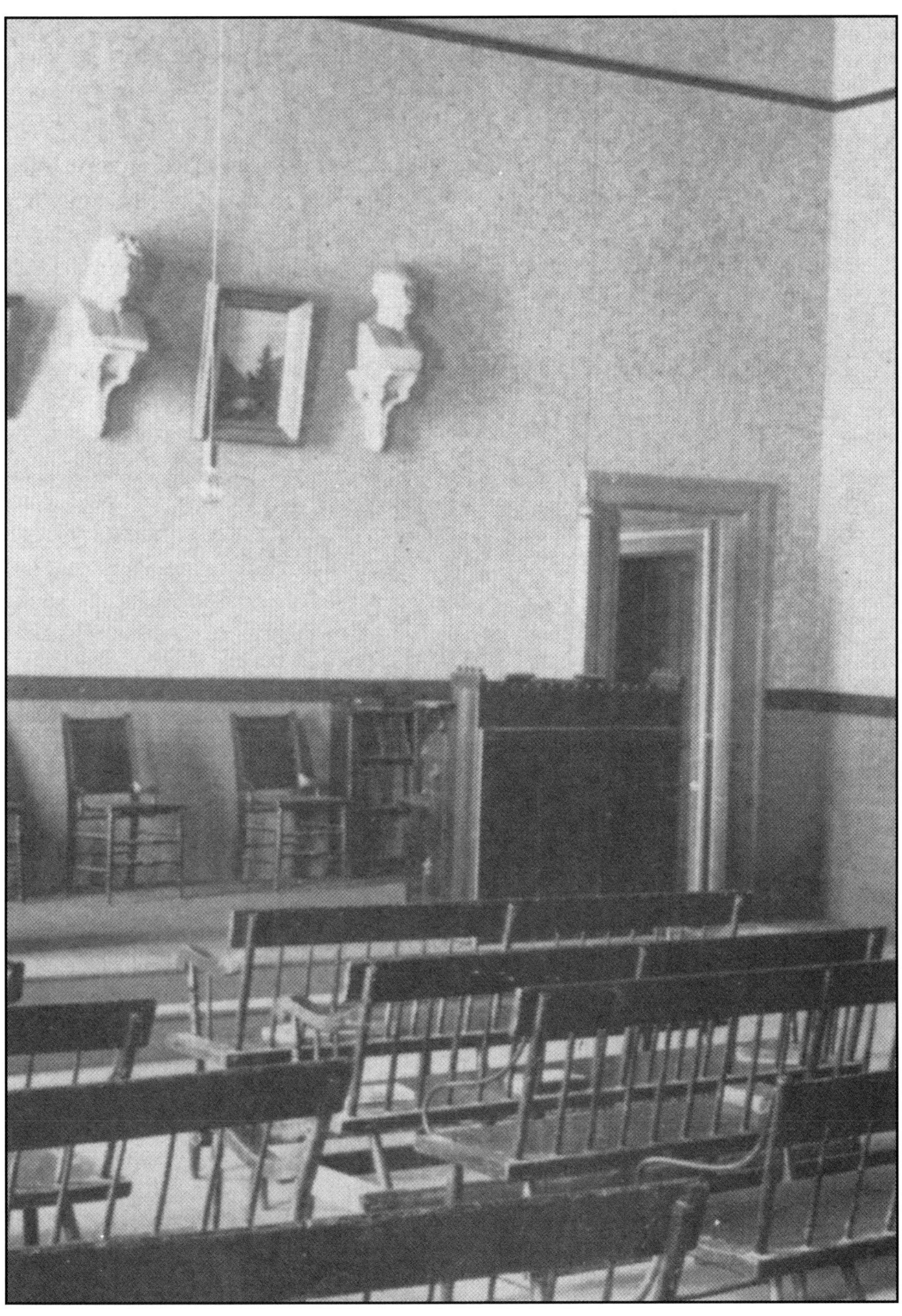

The old chapel at Wayland Academy in Beaver Dam where Colman attended daily services as a student (Courtesy, Wayland Academy).

1. To William Barber:

Beaver Dam, Wisconsin
July 1, 1891

Dear Sir,

Many thanks for check, which came tonight and for which I enclose a receipt. Work is progressing. Regards to Fred and Edith.

Yours in haste.

[Receipt] Beaver Dam, Wis., July 1st, 1891. Received of W.A. Barber one hundred dollars to be used in perfecting and testing my invention for drawing in cotton warp.

This is Howard Colman's earliest letter to William Barber.

2. To William Barber:

Beaver Dam, Wisconsin
July 16, 1891

Dear Sir,

The man whom I had engaged to do most of the work on the machine has just informed me that he is going to leave Monday to take the place of [a] machinist and engineer at the State Prison, and there is no one else in Beaver Dam who can do the work, and so in order to get out those cams properly, I will probably have to go to Milwaukee. Of course this will increase expenses considerably, but if nothing else happens, the money you sent will be sufficient to put up the machine. It won't leave, however, but a small margin for changes and experiments in case the machine should not work at first. Would you feel like putting in any more if it should prove necessary?

Have already made the end cams of iron, but the two middle ones, which are by far the hardest to make, are not commenced. Expect to make them in brass.

Yours truly.

3. To William Barber:

[No date or inside address,
but probably written from
Beloit in 1893]

Dear Sir,

I believe that I have now overcome the last serious difficulty in the way of the success of our machine, and that there is now absolutely no room for a reasonable doubt of its ultimate success. Of course there is indefinite room for improvement, as there is in all new machines. The present machine, having undergone so many changes, is rather a patched-up affair and will never be a thoroughly practical machine, but I believe that it has already accomplished its purpose - i.e. it has proved the possibility of constructing a thoroughly practical machine.

I have secured drawings and specifications of the patents in the United States for doing this work. The first patent was issued in 1882 to two men in Maine who appear to be working together. All other patents are to one or the other of these two men and are for improvements on the original invention. I understand from cotton-mill men that it is not a success and is attracting little or no attention. So far as I have discovered, their patents would not at all interfere with us. So the field seems to be clear.

I do not think that you have fully realized the value of this invention. I had a talk with a gentleman who has been for some forty years engaged in selling mill machinery. He assured me that there was enough in [it] to yield a handsome return if we sold only to the new mills as they are built and left the old ones alone. I had estimated the present number of mills in the world at about 5,000. He thought there were more than twice that number. Many mills would need two to a dozen machines. He said $30 to $50 would be a fair royalty on such a machine. Supposing only 5,000 machines sold at only $25 royalty, we would get $125,000. Supposing 10,000 machines sold at $50 royalty, it would be $500,000. These figures do not consider the fact that machines wear out and have to be replaced, that we would doubtless improve and displace our first machines by better ones, and that we could in all probability so modify the machine as to adapt it to flax, silk, and wool.

But if you wish to invest in the enterprise any considerable amount of capital, we could make far more than this. The shoe factory here has certain machines for which they paid [a] $100 installment and continue to pay [a] $100 yearly rental for each machine.

This scheme would not be at all unreasonable, it seems to me, applied to our machine. Each machine would save the manufacturer in wages at least $1,000 per annum - probably more - and he certainly ought to be willing to give us one-tenth of what we save him. Supposing 5,000 machines to be installed on this scheme, this would be $5,000 per annum. The cost of manufacturing the machine in quantities ought not to exceed $50 each and certainly would not exceed $100. If we charged the installment fee, that would pay the cost of manufacturing right at the start. We might at least try this scheme with a few machines, and if we did not find it successful, we could then dispose of our rights on a royalty or by sale.

The figures I have mentioned may, at first, strike you as extravagant, but I think if you will consider them carefully, you will find them an under- rather than an over-estimate.

Whatever you wished to do about it, I shall wish to spend some time yet on the present machine, not so much for the purpose of making it work better, as for learning how best to design another machine.

If you wish to go on with it yourself, wouldn't it be a good idea to build a new machine, as perfect as the best machinists can make it, regardless of expense, and place it on exhibition at the World's Fair? There is, I am sure, time to do it yet, but we will have to rush things and spend money without stint.

I should like it if we can have a meeting soon. The machine will not be in good shape for exhibition for two weeks or so yet. I have been concentrating my attention on the difficulty that I wrote about last, and while I have overcome that, I have not yet got the rest of the machine to "jibe" with the new arrangements. Of course, if you are willing to take my word for the condition of the machine, I can come up to Warrens and thus save your time.

Hoping to hear from you at your earliest convenience, I am

Yours respectfully.

4. To William Barber:

Beloit, Wisconsin
October 4, 1894

Dear Friend,

Perhaps you have noticed that Father has moved to Oakland Ave., Milwaukee. The difficulty that I spoke about last June as possible has now arisen, and I feel that I must not be a burden on Father any longer. His income at Oakland Ave. will be less than here, and of course his expenses will be greater, and even here it has been a struggle to make both ends meet. You promised me your advice as a friend in this contingency, and I certainly need it now.

There is a phase of our present arrangement which I presume has not presented itself to you and which I take the liberty of mentioning, knowing that, if my point of view is the correct one, you will be entirely ready to acknowledge it, and trusting that, if it is not, you will find an equally fair spirit in me. The case is as follows:

I am making drawings which, if I were unable to draw and we had to hire the work done, would cost at least $400.00. I do not refer to the inventing but to the part of the working involving drafting ability and mechanical skill and judgment. It is often the case, you know, that a man can invent but has to hire that part of the work done, and it is just as much a part of the legitimate expenses of experiment as the machine work. It seems to me that my inventive ability fully balances your investment, for, judging by the few other cases that I know of, it would be impossible to hire done what I have done for anything like the sum you have invested. I did not mention this at the start because I believed the expense of the blunders I would make through inexperience would balance the value of my services as draftsman and designer, but it has been the universal testimony of those who have had experience in experimental work that I have got along with remarkable economy. Refer you to Spengler or W.S. Bates, 1144 Monadnock Bldg. of Chicago, and there are others whose testimony I can get if you wish.

Now if we try to sell without building again or try to interest new capital, it would seem to me beyond question that the value of having these drawings will greatly exceed their cost. We considered ourselves even before I began these drawings (I do not make the slightest claim for work on drawings for [the] present machine), [so] why should I bear the whole burden of the present work? I would propose for your consideration that you pay me $10 a week from now until the drawings are completed (probably three months) and that the drawings be then submitted to competent judges to decide what they are worth (as drawings and working plans and not as an invention), and that you then pay me half that amount, the $10 a week to apply on said payment, or if the $10 a week is the amount, then I refund the difference. Then if we sell, we will be even, at least I will be willing to call it so, altho' it would perhaps be fair to say that the inventive ability I am investing fully balances all expenses, including payment for drawings and building [the] new machine, thus making me entitled to full payment for drawings in any case. But please understand that I consider your judgment of what is right and fair in the case as better than my own, and that I make these remarks merely to call to your attention a phase of the case which you may not have thought of …

Yours truly.

Please reply as soon as possible, for I fear I must seek remunerative employment unless you and I can make some such arrangement as above or unless you have some other scheme to propose.

5. Colman's negotiations with the Draper Company of Hopedale, Massachusetts over the sale of the D.I.M. reached an impasse in 1895 when the company's lawyers claimed that Colman's design infringed on an existing patent. Colman asked his own attorney, L.I. Morrison, to investigate this possibility and to conduct a review of the existing patent literature. Colman also studied ways to alter the D.I.M.'s design. The Drapers' suggestion to Barber and Colman that they wait for the existing patent to expire - that they follow, in the interim, a "course of masterly inactivity" - produced the following response from the inventor.

To William Barber:

Milwaukee, Wisconsin
June 10, 1896

Dear Friend:

… I hope we can have a conference soon. It would undoubtedly be better if we had Morrison's opinion about the file wrapper and contents first, but there appears to be a probability of considerable delay in getting copies. I enclose a letter from Morrison in which he says that he has instructed his correspondent not to order copies of British patents cited. I wrote him at once, telling him to order them but placed a limit of $20 and shouldn't be surprised if that would prevent his doing so.

I hardly expect them to get any results in that direction in less than four weeks. Meanwhile I will be getting deeper in debt and accomplishing nothing. Wish we could meet and decide on some course of procedure at once. It seems to me if we are going to submit to simply wait the pleasure of patent lawyers, we will have the privilege of doing so forever. This does not mean that I am necessarily opposed to the adoption of Draper's suggestion as to "a course of masterly inactivity," but if that is to be our course, I want it decided so that I can write Draper, Merrimack, and Cumnock for a job, without danger of injuring our case thereby.

I think "emasculating" would describe my present inactivity more accurately than "masterly."

If we do not simply wait, should think we would better go on with [the] new machine in hope that time will smooth things in some one of several possible ways, and I think you will agree with me after we have discussed it that we can do this pretty safely without waiting for Morrison.

Of course your interests and mine clash at this juncture in this: - that my investment goes on as heavily as ever, while yours stops altogether if we wait, and perhaps the shoe pinches me so hard that I am inclined to be unjust to you.

Yours truly.

6. In 1896-97 Colman designed and patented a check pump for the weighing out of skim milk at creameries. He and Barber authorized Cornish, Curtis & Greene (C.C.& G.) of Ft. Atkinson, Wisconsin to manufacture and sell the device on a royalty basis. Colman refers below to C.C. & G.'s delay in making royalty payments.

To William Barber:

Rockford, Illinois
May 5, 1898

Dear Friend:

I fear I will never be an inventor and man of business at the same time. I am surprised to find today that I have overdrawn [my] bank account about a dollar, and American Heating Co. want $18.18 for pipe, labor, etc. They are very accommodating about furnishing things, etc. and taking them back afterwards if I don't want them, so I hate to stand them off - especially as they want the money, so I promised it Saturday. Please send $25.00 at least. I think I can get along with that until something comes from C.C.& G. I hand you herewith [a] copy of [a] letter which I sent them, and which I hope will bring them to time. If I hear nothing from them by the 11th, I think I will telephone them. I think that, better than writing, can make them promise, whereas a letter they can simply ignore.

You and Edith are very kind to send me so much arbutus. My friends (including three sick people) and myself have all enjoyed it very much indeed and thank you most heartily.

Yours sincerely.

7. Colman experimented with the D.I.M. throughout the 1890s, even though much of his time was spent on other projects, such as the check pump, water lift, and spiral separator.

To William Barber:

Rockford, Illinois
December 7, 1898

Dear Friend:

Since my last writing [I] have devoted myself almost exclusively to D.I.M. and have been (and am) astonished at the old girl's good behavior. Had been having troubles innumerable before - as soon as one trouble was fixed, another more serious appeared. But during the past few days every touch has seemed to help matters - until today, I drew in a perfect warp - the first I ever did. This, however, is at a slow speed (about 90 threads per minute) because, as the machine is at present, I do not dare run fast on account of the dangerous pound occurring when the automatic stop acts. This is much worse than in the old machine because everything is much heavier. Have devised a change which I hope will make this stop less abrupt and permit any speed desired so far as that is concerned.

The machine is running as I write. I just stopped to "look up" the last warp drawn and start another. Found work nearly as good as that mentioned above - one thread broken was the only fault. By the way, it seems very likely that today is the first time in [the] history of the world that a perfect warp has been drawn by machinery.

Have had a great time trying to get a pick-up that wouldn't draw "doublers." Had one yesterday that drew six warps in succession without any doublers - then an accident broke it. The next one I tried drew 37 doublers in one warp. The next one drew three warps without doublers, then two warps with one doubler each, and now two warps without any - one of these being the famous "perfect warp." The last two have been drawn with a slight change in the arrangements, which seems to be an improvement.

All this is very encouraging, but no end of troubles are [sic] likely to develop when the speed is increased to 150 or 200, and even though the action were perfect, several minor things remain to be done to make the machine convenient and complete …

Very truly yours.

8. In 1899 Colman traveled to Lowell, Massachusetts to work on adjustments to the facer jaws of the D.I.M., which was being exhibited in the local Merrimack Mills. Here he recalls an amusing conversation with one of the Mills' maintenance mechanics:

To William Barber:

Lowell, Massachusetts
July 19, 1899

Dear Friend:

… The man who did the work [facer adjustments] for me is an old fellow they have in the tool room of the machine shop, whose principal business (I gather from his account) is to do odd private jobs for the overseer, etc. His brother is the master mechanic and (the superintendent tells me) is an unusually fine mechanic. He is rather gruff but is interested in D.I.M., and is very much taken with our double-movement cams. [His] name is Walcock …

[Walcock] … I found to be slow, very slow, but intelligent and accurate. Some pieces of work he showed me I have never seen excelled, so he proved to be just the man I wanted. He was very much interested in seeing the machine run and was very appreciative of its points. Finally he said:

"Must have spent a good deal of money in it, ain't ye?"

"Oh, yes, of course," said I.

"How much would ye take for it?"

"You mean the patent rights?"

"Yes, the whole thing."

"Oh, I hardly know."

"Ye must have some idea. Come now, what would tempt ye?"

Meanwhile I had been considering, not wanting to turn him down, because he is useful and likely to be more so, and concluded that it would do no harm to name our outside figure, especially as it would not be in any sense binding, so I said:

"Oh, perhaps $50,000.00"

"Well," said [Walcock]. "I'll tell ye something. Old man Pead was talking with my brother about it, and he said that, if the thing worked as he thought it would, it was worth $100,000.00 of any man's money. Of course, ye mustn't let on that I told ye, fer I ain't no business to say anything, but that's the fact."

And he gave me a lecture on the folly of letting a good thing go too cheap …

Very truly yours.

9. Colman's imagination ranged over many scientific fields. During the D.I.M. exhibition in Lowell, he worked out in his head the design of a new gasoline engine.

To Luther Miller:

Merrimack House
Lowell, Massachusetts
August 7, 1899

Dear Luther:

… To-day my stomach has been so bad that I have not gone to the mill at all, but am feeling better to-night and think I will be all right tomorrow.

For a week I have been, at odd times, considering a new idea for [a] gas engine, and getting the scheme into tangible form in my mind. It seems to me that it has important points of advantage, especially as an automobile engine. It expands the gases to atmospheric pressure before exhausting, thereby gaining a trifle in efficiency and making the exhaust noiseless. It has a continuous impulse - i.e., each impulse begins before its predecessor ceases, so no fly wheel would be required. To gain this I use 6 or 8 cylinders, but nevertheless I consider the whole machine simpler than the ordinary one-cylinder engine, for all parts are either stationary or revolve with the shaft (without other motion), except the pistons. The gases are inducted and e-ducted without valves (by ports), the burnt gases are thrust out entirely before new ones are drawn in, and ignition is accomplished without valves, hot tubes, or electricity. Also the whole machine would be lighter and more compact than any other scheme I know of. The wonderful simplicity referred to doesn't include [a] governing apparatus, but it does include [a] means for circulating water-jacket water other than the natural circulation of heating.

Am really quite in earnest about the matter and have started drawings so as to have something definite with a date to it. You told me once how many patents there are in this class, but I have forgotten. Wish you would look it up again. If they are not too numerous, I may decide to order the whole class. Am anxious to show drawings to Barber and get his opinion.

What is the price of patents when you take the whole class?

Sincerely.

10. Colman met Bertha Maguire in 1900, and their relationship gradually deepened. She was one of his main correspondents on business trips to New England and Europe. They married in 1902.

To Bertha Maguire:

Young's Hotel
Boston, Massachusetts
November 1, 1900

My Dear Bertha:

Your letter came yesterday morning and made glad the heart of this wanderer, I can tell you. It was awfully good of you to write when I had not written again as soon as you naturally expected, nor as soon as I would have done had I not been so much under the weather that it was hard for me to do anything. I appreciate it very much.

I went to a doctor Saturday and told him I needed to be braced up as soon as possible, and told him my symptoms. Guess he was on to his job for he seemed to think he could relieve me of the headache I had been having, but he said I must spend as much time as possible on my back, and ever since then I have been the laziest man you ever saw but not in any pain. Whether the laziness is the result of his advice and my natural indolence or whether it is partly due to his medicine, I don't know; but anyway, I was never so diligent in taking medicine before in my life …

Devotedly.

Howard Colman's 1902 wedding photograph.

11. To Bertha Maguire:

The Lake Shore Limited
New York Central, Boston,
Albany Lake Shore, and
Michigan Southern Railways
May 13, 1901

My Dear Bertha:

I wrote you yesterday afternoon very hastily because I still had some errands and not much time before the train left. Am going to write again now because I suspect there will not be much time in Boston and just now [Luther] Miller is busy preparing for a visit he has in Boston tomorrow.

We are running along besides the Erie Canal between Rochester and Syracuse, thru' a country bright with apple blossoms and dandelions. Just now I think of you as dressing for church, and I wonder whether the day is as fine in Rkfd. as here. If it is, I hope you will take Flora and go driving - but lately you will have other invitations.

Thanks to Miller's company in part, but more to your kindnesses when I left, I am having a very pleasant trip - so pleasant as I can hope to have under present circumstances.

As you probably inferred from my hasty note, my interview with the Dr. was very satisfactory, but I had quite a time getting it. I went to his office as soon as possible after arriving in Chicago, only to learn that his time was all spoken for until Tuesday, but upon my explaining my situation, I was told that I could come again at one and if any one failed to keep an appointment, I could have it. I went but thought my chances very slim. You can imagine how surprised I was when the young lady clerk told me that some one from Rockford, Ill. had cancelled his date, and I could have it!

The Dr. and his assistant put me through a regular examination such as I have never had before, made me strip, and kneaded me all over, listened to my heart and lungs with a stethoscope, looked into my eyes with an ophthalmoloscope, etc., besides no end of questions. Finally, when I was again clothed and in my right mind, the Dr. told me that I was absolutely sound and that my whole trouble is nervous, due to overwork and worry. He doesn't think it all serious and went on to tell me how to avoid it and gave me some stuff to take temporarily - during my present trip anyway. I understand it is merely to quiet my nerves. Anyway, he said it was "simple and harmless." He gave me some advice about eating and working, but he put the most emphasis on taking some outdoor exercise, which I enjoy and, I must say, I'm a little stumped as to what that will be. Guess I'll have to beg you to take me rowing frequently ...

We have just arrived at Syracuse, and I want to mail this here. So please excuse mistakes, awful handwriting, and lots of other things ... This is horribly written, worse expressed. Please be indulgent.

Devotedly.

12. On a trip to Europe in 1901, Colman wrote Bertha Maguire daily installments of a long letter aboard the U.S.M.S. "St. Paul." Bertha, in turn, sent short notes with him to be opened in sequence according to the dates on the outside of each envelope.

To Bertha Maguire:

U.S.M.S. "St. Paul"
October 26, 1901 [postmark]

My Dear Bertha:

It is the evening of the second day out, and all conditions have been ideal so far - warm and clear air and no waves that can affect this great boat. Except for a slight vibration from the engine, this table is as steady as your own writing desk.

I have been doing as you said in your dear note for today - enjoying every minute of it. The passenger list is very small, but there is no lack of pleasant company - in fact, one has to do a little dodging to avoid too much of it. I am particularly pleased with the people who sit near me at table: a man and wife from N.Y. The lady, it seems to me, must be just like my mother was twenty years ago. They sit just across. Next [to] me is a gruff old Englishman whom I thought, when I first saw him, would be intolerable, but who turns out to be extremely interesting. Just beyond him is a patent lawyer from Albany who is fine. I sit at the end, so there is no one on the other side. A couple of young fellows from Boston - college boys, I should judge - sit next to me on the deck, and they are very agreeable, too. Have played "shuffle board" with other young fellows and promenaded with still others. Everybody promenades miles and miles every day. But I must stop or I will have nothing to write you next time. I wish you were here to enjoy it with me.

13. Howard and Bertha spent the first year of marriage living with her parents in Rockford. After the birth of son Walter in May 1903, Howard was increasingly impatient to move out.

To Mrs. Howard D. Colman:

Barber and Colman Office
Boston, Massachusetts
September 17, 1903

My Dear Bertha:

... Hope you are ready to go about making a nest of our own for just us three as soon as I return and [am]very sorry that you have not written me that such is the case. It is the only possible way for us to live happily, and any delay only makes it harder.

Good bye, dearest.

14. The following memorandum was filed among Colman's experimental papers under the heading of "Arguments Affecting Decisions." It was occasioned by a slump in the textile market.

Rockford, Illinois
August 7, 1907

The attached estimate was prepared for me for the purpose of discussing with Mr. Barber the possibility of going into some line of manufacturing of a kind more stable than our present patent-protected business, the manufacture of automobiles being the particular line in mind. The portable business is estimated on a liberal basis and also on a conservative basis. The liberal basis is what [Harry] Severson and myself are agreed is just a fair probability - in other words, it is the state of affairs which we think is most likely to occur. The conservative basis is the least amount of business which we think [we] are likely to have, provided general business conditions and conditions in the cotton trade, in particular, continue as they now are and, also, provided that no special misfortune of our own occurs.

The larger estimate of proposed expenditures is thought to be all that we can organize to expend with any reasonable economy, and it is thought that the smaller estimate of expenditures is all that we are likely to be in a position to spread.

Mr. Barber and myself went into these figures as thoroughly as possible on August 3rd, 4th and 5th, and we decided, together with Mr. Severson, that we ought to go into some stable line as proposed, and we have further concluded that nothing at present appears to offer as good attractions as the automobile line. We, therefore, decided to take preliminary steps, looking toward our going into the manufacture of automobiles, reserving the final decision until later.

[Colman next provides "liberal" and "conservative" forecasts of Barber-Colman knotter and warp-typing machine sales, manufacturing costs, and operating expenditures in Europe and the U.S. from August 1907 - January 1, 1909. This is followed by a list of the expenditures "outside regular expenses" that Colman estimated would be needed for an automotive start-up.]

LIBERAL BUSINESS ESTIMATE

Building & Equipment	$100,000.00
Automobile Development	100,000.00
"X"	100,000.00
"T"	100,000.00
General Experimenting	50,000.00
Reserve for Litigation	50,000.00
Total	500,000.00

CONSERVATIVE BUSINESS ESTIMATE

Building & Equipment	$ 75,000.00
Automobile Development	75,000.00
"X"	75,000.00
"T"	75,000.00
General Experimenting	25,000.00
Reserve for Litigation	25,000.00
Total	375,000.00

STOCKPORT AND DISTRICT

Weavers, Winders, Warpers & Reelers'

ASSOCIATION.

All Winders who work at the following Mills :

Stockport Ring Spinning,

Kingston Mill, India Mill,

AND

Travis Brook Mill,

ARE URGED TO

REFUSE TO USE THE BARBER KNOTTER

AFTER

WEDNESDAY Afternoon, APRIL 9th,

And reduce the number of ends by 20 per cent.

Example : 60 spindles—mind 48.
„ 70 „ „ 56, and so on.

All Winders are urged to act together.

On behalf of Committee.

J. PHILIP RIDING.

J. S. Dutton, Printer, Market Place, Stockport.

An undated flyer (c. 1902) protesting against the introduction of the Barber knotter into the mills of Lancashire, England. Many manual workers, in the U.S. and England, initially opposed the use of the knotter because of its labor-reducing potential.

15. To Lucinda Colman:

Rockford, Illinois
March 1, 1920

My Dear Mother:

Bertha was at her high school lunch room work as usual this noon, so I have read to Dorothy her mail. She was greatly delighted with her missive from her poetical grandmother, and I am sure will prize it more highly in future years ...

For some time I have been looking for a chance to run up to Milwaukee & see you, but the pressure of business seemed to make it impossible, altho' I ought not to let it be. In a few weeks now, the roads will be passable & then it won't be quite so difficult.

Much love.

16. In order to establish his rights as a pioneering inventor and prepare the way for later patent applications, Colman went to great lengths to document his "idea trains" while conducting experiments. These self-reflections were filed in the Barber-Colman Experimental Department. The following discussion of "Telegraph Signaling" indicates that the genesis of Colman's interest in telegraphy was his work on a radio-controlled garage door opener in the 1920s.

April 28, 1925

This scheme is described in an article written by myself, dated February 11, 1925, entitled "Description of Proposed Method of Telegraph Signaling," and an article written by Mr. Duncan J. Stewart, dated March 6, 1929, entitled "Telegraph Signaling."

This idea was suggested by my work on "DO" [Door Operator] where we use a combination of pins pushed and not pushed to form a mechanical lock having many different combinations. (See my application for Patent on Remote Control Apparatus [DO], Serial No. 1,808, filed January 12, 1925.) This work called my attention to the large number of combinations possible with a small number of pins, as shown by the law N = 2n where N equals the number of combinations, and n equals the number of pins. I do not recall the exact date on which this idea first occurred to me, but I think it was about December 27, 1924, until January 4, 1925, during which time I had my son, Walter, look up the article in the Britannica Encyclopedia on Submarine Telegraphy, the pertinent parts of which I read. I also had Walter call up Mr. D.S. Sprague and find out how many words there are in an ordinary dictionary, and how many words per minute a typist can write. Mr. Sprague tells me that it was on a Sunday or holiday that Walter called, because he remembers being at home when Walter called. As Walter left for Seattle [on] Friday, January 2, it must have been either New Year's Day or Sunday, December 28, 1924, when he called Mr. Sprague, and I think it was the latter date.

I disclosed the scheme first to Mr. Duncan J. Stewart and, I think, but I am not just sure, that I disclosed it to Mr. Earl C. Carlson on December 31, 1924, which day he spent at my house going over the papers in the application for Patent, Serial No. 1,808, previously mentioned.

At any rate, Mr. Duncan J. Stewart and I discussed the code extensively during my illness and read everything we could find on the subject, including an article regarding Colonel George W. Fabyan in the *American Magazine* for January 1925 entitled "He Solves the Secrets of Cipher Writing" by John Kidder Rhodes ...

17. This report from the Barber-Colman Experimental Department file is stamped "H.D.C."

November 25, 1926
[date-stamped]

SUBJECT: Automatic Tailoring Machine

I conceived the idea today of an automatic machine for making men's (or women's) clothes to fit the individual just as the tailor does.

A measuring machine measures the individual & records the results by punching holes in a tape. The machine does the measuring by means of a feeler (or a number of feelers) which touch the individual at the required number of places. These feelers will perhaps work on the "condenser feeler" principle. There may be enough of them to touch the required number of places all at once or there may be a much smaller number (perhaps only one) which touch the required number of points in succession, but if so, the individual must be held in position so that he (or she) cannot move during the measuring operation, which will probably not occupy more than a few seconds.

The tape so punched controls an automated machine (or machines) which completes the suit without other attendance than to put the tape and material in position, set a dial indicating the type of suit (or perhaps special holes in the tape will control the type of suit) & start the machine. Perhaps one machine will be required for coat, another for suit & another for trousers, or perhaps one machine will make the three garments in succession. Or perhaps the three machines will be used in large shops to increase capacity & only one in small shops.

Assume that a battery of 3 machines can finish a suit in 5 minutes (whether they specialize on the different garments or not) & that they run an average 15,000 suits a year. This would require running 15,000/12 = 1,250 hours per year or say 12 ½ hrs. per day during 100 days of the year, which seems reasonable in view of the seasonable demand for clothes.

Will suppose that one concern (called the company) owns the machines & leases them to the local merchants for $5 per suit, including services & repairs but not operating attendance, which requires two men for the 3 machines @ 75 cents per hr. each, which would make during continuous running a labor cost of $1.50/4 = 12 ½ cents per suit, but owing to irregular running (idleness & overtime), this becomes 25 cents or possibly 50 cents per suit.

The merchant will carry only a small inventory (as compared with that of a dealer in ready-mades) & the customer will have the advantage of made-to-measure at the same (or lower) cost as ready-mades at present.

The company will receive $5 X 5,000 = $25,000 per annum for machines. The company manufactures the machines at a cost of $5,000 each & depreciation & obsolescence amount to 20% or $1,000 per year & sales, service & repair amount to another $1,000 per year. Average investment per machine = about $3,000. [Therefore] return of average investment 23,000/3,000 = 766.7% per annum.

If an average of 1 suit per year is made for each man & boy (not counting women & girls), then the gross income of the company is $5 X 50,000,000 = $250 million per year.

> 10,000 machines capital 10,000 X 3,000 = $30,000,000
> Expense $2,000 X 10,000 = $20,000,000
> Number of machines required per year to replace depreciation & obsolescence = 10,000/5 = 2,000
> Manufacturing cost per year = $5,000 X 2,000 = $10,000,000, which would require factory 2 to 3 times as large as B-C Company's present factory.

The principal obstacle in the way of realizing these nifty little sums seems to be to produce the very nimble machines required & to do so at the costs stated & before I'm called to shovel sulfur or play a harp*

> * *Nota bene.* Before the occurrence of this last-mentioned event, there will be ample time.

18. Colman's existing letters to his daughter Dorothy cover the last eight years of his life (1934-42). This one is written to her in care of the Choate College Preparatory School for Women in Brookline, Massachusetts, where she was employed as an English instructor.

To Dorothy Colman:

Rockford. Illinois
May 16, 1934

My Dear Dorothy:

I have your extended and interesting discussion of your possibilities and prospects for next year, and I assure you that I have given due and serious thought to all the considerations which you mention, even though my remarks in regard to some of them may sound otherwise to you. Probably you can stand a little flippancy after my first remark, which is:

1. I advise that you stay at Choate and finish your M.A., and take no money from Miss Choate even though she offers it to you.

2. I contemplate with sadness the lost joys which you might have had during the last seven years had a wiser parent directed your course, but the gloom is somewhat lessened by the thought that you have at least one boy friend, and thinking that the next time you write him, you might wish

In the 1920s Howard Colman redesigned the standard shaded-ring induction motor to make it smaller, quieter, and more powerful, using the machine as the linchpin of a new Barber-Colman electric system of temperature control. The motor was also sold to manufacturers of a wide range of commercial products, including fans, heaters, blowers, phonographs, timers, record-changers, business machines, vaporizers, and movie projectors.

to intersperse your billings and cooings with a reference to the astonishing exploits of his son, I enclose a clipping from the current issue of *Time.*

[The enclosed clipping, from the "Press" column of the May 14 issue of Time, is about the 1934 Pulitzer Prize-winner for journalism, the Medford (Oregon) Mail Tribune and its editor, Robert Waldo Ruhl.]

3. I do not seriously disapprove of a little back-breaking, for I have known broken backs to heal, but I am not going to fall in with my proposal to amputate a healthy and sound right arm. Such a thing would [be] so definite and final and, moreover, it would not accomplish your purpose.

4. I am interested to know of your prospective ride home in a motor car. In that connection, I have found that the railroad will redeem the unused portion of your ticket for about $13.25, and therefore you should not sell it for less than that. You should also bear in mind that either selling or redeeming the ticket will prevent your checking any baggage home, and the express company is quite careful not to handle the trunks for nothing.

5. The legend of the twelve Trojans is true, at least to the extent that they are again enjoying an existence which for a time was miserable indeed.

Your affectionate father.

19. The following letters were written to Dorothy after her marriage to Richard Wallace.

To Mrs. Richard H. Wallace:

Rockford, Illinois
June 27, 1936

My Dear Dorothy:

I cannot write you in answer to your great news. The words do not come, and the ones I have tried to force are detestable. So I'll just pray from the bottom of my heart that in your career as mother, your sufferings and sorrows may be [at] a minimum & your joys and pleasures beyond your fondest dreams. My own dominant emotion is not of pleasure but rather a feeling of responsibility for having even an indirect part in the starting of a new life.

[This note, written on a sheet of paper with the "Barber-Colman Company Experimental Department" letterhead, lacks a complimentary close and is simply initialed "H.D.C."]

20. To Mrs. Richard H. Wallace:

Rockford, Illinois
February 19, 1937

My Dear Dorothy:

God's nightgown! Surely other things besides the easy and romantic life of the aristocratic South prior to the Civil War have "Gone with the Wind"!! And yet I am expected to be gay!!!

But let's get to the extenuating circumstances, if any.

Confronted with the sudden necessity for an instant decision, I chose the Scylla of your displeasure rather than the Charybdis of shameless mendacity. And now my battered bulk, pierced by a dozen jagged rocks, rolls wretchedly and sinks, along with our cherished Constitution, rendered and wrecked by the resounding attacks of a ruthless Roosevelt.

The agonies of death are made ten thousand times worse by the realization that had not the lookouts been staging a sit-down strike and the helmsmen gone sound asleep, the narrow passage might have slid through without scraping a side.

I admit that these circumstances are poor extenuators, and if discretion is in you, no stork circling shall occur over your dwelling in the future except in densest fog.

I will attend [to] the proposed propitiating present tomorrow and cheerfully, for when sinking to Davy Jones's locker, what would be the sense of complaining that one leg is two inches longer than the other?

You will find no gaiety in this lugubrious confession, but possibly you can derive a delight from the deadly diameter of your dashing, degenerate, darling dad, as revealed by one of the enclosed shots of light. Anyway, how do you like my lagoon as a skating pond and a background?

[Colman had enclosed a photograph of a skating pond on his Cunningham Road property west of Rockford.]

Surely illness will be history ere this reaches you, at least I most earnestly hope so, and please don't let your righteous indignation prevent my being promptly advised.

Your affectionate father.

P.S. Remembering your contempt for Gilbert & Sullivan, I mention the fact that I am going to Iolanthe in Chicago tonight only as further evidence of degeneracy.

21. To Mrs. Richard H. Wallace:

Rockford, Illinois
September 3, 1938

My Dear Dorothy:

I am delighted to have your note of August 31, with the cheerful news that more movies and stills of your daughter are about to be sent to me. However, there is one part of your

A Colman family gathering at Lake Geneva, Wisconsin, in 1917. Colman had lived in Lake Geneva as a boy (1885-87) and enjoyed vacationing there with his family as an adult. In 1917 he purchased a dwelling known as "The Cabins." The property, which was later enlarged to 1,250 feet of lake frontage, became the home of his wife and children during the summer, with Colman sometimes joining them on weekends. Pictured above (l-r) are Alice Pearce, the family nurse; Adella Maria Woodruff Maguire, Bertha's mother; Ruth Colman (age 10); cousin "Lena" Woodruff, a relative of Bertha's; Bertha; Edwin (age 12); Dorothy (age 4); Howard; and Walter (age 14).

letter that is rather depressing, though it hasn't quite got me down yet. I refer to the fact that you seem seriously to entertain the idea that I am old enough to start writing a biography. Surely you must recognize the fact that I am not and if I were, it would be disgustingly conceited of me to even think of such a thing. However, since you ask for it, I'll give you one which, while necessarily not quite complete, seems at least to avoid my last objection. Here it is:

Created	1873
Mated	1902
Cremated	- - - -

Aunt Lu is home from Seattle, and I expect her here tomorrow morning to stay over Labor Day. I think she has had enough of traveling and visiting so that she will be glad to pass the time very quietly while I try to do a little work.

… Edwin and Elizabeth were here for dinner Thursday evening and brought with them a rather interesting Bulletin issued by your grandfather Colman, July 23, 1864, when he was principal of the Evansville Seminary. I have made photostatic copies and am enclosing one, thinking that you may be interested in the fact that he expected students to "refrain from walking, riding, or visiting with those of the opposite sex."

This interesting document was loaned to Edwin by the Librarian of Lawrence College, to whom I am now expected to return it. As you doubtless know, Edwin and Elizabeth attended the Regatta at Neenah and on one afternoon, when the race was called off on account of rain, they went to Appleton and poked around a bit …

Your affectionate father.

22. *This note, written on Barber-Colman Experimental Department letterhead, is evidently in response to a question about the origin of one of Mark Twain's humorous anecdotes. It is the last remaining document in Colman's handwriting.*

To Mrs. Richard Wallace:

Rockford, Illinois
June 7, 1942

Dear Dorothy,

Mark Twain.

A Tramp Abroad.

[Many of the words in the letter are illegible. The gist of the message seems to be that Colman has looked up the passage in question] … and found it all in about two minutes.

Vol. I, Chapter XXV, p. 250
I am heartily ashamed of myself.

Your loving Dad.

Colman was killed, eighteen days later, in an automobile crash near St. Charles, Illinois.

A family photograph of Howard Colman and daughter Dorothy at Lake Geneva in 1936. Among his existing photographs, this is one of the few that shows him laughing and relaxed.

Chronology

1873 Birth of Howard Colman (July 9) in Waukesha, Wisconsin, the fourth child of Henry Colman, a Methodist minister, and Lucinda Darling Colman.

1874 Colman family moves to Ft. Atkinson, Wisconsin.

1876 Colmans move to Milwaukee, Wisconsin, where Henry becomes the minister of the Spring Street Methodist Church.

1880 A workshop is provided for Howard in the Colman parsonage. He enters the primary department of the Fourth Ward Public School in Milwaukee and is promoted to the second grade.

1882 Colmans move to Whitewater, Wisconsin, where Henry takes over a new church.

1885 Henry is assigned to a Methodist church in Lake Geneva, Wisconsin.

1888 Henry becomes the minister of the English Methodist Church in Beaver Dam, Wisconsin. Howard enters Wayland Academy. Studies under Winfield Sweet, Wayland mathematics instructor.

1889 Howard constructs a wooden model of a warp drawing-in machine (D.I.M.) after visiting the Beaver Dam Cotton Mills. D.I.M. exhibited to mill superintendent, Alex Kingbury, at Thanksgiving. Henry agrees to pay for the construction of a metal prototype.

1890 Graduation from Wayland. Howard re-enrolls for a postgraduate term in September.

1891 Howard stays out of school during the winter to work on the D.I.M. but then re-enrolls for the spring semester. Introduced in June to William Barber, a Wayland benefactor who agrees to subsidize his work on the project.

Enters Northwestern University in September. When Henry is assigned to a Methodist church in Beloit, Wisconsin, Howard withdraws from Northwestern and enrolls in Beloit College. The D.I.M. is set up in a woodshed behind the Colman parsonage.

1892 Tests of the D.I.M. in the Janesville Cotton Mills, Janesville, Wisconsin. Howard drops out of Beloit College in order to spend full time on his experiments.

1893 Spengler Brothers Company of Rockford, Illinois, hired to build a new D.I.M. model incorporating various improvements.

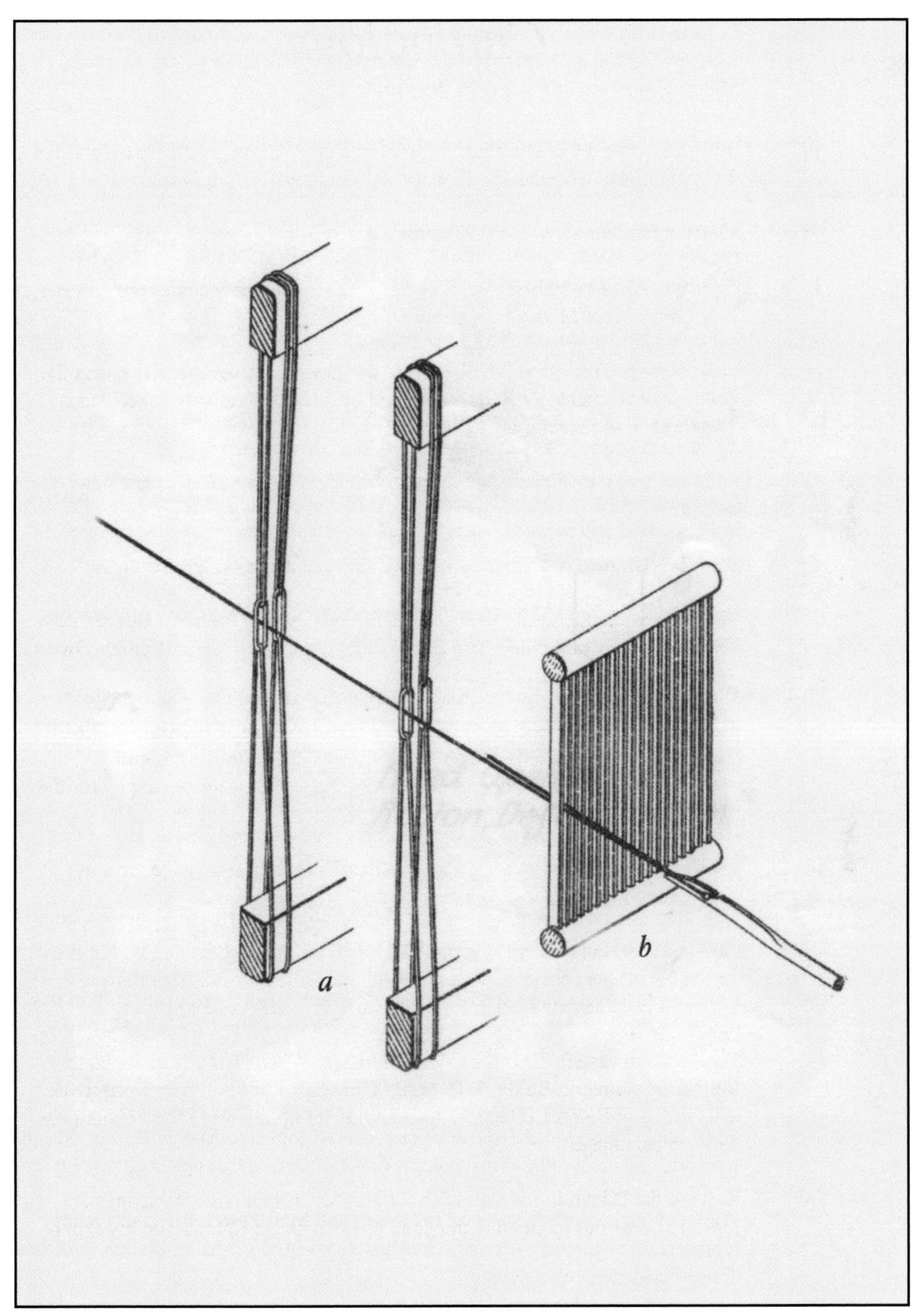

Preparing warp beams for mechanical weaving in the 19th Century required operators to pull tiny cotton threads by hand through the openings in the harnesses (a) and reed (b). Because of the size and irregularity of the openings, the process resisted mechanization before Colman's creation of the D.I.M.

1894 Colman sets up an experimental laboratory on the second floor of the Spengler Brothers building. Introduced to Luther Miller, Rockford patent attorney. Moves into a rooming house in Rockford.

1895 Colman conducts tests of the D.I.M. at the Boott Mills in Lowell, Massachusetts.

1896 Discussions with George Draper and Sons of Hopedale, Massachusetts, about the possible sale of rights to the D.I.M. Colman develops model of a check pump for the measurement of skim milk; Miller files patent application.

1897 Sales of check pump provide first earnings of the Barber and Colman partnership. Patent issued for the pump.

1898 Cornish, Curtis & Greene of Ft. Atkinson, Wisconsin licensed to manufacture the check pump. Tests of the D.I.M. yield a perfect warp.

1899 Colman exhibits D.I.M. at Merrimack Mills in Lowell, Massachusetts. Period of exhaustion and nervous strain. Idea for a manual knot-tying mechanism conceived.

1900 Hand-knotter tested at Merrimack Mills; Spengler Brothers begin manufacturing the device. Sales representative hired in Boston.

1901 Knotter patent issued. Spengler Brothers increase production. Colman travels to Europe to hire overseas sales representatives. Harry Severson, a civil engineer, becomes first regular company employee.

1902 Marriage of Howard Colman and Bertha Maguire (June 17) in Rockford. After a honeymoon in Alaska, the Colmans sail to Europe, where Howard markets the knotter.

New Barber and Colman factory building erected in Rockford. Louise Culver, an office worker ("cashier"), joins the company.

1903 Colman crashes his Pope-Toledo touring car into a Rockford trolley. Accident makes headlines of the *Register-Gazette.* Birth of Walter Colman (May 12).

Barber and Colman Company purchases machinery from Spengler Brothers and takes over knotter production. Earle Parker joins the company as a draftsman. Three former Spengler machine assemblers - Martin Noling, Martin Johnson, and John Skorberg - hired as first Barber and Colman shop employees.

Company branch offices opened in Boston and Manchester, England. Sales representatives hired in Atlanta; Dresden, Germany; and Lille, France. Colman designs a warp-tying machine.

1904 Warp-tying machine tested in Olympia Mills, Columbia, South Carolina; patent application filed. Orders for the machine lead to the construction of an enlarged Barber and Colman facility in Rockford. Bert Peterson joins the company as a draftsman.

1905 Barber and Colman partnership replaced by Barber-Colman Corporation. Birth of Edwin Colman (March 19). Worldwide demand for knotter.

1906 Beginning of patent dispute with American Warp Drawing Machine Company of Boston.

1907 Colman buys residence at 929 N. Main Street in Rockford. Birth of Ruth Colman (June 12).

Economic depression and collapse of textile machinery market causes Colman to investigate ways to diversify his company.

1908 New company offices opened in Chicago, Milwaukee, Detroit, and New York. Barber and Colman G.m.b.H. incorporated in Germany. Founding of Small Tools Division for the manufacture of hobs and milling cutters.

1909 Barber sells his shares in the company. Barber-Colman Corporation reorganized as a limited partnership between Colman, Miller, and Severson, with Colman owning 75% of the stock. Contract with the Ford Motor Company for the manufacture of thrust-bearings. Development of portable machine for warp-tying operations.

1910 Colman designs gear-hobbing and doffing machines. Start of Machine Tools Division. Family vacation in Colorado.

1911 Experimental installation of doffing machines in New England cotton mills. Barber-Colman develops new process for manufacturing steel hobs.

1912 Death of William Barber in Warrens, Wisconsin. Colman designs automatic spooler and begins tests in Bemis Brothers Bag Company, Bemis, Tennessee.

1913 Birth of Dorothy Colman (March 1). Patent received for automatic spooler.

1914 Initial sales of automatic spooler. Colman vacations with his family in White Mountains of Vermont and later visits Panama Canal in the company of Luther Miller.

1915 Colman makes rare public appearance in Rockford "Military Preparedness Parade" (November 11).

1916 Barber-Colman Company reaches 900 employees.

1917 U.S. entry into First World War. Barber-Colman factory dedicated to military production. Tools and special machinery supplied to Rock Island Arsenal. Parts manufactured for guns, sights, and mounts for U.S. Navy. New plant constructed in Manchester, England; "aero engine" parts produced through remainder of War.

Colman purchases summer home at Lake Geneva, Wisconsin.

Howard Colman in his mid-forties.

1918 National influenza epidemic. Barber-Colman discontinues manufacture and sales of doffing machines. Family vacation in state of Washington.

1919 Barber-Colman acquires rights to the drawing-in machine of the American Warp Drawing Machine Company, ending a 13-year patent dispute.

1920 Colman purchases key-operated electric door-opener system for Barber-Colman executive garage. U.S. economic depression.

1921 Development of Simplex knotter, a low-priced model made from sheet metal, and new automatic spooler and high-speed warper. Beginning of an extended period of depression and nervous exhaustion. Colman is absent from work for much of the summer and fall while recuperating.

1922 Colman's convalescence continues. While at home, he develops a design for a radio-controlled garage door opener. Begins to experiment with a model of a small synchronous motor.

1924 Development of hob-sharpening and reamer-sharpening machines. Duncan Stewart, an electrical engineering graduate of the University of Wisconsin, becomes Colman's personal assistant.

1925 During an illness, Colman studies military codes, ciphers, and submarine telegraphy. These studies lead to the development of a printing telegraph, repeating typewriter, and high-speed loom.

1926 New electrical department launched by Colman as company skunkworks; he personally underwrites 100% of operating costs.

1927 Death of Henry Colman (May 25).

1928 Patent application submitted for multiplex telegraphy.

1929 Production of Barber-Colman radio-controlled garage door openers, electrical temperature controls, furnace regulators, garage doors ("OVERdoors"), and electric fans. Branch offices for the sale of temperature-controls established in Chicago and Milwaukee. Company reaches 1,700 employees.

1930 Death of Lucinda Colman (December 20). Molded Products Division started after purchase of Rockford Phenolic Products. Collapse of U.S. stock market. Beginning of a period of personal depression.

1931 Colman sells electrical department to Barber-Colman to help the company raise working capital. $200,000 budgeted for Barber-Colman Experimental Department.

1932 Colman draws up his last will and testament.

1934 Howard and Bertha Colman separate. Howard moves to 26-acre homestead on Cunningham Road ("Hawthorne Hills") west of Rockford, while Bertha continues to live at 929 N. Main.

KEEPS YOU COOL — *QUIETLY!*

BARBER-COLMAN

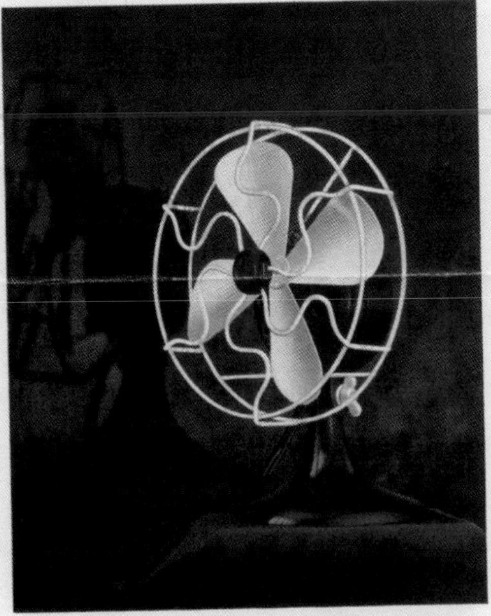

ELECTRIC FAN

SPECIFICATIONS

Blades (4)	6" diam.
Overall Height	8¾"
Net Weight	2¼ lbs.
Speed of Blades	2400 r.p.m.
Air Velocity (at guard)	1300 f.p.m.
Air Moved (free delivery)	600 c.f.m.
Circuit	115 v., 60 c.
Power Consumed	24 Watts
Material—Case	Moulded Bakelite
Pedestal	Moulded Bakelite
Metal Parts	Cadmium Plated

Motor—Induction Type—No Brushes—No Commutator. Quiet, Economical Operation—No Radio Interference.

Equipped with 6-foot Cord and 2-part Plug.

A High Quality Product at an Extremely Low Price . . . Good for Years of Service . . . Beautiful in Appearance . . . A Home and Office Convenience of Lasting Value . . . Keeps you Cool — *QUIETLY!*

BARBER-COLMAN COMPANY - ROCKFORD, ILL., U.S.A.

The Barber-Colman electric fan, one of the company's best-known commercial offerings, was made possible by Howard Colman's redesign of the shaded-pole induction motor in the 1920s.

1935 Colman and associate Bert Peterson awarded Longstreth Medal by the Franklin Institute of Philadelphia for outstanding contributions to the textile industry. Company begins manufacturing air distribution products after purchase of Uni-Flo Corporation of Detroit.

1937 Automatic temperature controls installed in Pan American "Clipper" flying boats.

1939 Creation of Aircraft Products Division.

1941 U.S. entry into Second World War. Barber-Colman military production includes filter motor-controls, gun director parts, tank and tank-engine air conditioning systems, and radar sets.

1942 Company reaches 3,000 employees. Colman and daughter Ruth vacation in California. He dies at the age of 69 in automobile accident near St. Charles, Illinois (June 25).

1945 Patent approved for multiplex telegraphy.

1971 Bertha Maguire Colman dies at the age of 96.

1984 Barber-Colman textile division sold to Reed-Chatwood (July). Barber-Colman acquires shares of five shareholder families (December); as a result, company management and outside directors assume control of 53% of voting shares.

1985 Barber-Colman hobbing, hob sharpening, and shaper lines sold to Bourn and Koch.

1987 Barber-Colman Company sold to Siebe plc of Windsor, England.

1988 Barber-Colman cutting tool product line sold to Pfauter-Maag.

1996 Reed-Chatwood textile assets sold to Hanjo-Rosen. (This business is acquired by Bourn and Koch in 1998 and re-sold in the same year to Gastex of Gastonia, N.C; Gastex is later purchased by West Point Foundry.)

2000 Smith Aerospace Ltd. purchases assets of Barber-Colman aircraft products division.

2002 Name of Barber-Colman Controls Division changed to Invensys Building Systems as a result of Siebe mergers and acquisitions.

2003 George Clubb, one-time Barber-Colman employee, purchases West Point Foundry assets.

2006 Invensys Building Systems sold to Schneider Electric SA.

The Barber-Colman Company's 22-acre manufacturing complex in the 1960s.

Colman's Patents

Title	Patent Number	Date
Check-Controlled Liquid Deliverer	581,149	April 20, 1897
Water Lift	650,167	May 22, 1900
Water Lift	650,168	May 22, 1900
Knot-Tying Implement	672,635	April 23, 1901
Knot-Tying Implement	672,636	April 23, 1901
Knot-Tying Implement	707,826	August 26, 1902
Knot-Tying Implement	755,110	March 22, 1904
Device for Correcting Drawing-in Errors	825,585	July 10, 1906
Tying Machine	905,793	December 1, 1908
Warp Carriage	938,124	October 26, 1909
Warp Carriage	942,247	December 7, 1909
Warp-Handling Apparatus	955,383	April 19, 1910
Knotter	955,384	April 19, 1910
Warp-Handling Apparatus	962,400	June 21, 1910
Means for Clamping and Stretching Warp Threads	963,871	July 12, 1910
Thread-Selecting Device	977,166	November 29, 1910
Doffer	983,858	February 7, 1911
Knot-Tying Mechanism	1,029,853	June 18, 1912
Doffer	1,044,993	November 19, 1912
Textile Machine	1,050,762	January 14, 1913
Warp-Drawing Machine	1,062,271	May 20, 1913
Doffer	1,062,439	May 20, 1913
Warp-Uniting Mechanism	1,069,081	July 29, 1913
Warp-End Supporting Means	1,069,082	July 29, 1913
Knot-Staggering Mechanism	1,070,116	August 12, 1913
Knotter	1,072,575	September 9, 1913
Spooler	1,078,574	November 11, 1913
Warp-Tying Machine	1,079,470	November 25, 1913
Warp-Tying Apparatus	1,082,474	December 23, 1913
Winder	1,105,065	July 18, 1914
Thread-Board Cleaning Apparatus	1,114,859	October 27, 1914
Machine for Preparing Warps for Weaving	1,115,399	October 27, 1914
Bobbin Cluster	1,115,509	November 3, 1914
Mechanical Movement	1,116,019	November 3, 1914
Method of Treating Warp Threads	1,129,849	March 2, 1915
Thread-Board Cleaning Apparatus	1,137,305	April 27, 1915

Textile Machine	1,149,499	August 10, 1915
Textile Machine	1,175,710	March 14, 1916
Textile Machine	1,183,276	May 16, 1916
Winder	1,184,077	May 23, 1916
Winder	1,187,971	June 20, 1916
Winder	1,191,102	July 11, 1916
Bobbin Holder	1,201,998	October 17, 1916
Warping Apparatus	1,207,138	December 5, 1916
Warping Apparatus	1,208,295	December 12, 1916
Warping Apparatus	1,209,122	December 19, 1916
Machine for Preparing Warps for Weaving	1,211,677	January 19, 1917
Bobbin-Handling Apparatus	1,226,606	May 15, 1917
Winder	1,227,754	May 29, 1917
Creel	1,228,410	June 5, 1917
Yarn Carrier	1,236,822	August 14, 1917
Traverse Mechanism for Winding Machines	1,239,669	September 11, 1917
Winder	1,239,670	September 11, 1917
Textile Apparatus	1,245,874	November 6, 1917
Container for Yarn Carriers	1,255,858	February 12, 1918
Knotter	1,255,859	February 12, 1918
Method of Winding Yarn	1,258,986	March 12, 1918
Waste Winder	1,262,644	April 16, 1918
Winder	1,267,977	May 28, 1918
Winder	1,268,684	June 4, 1918
Winder	1,274,386	August 6, 1918
Yarn-Carrier Support	1,274,387	August 6, 1918
Creel	1,275,850	August 13, 1918
Winder	1,293,042	February 4, 1919
Textile Apparatus	1,304,661	May 27, 1919
Warp-Handling Machine	1,306,138	June 10, 1919
Winder	1,311,498	July 29, 1919
Support for Yarn Carriers	1,329,504	February 3, 1920
Machine for Operating upon Warps	1,342,896	June 8, 1920
Knotter	1,348,929	August 10, 1920
Winder	1,366,447	January 25, 1921
Machine for Operating upon Warps	1,442,776	January 16, 1923
Bobbin and Yarn Package	1,444,414	February 6, 1923
Eccentricity-Preventing Means for Warpers	1,444,415	February 6, 1923
Stopping and Restarting Mechanism	1,446,451	February 27, 1923
Knotter	1,450,941	April 10, 1923
Machine for Operating upon Warps	1,450,942	April 10, 1923

Winder	1,475,688	November 17, 1923
Comb Used in Textile Art	1,503,637	August 5, 1924
Winder	1,517,279	December 2, 1924
Feed and Adjustment for Textile Machines	1,531,736	March 31, 1925
Thread Clamping and Shearing Means	1,539,076	May 26, 1925
Warping	1,544,055	June 30, 1925
Tension Equalizer	1,550,881	August 25, 1925
Loom	1,551,732	September 1, 1925
Warp-Drawing Machine	1,589,587	June 22, 1926
Winder	1,596,807	August 17, 1926
Winder	1,611,890	December 28, 1926
Spinning Machine	1,614,718	January 18, 1927
Method of Spinning	1,614,879	January 18, 1927
Warp-Drawing Machine	1,624,928	April 19, 1927
Yarn Mass Support	1,641,661	September 6, 1927
Winder	1,661,817	March 6, 1928
Textile Apparatus	1,666,735	April 17, 1928
Bobbin Skewer	1,678,806	July 31, 1928
Thread-Handling Mechanism	1,684,945	September 18, 1928
Heddle Frame	1,686,073	October 2, 1928
Machine for Generating Gear Wheels	1,712,254	May 7, 1929
Grinding Wheel	1,712,255	May 7, 1929
Gear-Cutting Wheel	1,712,256	May 7, 1929
Winder	1,727,534	September 10, 1929
Winder	1,727,749	September 10, 1929
Gasoline Gauge	1,723,681	September 24, 1929
Automatically-Controlled Clutch	1,734,998	November 12, 1929
Gear-Cutting Machine	1,737,217	November 26, 1929
Warper and Method of Warping Yarn	1,741,757	December 31, 1929
Telegraphy	1,745,007	January 28, 1930
Telegraphy	1,745,008	January 28, 1930
Selective Signaling Apparatus	1,760,478	May 27, 1930
Radiant Energy Control System	1,760,479	May 27, 1930
Operating Means for Doors and the Like	1,773,219	August 19, 1930
Lacing Machine and Method of Lacing Skeins	1,774,591	September 2, 1930
Skein Lacing Machine	1,774,592	September 2, 1930
Lacing Machine	1,784,984	December 16, 1930
Thermostat	1,807,306	May 26, 1931
Overload Release Mechanism	1,815,345	July 21, 1931
Motor-Driven Operator	1,815,397	July 21, 1931
Motor-Control Mechanism	1,815,398	July 21, 1931

Signaling Apparatus	1,844,205	February 9, 1932
Heat-Regulating System	1,844,841	February 9, 1932
Connected Series of Heddles	1,848,869	March 8, 1932
Dressing Device for Grinding Elements	1,850,201	March 22, 1932
Thermostat	1,875,369	September 6, 1932
Machine for Producing a Connected Series of Heddles	1,884,575	October 25, 1932
Electric Valve Operator	1,903,229	March 28, 1933
Electric Control Unit	1,903,231	March 28, 1933
Gate Operating Mechanism	1,913,976	June 13, 1933
Temperature Regulating System	1,921,154	August 8, 1933
Storing Transmitter	1,962,136	June 12, 1934
Clutch	2,013,649	September 10, 1935
Clutch Mechanism	2,091,268	August 31, 1937
Clutch Mechanism	2,091,269	August 31, 1937
Clutch Mechanism	2,091,270	August 31, 1937
Self-Adjusting Brake	2,106,167	January 25, 1938
Self-Adjusting Hydraulic Brake	2,130,875	September 20, 1938
Bellows Piston	2,160,248	May 30, 1939
Self-Adjusting Hydraulic Actuator	2,193,190	March 12, 1940
Printing	2,196,354	April 9, 1940
Clutch Mechanism	2,207,051	July 9, 1940
Storing Transmitter	2,232,166	February 18, 1941
Hydraulic Power Brake	2,246,667	June 24, 1941
Selectively-Operable Mechanism for Typographical Machines and the Like	2,294,385	September 1, 1942
Control-Strip Composing Machine	2,324,280	July 13, 1943
Record Mechanism	2,334,145	November 9, 1943
System of Communication	2,380,894	July 31, 1945
Gearing	2,397,777	April 2, 1946
Message Intercepting and Relaying Circuits in an Automatically-Directed Message Telegraph System	2,424,223	July 22, 1947
Automatic Multiple-Stage Telegraph System	2,472,885	June 14, 1949
Clutch and Control Mechanism Therefor	2,564,324	August 14, 1951

Colman's Designs

Howard Colman's powerful visualizing capacity enabled him to summon an endless stream of mental images in the development of his inventions. The play of forces and motions in his imagination was the beginning of a process that found expression in sketches, drawings, prototypes, and production models; and the same considerations of balance, scale, and proportion that shaped the work of his contemporaries in the visual arts also influenced his designs. Working without written notes or other kinds of physical cues, he spent long periods of time "in cogitation," allowing schemes to evolve in his head and calling upon memories of past experiments to test and refine these images. When a concept had sufficiently matured to be worthy of a practical trial, he disclosed it to a draftsman, usually with the help of pencil sketches. A general drawing (i.e. two-dimensional line drawing) was then completed, as well as a series of shop-detail drawings for the fabrication of a prototype. In his early career, Colman made these drawings himself, using his Chicago draftsman, L.T. Mann, mainly for the illustrations that accompanied his formal patent applications. After the invention of the hand-knotter, however, Colman was able to take advantage of draftsmen and machinists within the company and to pursue his investigations in a much more systematic fashion. Harry Severson remembered (apropos of the warp-tying machine) that Colman liked to disclose a scheme to the members of the Experimental Department while plotting it on a drawing board. He would give verbal descriptions as he sketched and outline the essentials of the project that he hoped to undertake:

> Mr. Colman's first explanation was verbal, though probably sketches were made to indicate roughly some of the features. Work was, however, immediately started on a drawing, and this drawing was shown and explained to me from time to time as the work progressed. Mr. Colman made this drawing, and from it both he and Mr. Parker made working drawings of the various pieces as the work on the general drawing progressed (Record of Warp-Tying Machine Interferences, Vol. V., U.S. Patent Office, 1915).

After the parts and assemblies of a new machine were completed, they were incorporated into a study model. Colman scrupulously monitored each step of the process and made "change drawings," as necessary, according to early tests of the device. Designing in this way - finding the right arrangement of machine elements to suit his purpose, re-jiggering the parts in light of the experimental results - was the practical side of his engineering work.

As an inventor, Colman's natural medium of expression was visual-spatial. It was also inwardly-focused. His line drawings were the first step in translating his mental images into tangible objects, his schemes boiled down to their bare-bones essentials. Understanding how a thing functioned was inseparable from knowing what it looked like, and the inventor's trick was to envision a new scheme without determining what its possibilities were, or even if it worked. On the following pages (and on the front- and back-inside covers of this book) are a sampling of designs from Colman's patent applications, drawings prepared by drafting professionals from two-dimensional studies that the inventor made himself. If his own sketches and prototypes are gone, destroyed in successive house-cleanings at Barber-Colman over the years, his patent drawings remain; and we can get an idea of the imaging process that produced his inventions by examining these designs. When we admire the spatial harmonies of his best work, the hand-knotter pre-eminently, we realize that an aesthetic impulse was an important factor in determining his final forms. We can appreciate the parts' complexities even if we're ignorant of their functions.

The Barber-Colman "Simplex" knotter (1921).

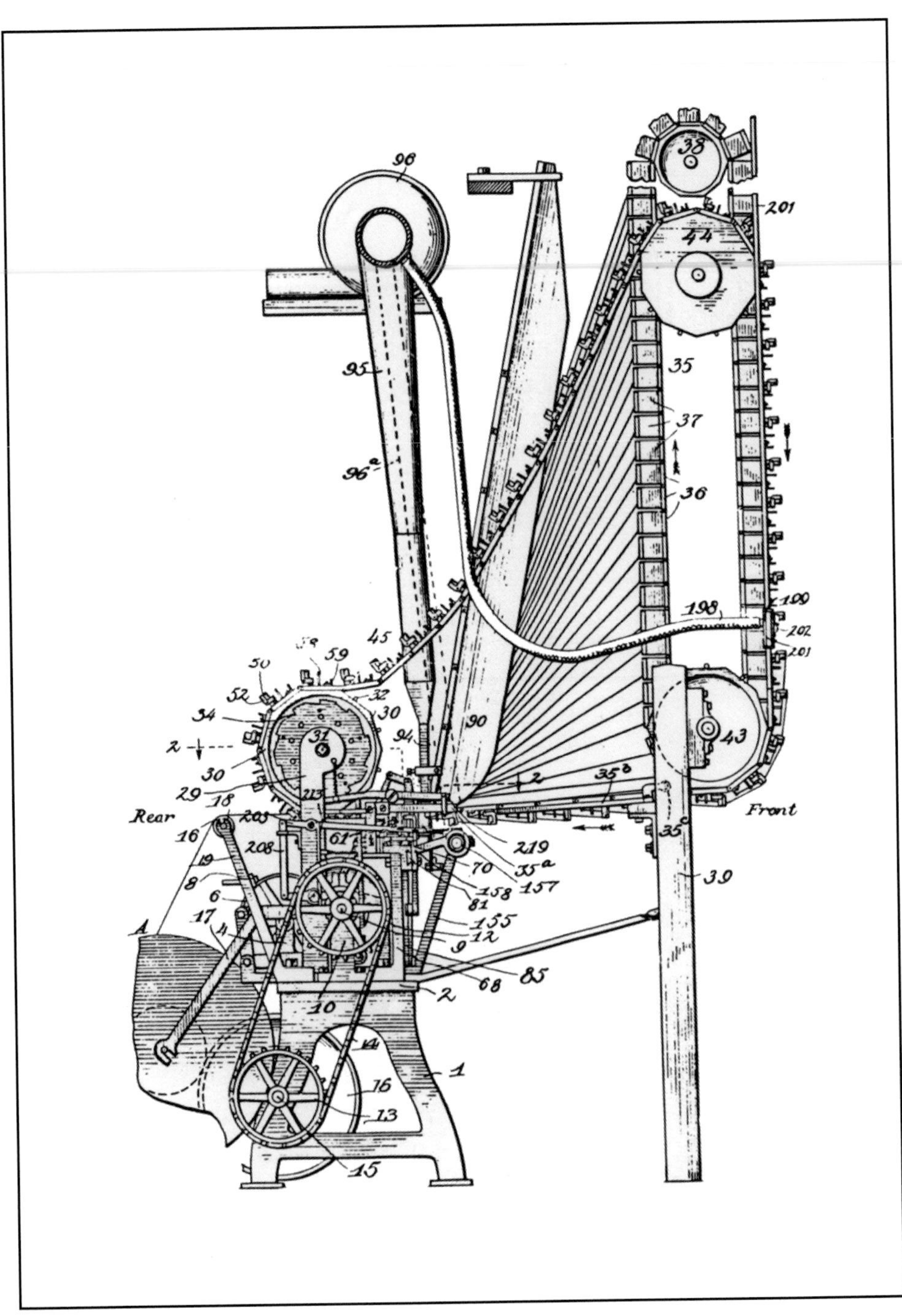

Winder (original patent application filed June 21, 1902; continued July 31, 1903 and September 13, 1911). This side elevation shows the machine winding threads from an endless chain (35) of bobbin-boxes (37), right, onto a section beam (A), lower left.

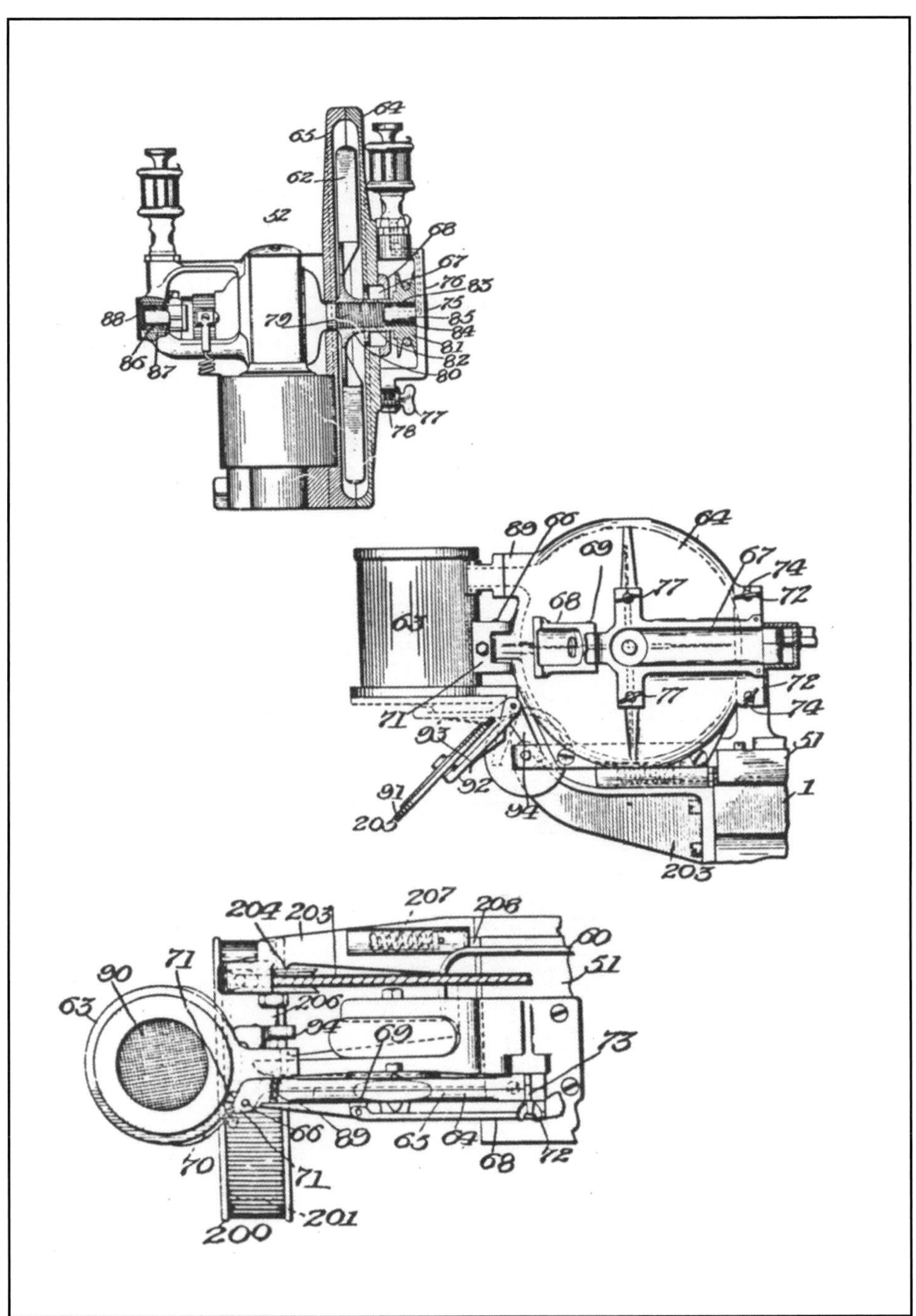

Warp-Tying Machine (original patent application filed October 5, 1906). The top drawing shows a fan used to blow away loose thread ends during the tying process. The middle view is a profile of a centrifugal collector for the thread ends. The bottom drawing is a top view of the same collector.

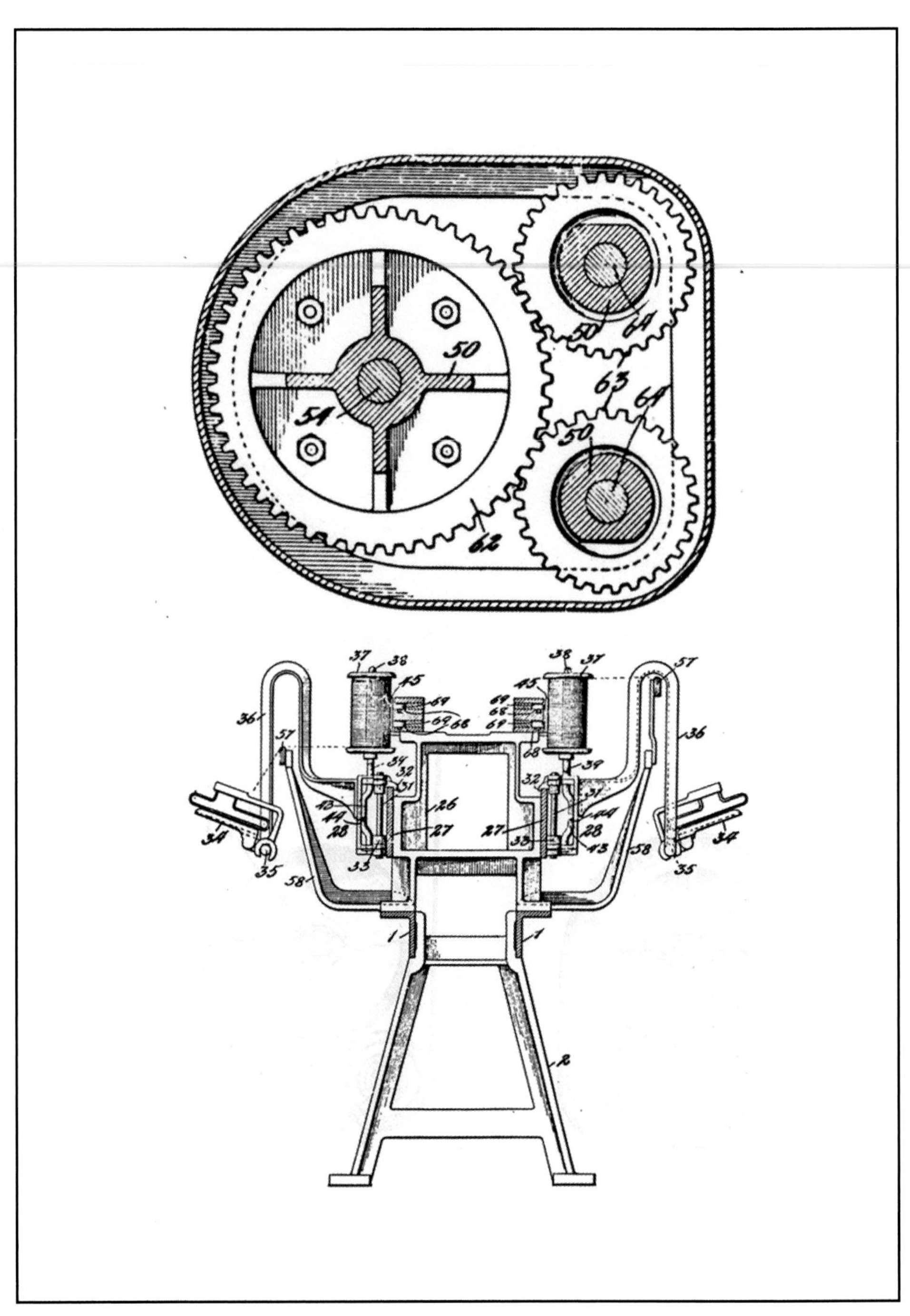

Spooler (original patent application filed December 26, 1907). The top drawing shows the sprockets that drive the machine's spool and bobbin carriers. The bottom transverse sectional view shows the base and standard (1-2), bobbin holders (34), spools (37), and spindle (38).

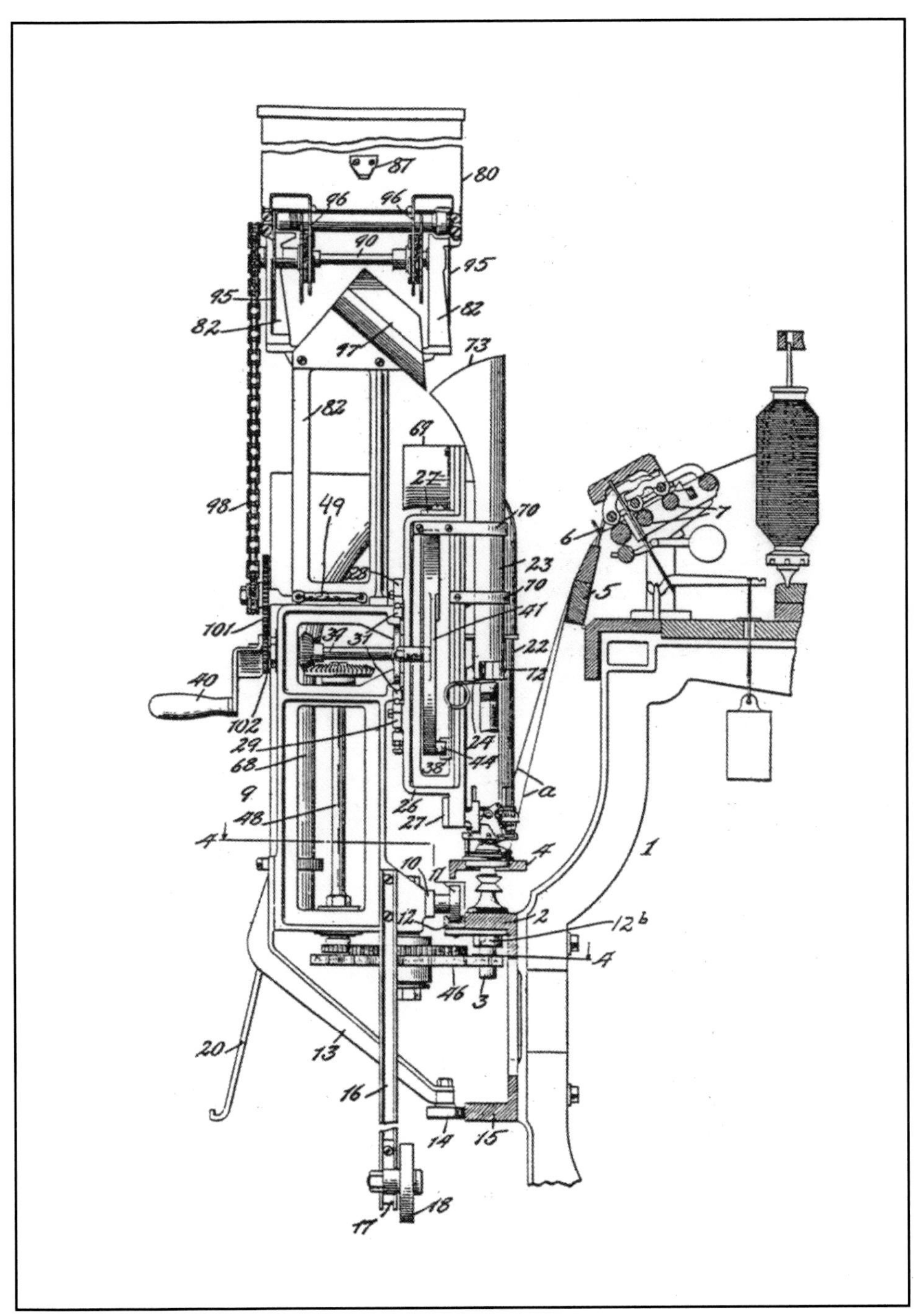

Doffer (original patent application filed November 5, 1908). A side elevation of the device illustrates how Colman's doffing mechanism ("doffer") is attached to a standard spinning frame, shown here in section. Pneumatically-controlled doffing (22) and donning (23) tubes for removing and replacing bobbins on the spinning frame are shown at the center of the drawing.

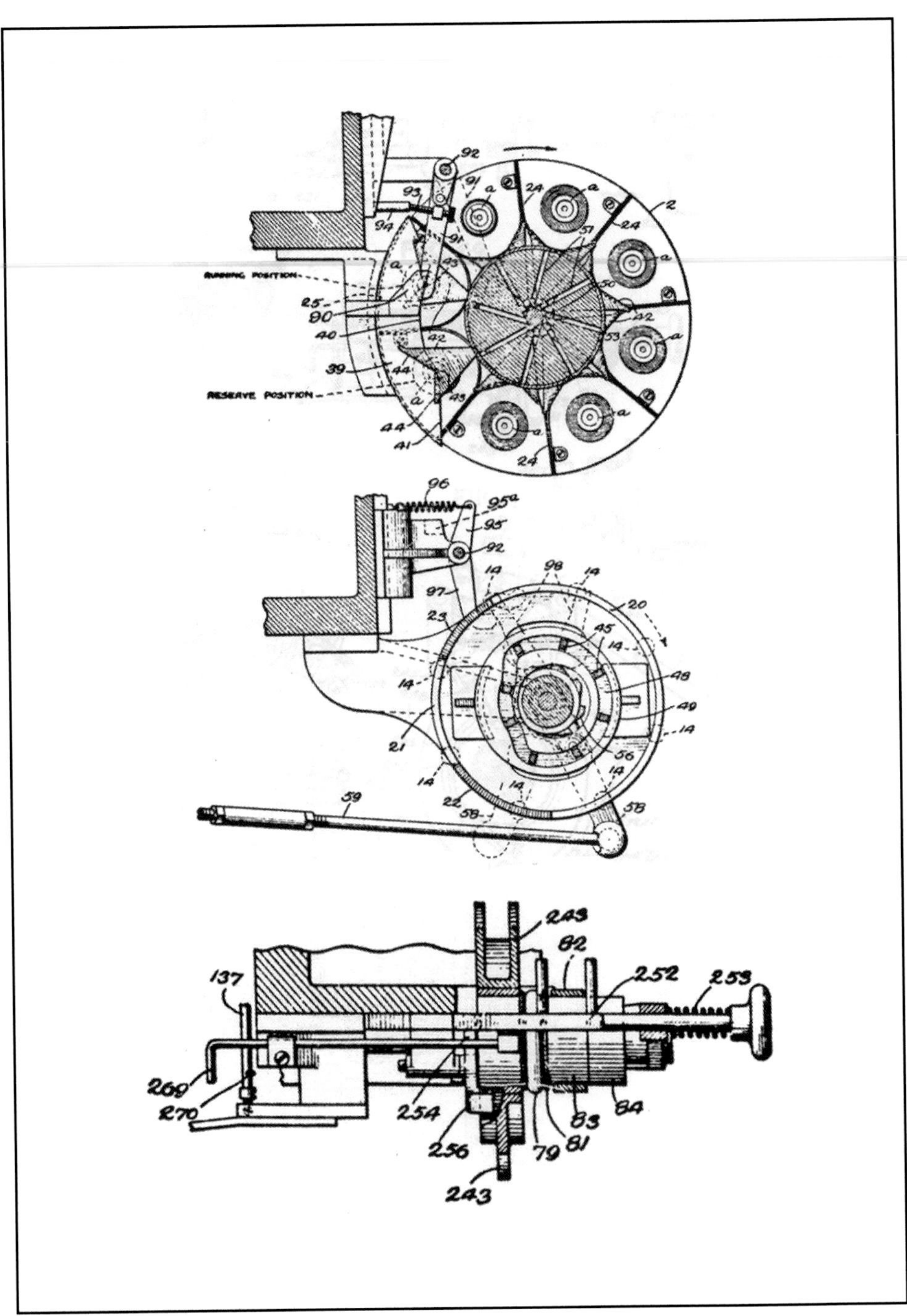

Winder (original patent application filed January 4, 1917). The drawings show various components of the device's yarn-clearing mechanism..

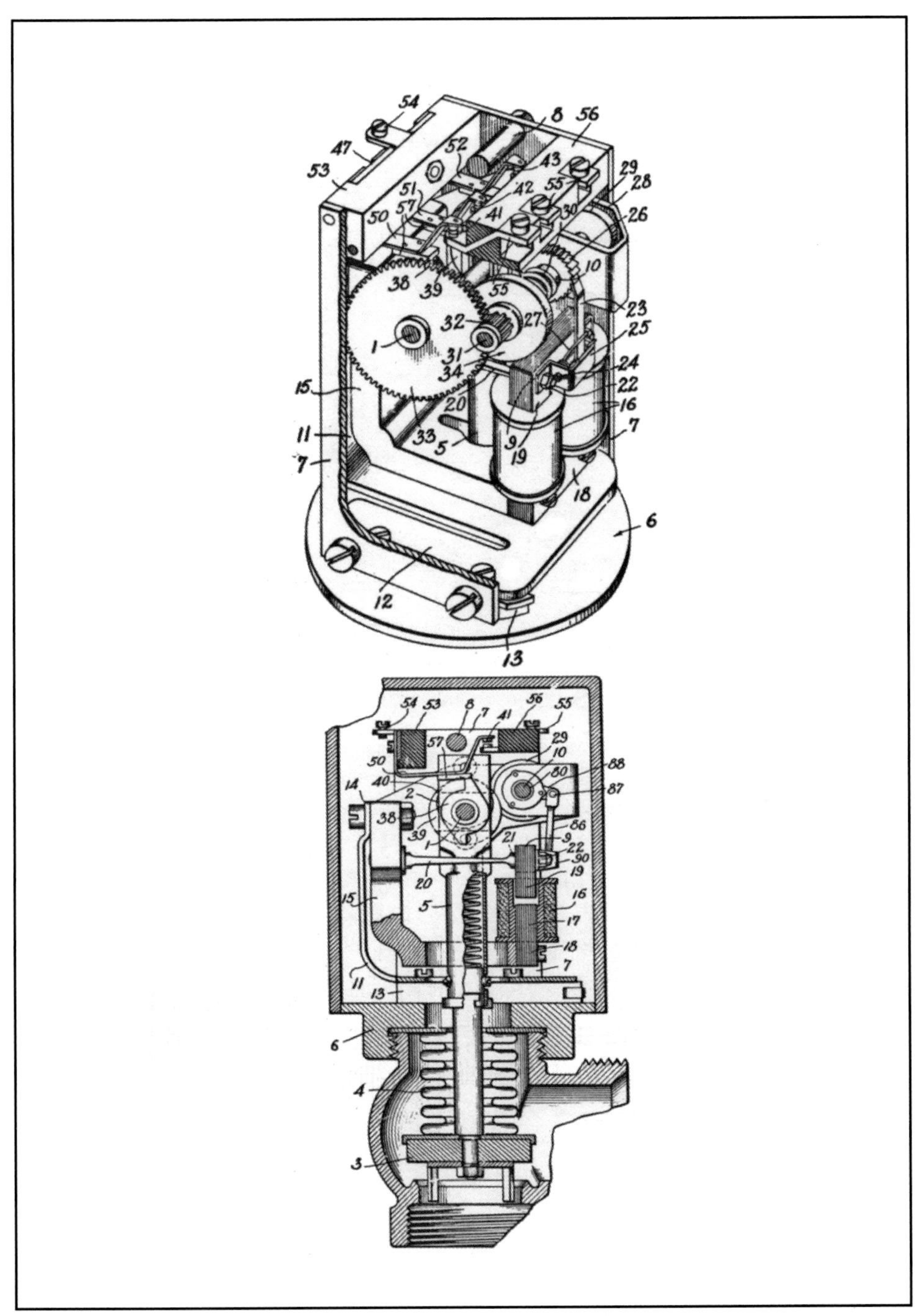

Electric Control Unit (original patent application filed February 15, 1929). The top drawing is a perspective view of the device as it applies to the operation of a radiator valve in an automatic temperature regulating system. The bottom drawing, a vertical section view, shows the cam mechanism (2) that moves the valve (3) from its seat in the casing.

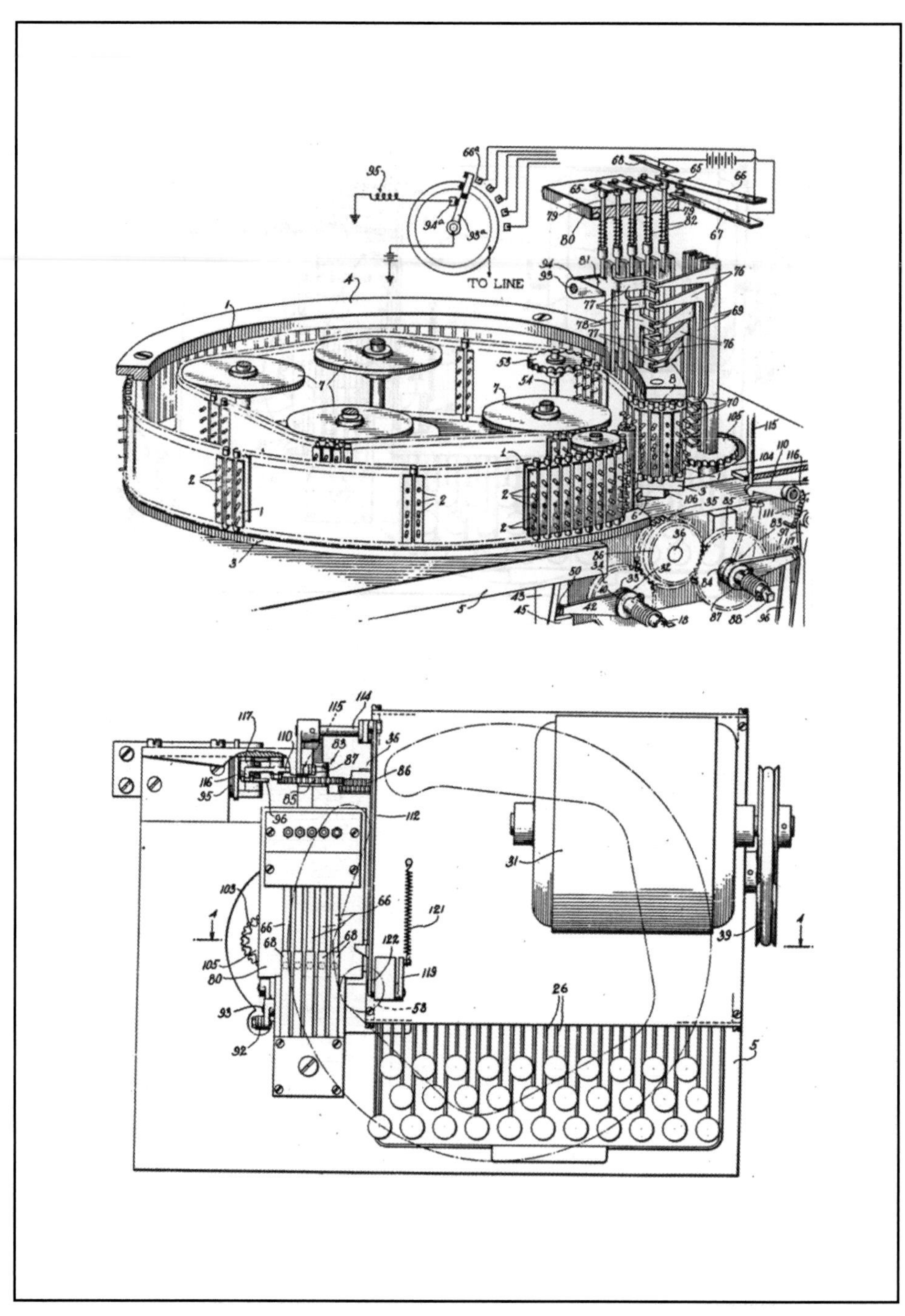

Storing Transmitter (original patent application filed August 1, 1930). The mechanism was intended to provide a flexible storage medium for messages transmitted from a remote keyboard. The top drawing is a perspective view and wiring diagram of the device. The bottom drawing is a plan view.

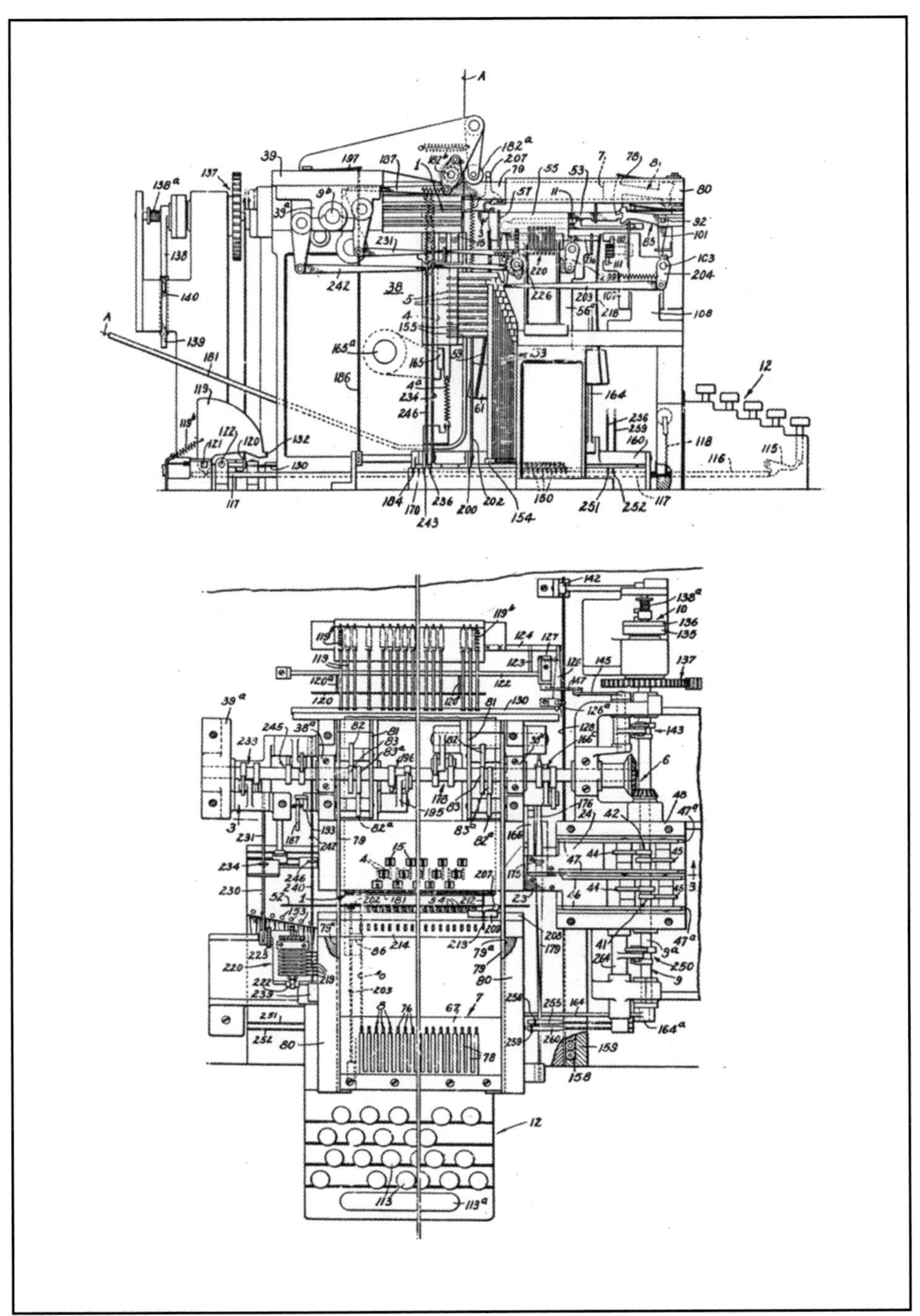

Printing (original patent application filed February 7, 1936). The top drawing is an end-elevation of a high-speed printing or typewriting device for the output of telegraph messages, adding-machine data, etc. The bottom drawing is a plan view.

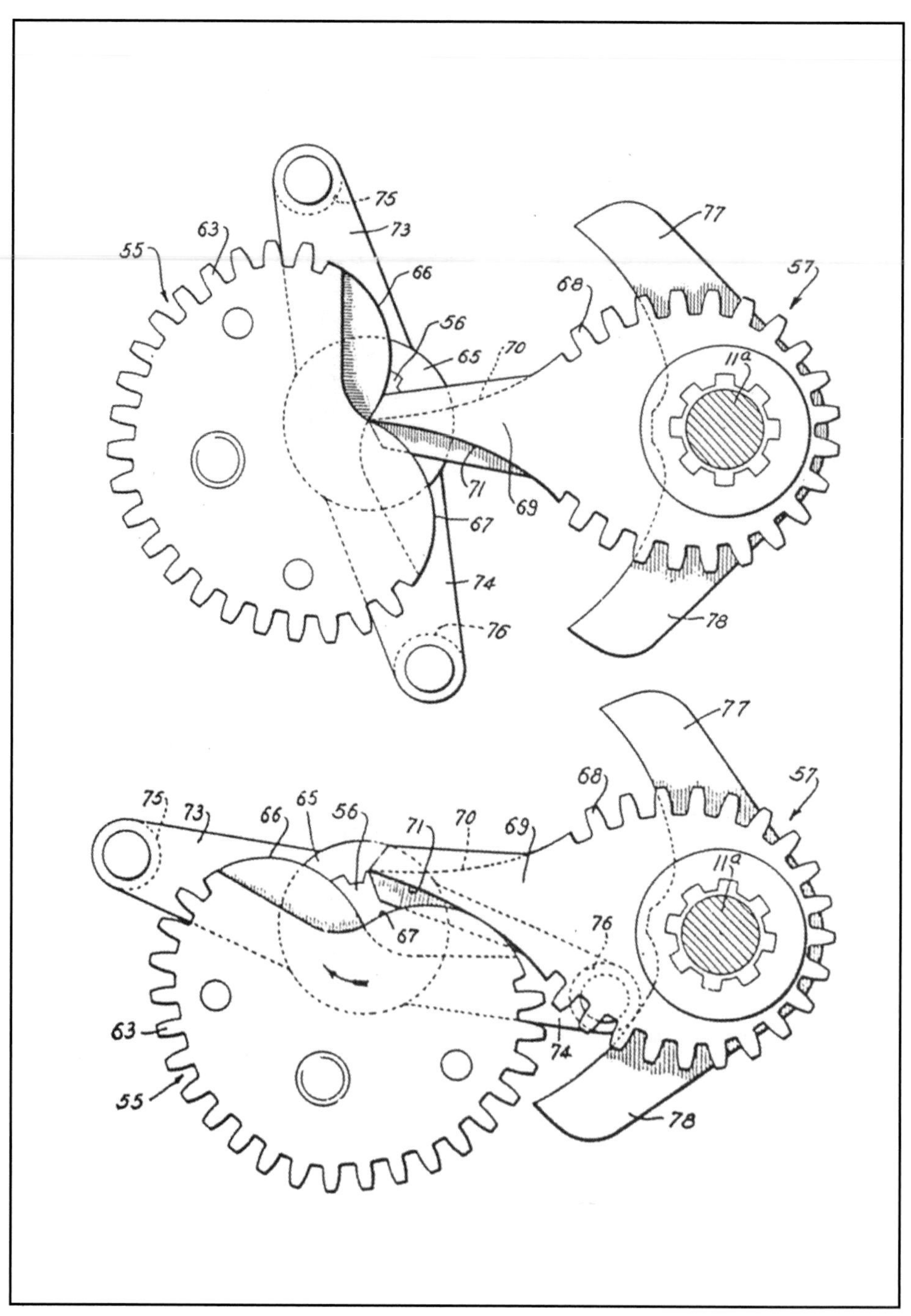

Selectively-Operable Mechanism for Typographical Machines and the Like (original patent application filed September 23, 1939). The drawings show gears of a variable drive mechanisms in different positions.

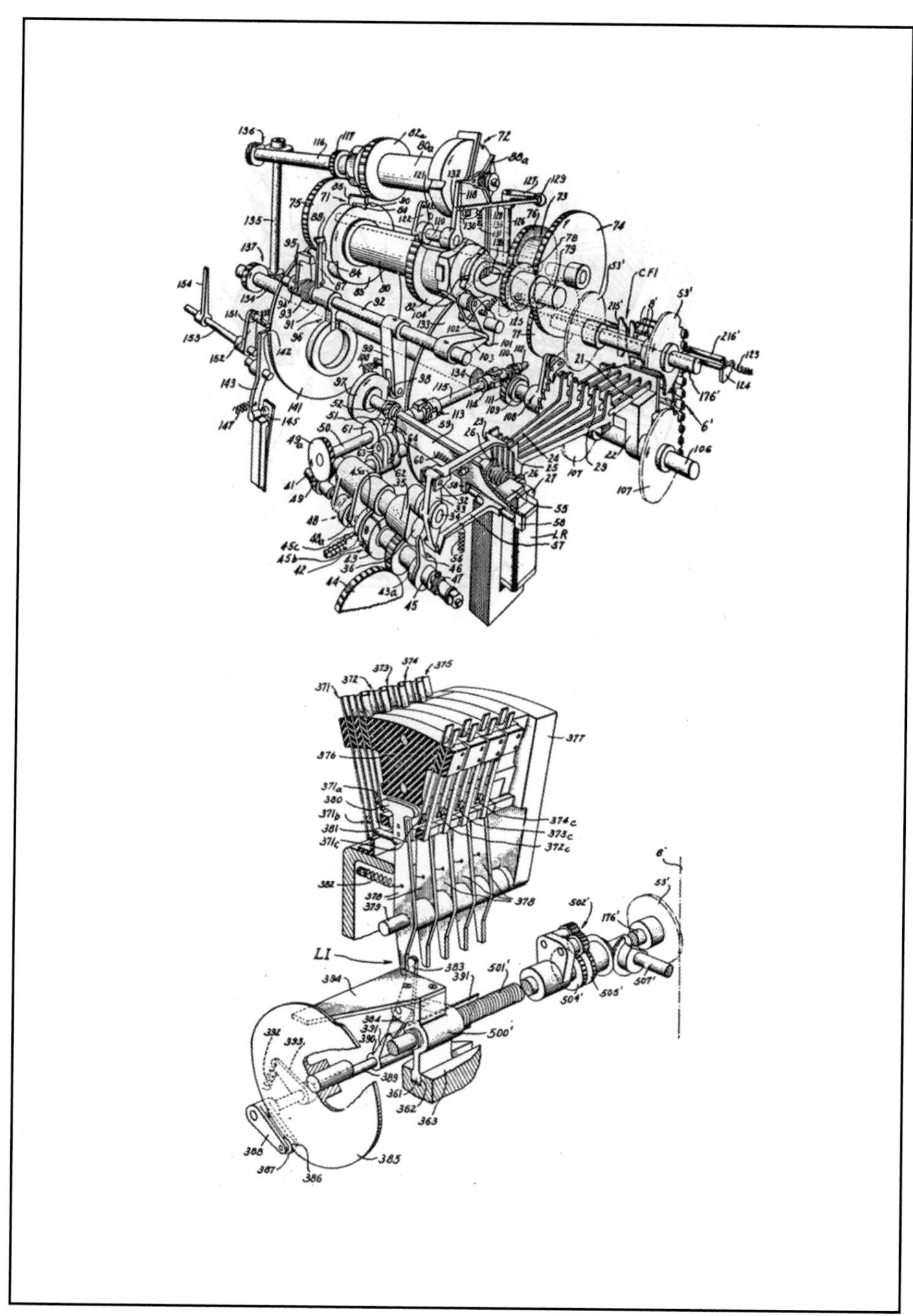

Message-Intercepting and Relaying Circuits in an Automatically-Directed Message Telegraph System (original patent application filed July 19, 1940). The top drawing shows the stop-start recorder of a storage unit for telegraph messages. The bottom drawing is a perspective view of its stop-control mechanism.

From Partners to Shareholders

The Barber and Colman co-partnership, which started in the summer of 1891 with a handshake and a $100 investment, lasted until December 1904, when it was reorganized as the Barber-Colman Company under the laws of Illinois. The reorganization was prompted by the need to raise working capital for the manufacture of the warp-tying machine, but it also formalized a de facto management change that had taken place over the previous three years, as Colman assumed control of the knotter project and Barber more or less withdrew from any involvement in the daily affairs. According to R.G. Dun and Company, Barber became solely an investor or "financial member" of the corporation from this point forward and "never [was] ... active in the business" again. Nearing his 62nd birthday and still engaged in operating George Warren and Company in central Wisconsin, he found the pace of the knotter production and the rapid deployment of new employees and new equipment in Rockford to be confusing from afar, to say nothing of his difficulties in keeping up with the progress of Colman's experimental work. On a practical level, his investments in the partnership had been fully repaid by earnings from the knotter sales; and it now seemed prudent, in view of his age and Colman's demonstrated ability to lead and finance a successful manufacturing operation on his own, to establish a limited liability corporation and distribute future earnings on the basis of the owners' shares of capital stock. The Barber and Colman partnership had been mainly concerned with prototyping and new product design. Both men hoped that a reorganized Barber-Colman Company would enhance its invention business with a robust production capacity.

The formal transfer of the partnership assets occurred on January 1, 1905. According to the corporate records, the new Barber-Colman Company was intended to "carry on the business of manufacturing, producing, selling, leasing, operating, and otherwise dealing in machines, devices, and apparatus used in and about the manufacture of textiles and fabrics;" nothing outside of this field, no other type of venture, was either planned or envisioned at the time. Barber and Colman agreed to give up the ownership of all properties, "real, personal, and mixed," including all American and foreign patents, all patent applications, all inventions and working models described in these documents, all un-patented inventions, and all related models, parts, appliances, and test devices. The new company issued 500 shares of capital stock at a par value of $100, with

Colman subscribing $26,500 and Barber $23,400. A single $100 share was sold to Harry Severson. The three men were then named to the company's board of directors. It was agreed that either Colman or Barber, as major shareholders (i.e. persons owning at least one-third of the capital stock), would be able to call meetings during the year to issue dividends after determining what the business's ongoing needs for working capital would be.

After transferring the business, Colman moved to consolidate his control of the daily operations by developing a series of "special contracts" for his services as an inventor. He signed an agreement with the company authorizing himself to "make improvements" to the warp-tying machine and to "produce and improve accessories;" he also sanctioned the design and development of mechanisms that would be useful "in or about" its manufacture. Colman, the inventor, proposed - and Colman, the majority shareholder, accepted - that all "improvements" eventually be turned over to the company in exchange for 40 shares of treasury stock, but that any experiments and inventions not specifically related to the warp-tying machine remain his personal property. (In a single exception, he granted the company permission to apply certain "features" from his "winders" to the design of the warp-tying machine.) If patent applications for inventions were to issue during the course of his contract, he said, the board of directors would be required to grant him "a personal license to make, use, and sell devices other than those manufactured or sold by the corporation." As an addendum to this agreement, Colman awarded himself a final "personal license" for the four hand-knotter patents that had issued between 1901-04, thus removing the single most valuable invention from the assets that were transferred from the partnership.

Colman held all the cards. As chief inventor, he controlled the development of new products. As general manager, he oversaw the flow of work through the company. As president and treasurer of the board of directors, he recommended (and approved) strategic expenditures on land, buildings, and equipment, as well as annual dividends from the company's "surplus funds." According to Barber-Colman policy, he was entitled to draw upon the company's reserves for personal loans up to $45,000, at six percent interest. He had the authority to invest in real estate near the Rock Street factory "at his discretion" and to hold the land in trust for the company until the time it was "needed" for expansion. He could also set up his own skunkworks if he wished, fund it with Barber-Colman revenues "off the books," and either fold it back into the company or write it off as a loss after giving it a chance to prove itself. We know that he paid himself separate salaries as "general manager" and "inventor," and when he later assigned the G.M.'s duties to Harry Severson, he adjusted his own pay upwards as part of the transfer. (The 1908 corporate minutes indicate that Colman, while being relieved of his management responsibilities, would still devote himself to "his duties as president of the company and to making and developing inventions.") In good times - and good times were the rule in the early Barber-Colman - the company issued ten-percent dividends at least four-five times a year. Colman also collected royalties from the use of his patents and from the sale to Barber-Colman of inventions of a certain vintage, "patented and unpatented, complete and incomplete." To "encourage loyalty" and "promote industry," he issued a limited number of shares of "employee stock," while insisting on the option to re-purchase the shares if their owners decided to sell.

By 1909 William Barber himself, at 67 and in declining health, was ready to liquidate his interest in the business. As was his right, Colman purchased the majority of Barber's stock and allowed Severson and Luther Miller to acquire the remainder. Upon surrendering the charter, R.G. Dun and Company noted,

> Mr. Colman states they took no funds out of the business, did not disturb assets and liabilities at all. The money due Barber for his interest is payable in installments, it is understood, Colman being in shape to anticipate these, but Barber does not need the money (1911).

Walter Colman, the inventor's oldest son, would later say that Barber, who died in 1912, received more than $300,000 from the company on a total investment of $15,000, and that it was the only one of his many business ventures outside of Warren and Company that ever earned a profit.

Barber-Colman records in the old basement vault of the Rock Street factory include a number of Colman's "special contracts" for services, but by far the most elaborate (and arguably the most important) is the December 31, 1931 agreement for the sale of his Electrical and Control-Products Division. This business, which had been initiated a number of years earlier and personally financed by Colman through a proprietary internal account, involved the design and manufacture of what was described at the time as "electrical fans and motors, adaptation of motors to fans, operators, overdoors and door-operating equipment, furnace regulators, draft control apparatus and systems, and temperature control apparatus and systems" - in essence, almost all the key non-textile inventions that had

Howard Colman at the wheel of his roadster, with his wife Bertha and sons Edwin and Walter, in 1909. William Barber appears on horseback in the background. The close personal relationship between Colman and Barber continued undiminished over the two decades of their business ventures.

been developed at the company since the mid-1920s.* When Colman sold his electrical and control-products assets in 1931, the U.S. was entering the third year of the Great Depression and Barber-Colman's Rockford factory running on reduced hours. Sales orders for larger ticket items like warpers, spoolers, and warp-tying machines had virtually dried up. Colman hoped that his sale would provide the cash flow needed to keep the textile business going.

According to the terms and conditions of the contract, Colman agreed to transfer his electrical and control-products patents, the rights to manufacture under these patents, and the tools, supplies, appliances, materials, and stock associated with their commercial production to the company in exchange for "an annual apportionment" of the profits from future sales. He proposed that the "apportionment" be calculated according to the following formula:

$$P = \frac{B_2}{1000 \text{ x square root of A}}$$

In Colman's formula, "P" stood for the proportion of the profits that were due to him, "B" for the division's annual profits, and "A" for the division's annual dollar volume. To calculate his apportionment, Colman said, the company would 1) record the profits from the new division; 2) record the total dollar volume; 3) find the square root of this volume; 4) multiply this number by 1,000; 5) find the square root of the yearly profits; and 6) divide this number by the total in #4. He agreed that his apportionment would be limited to 25% or less of the division's profits, depending on operations.

---

* One notable exception was the group of devices associated with the "multiplex telegraph" or "system of communication."

Acknowledgments

Ruth Colman Tower, the inventor's older daughter, was the driving force behind this book. She assembled much of the archival material upon which the story of her father's life and experiments is based, and along with her sister Dorothy Colman Wallace, was the principal source of anecdotal information concerning his personal affairs. Ruth was always available to answer questions and never ceased to amaze me with her memory of events of seventy-eighty years ago and her ability to describe them in detail. Dorothy, likewise, enthusiastically recalled her relationship with her father and shared with me a number of stories that helped to throw light on his complex personality. After Dorothy's death in 2002, her daughter Connie Gordon furnished me with copies of letters that the inventor had written to her mother between 1934-42. Though often flippant in tone, they are revealing of his private life to a degree that is unprecedented in the rest of his writings. Edwin Colman, the inventor's younger son, and his wife Elizabeth, the daughter of former Montana Senator Burton K. Wheeler, graciously entertained me at their home in Pine Lake, Wisconsin and answered many questions about the Colman family and its patriarch. I did not have the privilege of knowing Walter Colman, the inventor's oldest child, but I greatly benefited from my friendship with his widow Janet, who scoured her home in Rockford for older Barber-Colman documents and turned up many things that have had a direct bearing on the contents of this book. It was her grandson Adam, on a visit from Chicago, who stumbled upon the large collection of letters, cash books, photographs, and drawings - the contents of "H.D. Colman's personal filing cabinet and case" - in the attic over her garage. His discovery, in effect, transformed my narrative from a reminiscence into a much more detailed study of the inventor's creative development. Other Colman family members, such as Ruth's children Jack and Nancy, were unfailingly courteous to me during the writing of this book and tolerant of my many delays. I should also mention here the kindness of Lee Mitchell, of Leydig Voit and Mayer, who helped to assemble the four-volume set of Colman's Letters Patent, and Keith Hyzer, the Colman family attorney.

Ruth Colman Tower at a Barber-Colman shareholders' meeting in 1977.

I was fortunate to meet Roger Schuette, one of the few non-family members to have known Howard Colman personally and probably the last person alive who worked with the inventor at the Barber-Colman Company. Schuette, an electrical engineer, helped me understand the importance of the inventor's work and elucidated some of the special functions of his electrical-mechanical gadgetry. John Nelson, a one-time owner of the Rock Street Barber-Colman facility in Rockford, took me on several guided tours of the old industrial complex, showing me the storerooms of textile-machinery prototypes, the inventor's "penthouse," and the drawers of "daily notes" in the Experimental Department files. He also persuaded Patricia Clubb of Barber-Colman/Siebe to open a vault in the basement of the Rock Street factory and allowed me to make copies of corporate documents there related to the beginnings of the Barber-Colman business. Peter Noling, the son of Martin Noling, Colman's close friend and chief model-maker in the Experimental Department, visited me on a trip from California and recounted some of the stories and shop lore about the inventor that were passed on to him by his father.

My thanks for services rendered to Dick Rundquist; Ed Schott; George Spengler, a direct descendant of the Spengler brothers who did Howard Colman's earliest machining; Gloria Wheeler of Wayland Academy; Fred Burwell of Beloit College; Joanne Wells and Mary Cudnehfsky of the Dodge County Historical Society; and the State Historical Society of Wisconsin. I would like to acknowledge former Barber-Colman employees Armer Severin, Chuck Leonard, Roger Reithmeier, and L.E. Lewandowski for providing information related to the recent history of the company (1971 - present). My thanks to Lewandowski, Tom Johnson, Kay Boyer, Tom McDunn, and Nick Parnello for reading early drafts of this book and suggesting needed changes. Dick Lewis and Shannon Halverson worked with me on the book's layout and cheerfully put up with my constant tinkering. Diane Fagen provided an invaluable service in helping to compile the index. Last but not least, I owe my wife an enormous debt of gratitude for her support during the writing of this book and for her forbearance in dealing with my regular absences from family activities.

Sources

Unless otherwise indicated, biographical information in this book is based on manuscripts and documents in Rockford College's Howard D. Colman Library, Rockford, Illinois. Specific inquiries concerning the Colman Archival Collection should be addressed to the College Archivist (mpryor@rockford.edu).

Index

Note: HDC = Howard D. Colman.

Illustrations and captions are identified by italicized page numbers.

I am not depressed by the fact that nature did not endow me with a great mind, but I see more and more evidence all the time that I might have done more with what I have if I had not been intellectually lazy.

- Letter from Howard Colman to Dorothy Colman Wallace, 1941

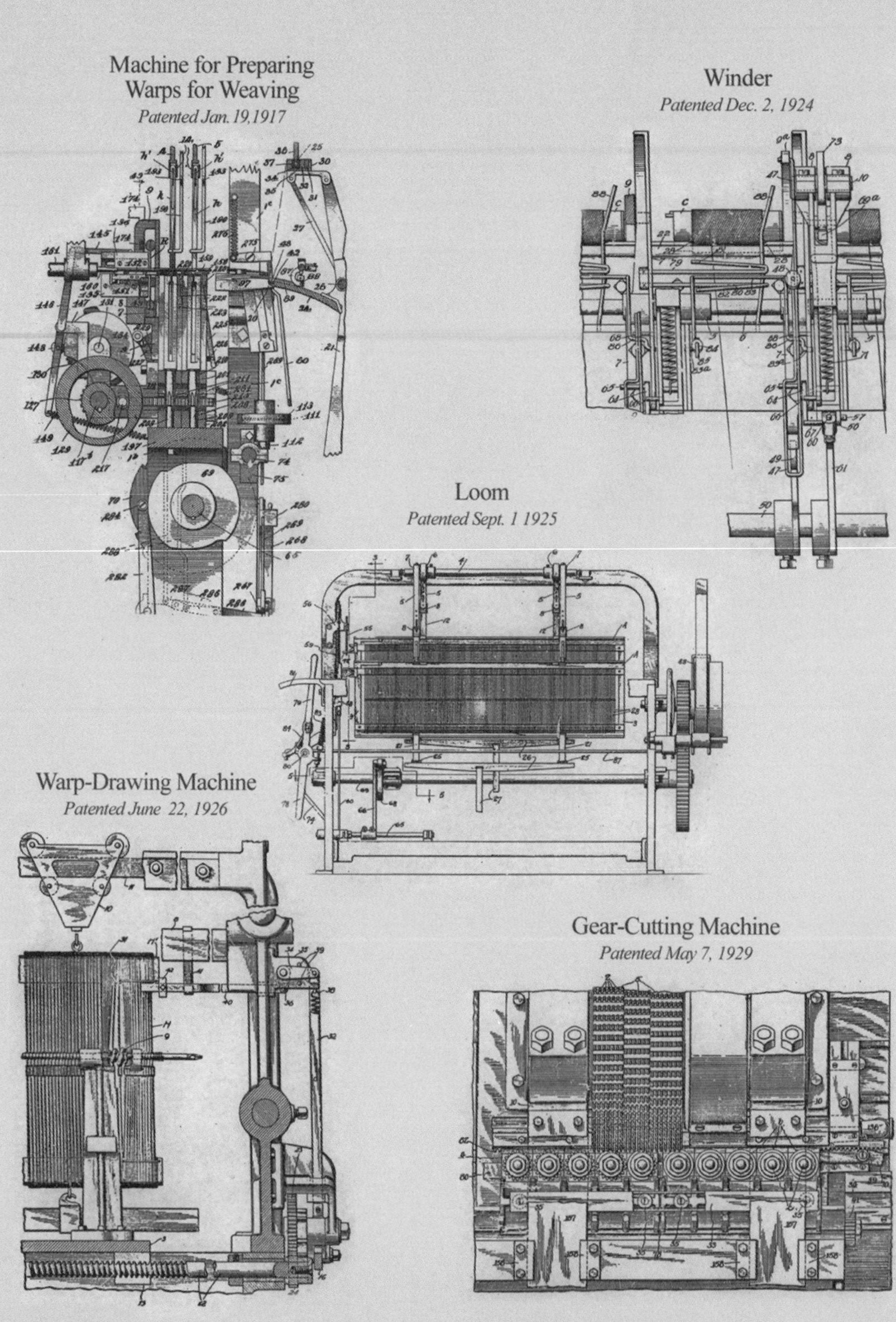
Machine for Preparing Warps for Weaving
Patented Jan. 19,1917
Winder
Patented Dec. 2, 1924
Loom
Patented Sept. 1 1925
Warp-Drawing Machine
Patented June 22, 1926
Gear-Cutting Machine
Patented May 7, 1929